Why Are Black Women Losing Their Hair?

The First Complete Guide To Healthy Hair

Barry Fletcher

Published by Unity Publishers, Inc.
6228 Addison Road
Seat Pleasent, MD 20743
for Unity Publishing, Inc.
1800 Fletch 4
www.BarryFletcher.com
301-336-0604

Printed in U.S.A.

Design: Artemis Productions
& Publications International, Inc.
Cover & Color Section: David Baker
Text: John McLaughlin
Printing: United Book Press

Creative Director: Barry Fletcher
Copy Editor: Marcia Davis
Cover Photo: Frantz Photography
Contributing Photos: Keith Cephus

Library of Congress Control Number: 00-091928

Why are Black Women Losing Their Hair?

Why Are Black Women Losing Their Hair?

Table of Contents

Introduction

Barry L. Fletcher, *World Class Hair Designer*
Mitchellville, MD

I have spent my entire adult life in the hair business; training, studying, lecturing, styling and kutting (the letter 'c' in cut will be replaced by the letter 'k', exemplifying my new Y2K Kut. See Chapter 20, "Hair 2000 and Beyond"). I have traveled the world, represented my country in the Hair Olympics, and spruced up celebrities from Tina Turner to Halle Berry to Maya Angelou. But after 21 years of mostly lauding the virtues of my industry, I've reached a disturbing conclusion: The industry is destroying black women's hair. That's right! Too many sisters are unwittingly victims of harmful products, drawn in by misleading advertisements that promise gold and deliver sand. These days I find myself doing more corrective work than creative work in the salon and that is truly distressing.

This book, like no other, will share tips and secrets about how black women can keep their hair healthy. It is a book designed to empower sisters, to give them a more complex understanding of their hair and its historical roots. With that knowledge, sisters will be better armed to maintain their manes between salon visits or eliminating those visits altogether. By the time you have finished this book, you will know the do's and don'ts of grooming and the deleterious effects of certain services commonly provided in salons across the country.

But First, Some Perspective.

Pull out your old family albums and look closely at your mother's hair when she was young, or your grandmother's, or great-grandmother's. You probably will notice that they had long, full-textured hair. In the early 1900s, sisters had, on average, 10 to 12 inches of hair, a length maintained through the first half of the 20th century. The main reason: Sisters didn't do much to their hair then but let it grow.

Over time, however, styles evolved, from plaiting to pressing, from naturals to curl perms, from relaxing to braiding, to weaving to locking. But here is the bad news: Today, sisters have an average length of four to six inches of hair. The truth is sisters don't learn of the impact of altering their hair until they try it. Then it may be too late.

Who is going to tell them? Not the fashion and beauty magazines, which rely on $45,000 a page ads from hair care manufacturers. And you know the manufacturers are not going to offer consumer tips that might jeopardize their profits. The hope is that hair stylists would be responsible enough to inform black women of the pitfalls of experimenting with certain styles and chemicals. But that is not always the case.

African Americans spend nearly $5 billion a year on hair products and services, but in no other period in history has black hair been as badly abused as it is today. White-owned companies are leading the charge. They have launched some of the worst products for black women on the market today: the no-lye and gel relaxer kits, the Rio products, the permanent colors and the high-alkaline shampoos. I wish I could say this bamboozlement was confined to white companies. It would be easier to attack that way. But sadly, I can't. Unfortunately, some black hair care companies are culprits too, mimicking their white brethren all the way to the bank.

Fearful of losing a sizable portion of their market to bigger corporations, these black companies are losing their integrity and selling their souls in the process. And that's too bad.

The black beauty industry has a noble history. Hair is the only business in the United States in which our presence is felt at every level. We have black schools, manufacturers, distributors, salons and barbershops servicing the black community. The black hair care industry should be a model of economic empowerment. But the tragic reality is that we have lost some of our edge and ingenuity, and we have become too greedy. Black women are complaining like mad about damage to their hair and scalp, but our researchers and scientists are not developing new remedies. Our schools cannot take eager students fast enough, but they are unwilling to pay good teachers what they deserve. Our manufacturers seem more interested in the quantity of their sales than in the quality of their products. And now that African Americans have lost their grip on the distribution side of the business, most consumers head to their neighborhood beauty supply store, where they can buy all kinds of junk. In some respect, the beauty supply store has turned into a chemical waste dump.

I remember 15 years ago when manufacturers would travel from city to city giving mini-tutorials on their wares. They would break down the chemistry of their products and teach stylists how and when to apply them. Companies wanted to make sure their products were not just sold, but administered properly.

But today, most beauty school graduates don't know how to professionally process a relaxer, press-and-curl, or use permanent color. And most state boards don't even require students to demonstrate these services to become licensed.

So Where Are We?

We are at a defining moment. Those of us who have given our lives to the beautification of black women can no longer afford to be simply stylers of hair and hustlers of products. We must be full-service cosmetologists, incorporating the principles of health and wellness into our practices. We must be, in some respect, image consultants, therapists and hair revolutionaries.

This book serves as a guide for consumers and professionals alike. It contains step-by-step instructions on how to care for every type of African American hair. There are self-diagnosing charts, cures for hair ills, holistic ideas, chemical explanations and natural methodology. The book includes essays and advice from an array of vantage points — dermatologists, psychologists, journalists, chemists and hairdressers. I know that my clients and associates want answers. So this is the beginning.

We have come a long way in hair care since the days of slavery, when butter was used as a conditioner and axle grease was used to dye away gray. When African slaves were brought to America, they were not allowed to groom themselves, and many came to view their matted, unruly, natural styles as hair in need of altering.

In most cases, the longer societal ramifications of hair have left us ambivalent. We keep suffering through an African heritage searching for a cure. Those sisters who are frequently flying from Africa to Europe on their very own hairplane should read on and find out how to qualify for a round-trip.

Today, the mosaic of black hairstyles is represented in public life, from Oprah's silky-straight relaxed hair, to Lauryn Hill's locks, to Susan Taylor's glorious braids. Our hair is as rich as the culture from which it emanates. Let's celebrate and protect it.

Designed to empower sisters!

Foreword

A'Lelia Bundles, *Madame C.J. Walker's Great-great-granddaughter, Alexandria, VA*

*I*n the ultra-glamorous, highly competitive international arena of hair fashion, Barry Fletcher is an undisputed champion. With flare and grace, he has waved his combs, brushes and curling irons like magic wands across the tresses of thousands of beautiful women, winning scores of trophies and the affection of his clients along the way.

If Barry Fletcher chose to do so, he could rest on his laurels. He has already reached the mountaintop of the hair care industry, displaying his artistry from the runways of the International Hair Olympics to the cover of Essence magazine. His master classes and training seminars are standing-room-only affairs in Paris, London, Canada, the Caribbean and throughout the United States. He has opened a salon in St. Croix, with more to come. He has created styles for movie stars, Congresswomen, fashion models and corporate executives.

All the accolades could go to a guy's head. Instead, they have moved Barry to a higher level of hair care consciousness. The result: He wants to go back to basics, to help black women recapture the power and vitality of their crowning glory.

During his 20 years as a hairstylist, Barry has treated the spectrum of emergency beauty ailments, chronic hair abuse, habitual scalp battering, chemically dependent perm disorders and tortured stress syndrome.

The cure, he has discovered, is Grooming! Grooming! Grooming! The medicine that he always prescribes is Conditioning, Conditioning, Conditioning. But the real miracle ingredient, he will tell you, no matter how you wear your hair is a generous dose of self-acceptance and self-love.

I first read about Barry several years ago when he dared to challenge the status quo of the prestigious International Hair Olympics. Instead of being oh-so-grateful for the invitation to compete in London, he made a revolutionary decision. His model, much to the U.S. team leader's consternation, would be a black woman, someone whom they declared would not do. Didn't black hair lack "certain versatility,"

they whispered amongst themselves? In the end, Barry prevailed, and he has not looked back.

My interest in Barry's work has continued ever since, because, like my great-great grandmother, the hair care industry pioneer, Madame C. J. Walker, he cares deeply about black women and their hair. Just as she discovered almost a century ago, he has learned that promoting hair care among his clients is more important than serving up the latest hair fashion.

In the late 1800's and early 1900's, thousands of black women were going bald, not only because of stress and poor diet, but because their hair had been neglected and mistreated. Too many of us believed an old wives' tale that it was bad luck to wash our hair more than once a month. In rural areas where there was a lack of indoor plumbing and electricity, many women left their hair unwashed all winter for fear they would catch a cold. The scalp disease that resulted is almost too horrible to imagine.

Like Madame C.J. Walker, he cares deeply about black women and their hair.

At a time when few were celebrating the beauty of black women, Madame Walker and Poro Company founder Annie Malone were among those who exposed us to a new way of viewing our hair. Today, Madame Walker is often identified with hot combs and hair straightening, even though she did not invent either. In reality, she was more concerned with hygiene and hair restoration. Calling herself a "Scalp Specialist," she once told a reporter, "Let me correct the erroneous impression held by some that I always held myself out as a hair culturist. I grow hair—I want the great masses of my people to take greater pride in their appearance and to give their hair proper attention."

"Giving our hair proper attention" is also Barry Fletcher's goal.

As you turn these pages, you will be treated to his vision of hair care empowerment. In the process, I hope you will discover ways to nourish your inner and outer selves.

Preface

The reason you have never read an educational guide as complete and informative as this book is because one person can't write it. It requires contributions from medical doctors, dermatologists, trichologists, nutritionists, and people who have experienced trauma and success with their hair – just like you. Without the politics or concerns of companies and individuals who profit financially from retailing products to consumers and beauty industry professionals, this vehicle of empowerment in your hand will take you on an educational, inspirational and emotional roller coaster ride. It will help you obtain a more comprehensive appreciation of hair and its care. Please do not be discouraged if you are losing your hair. This book will have some answers for you. It is information that will be discussed in hair salons, at social gatherings and in black families the world over for years to come.

I hope you find pleasure in the changing personalities of each chapter. Remember, health plus wellness equals beauty.

Thank you for your support.

Living With Your Hair

By Barry L. Fletcher

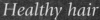

Healthy hair begins with how we view it.

*I*n our fashion-conscious society, it seems we are inclined to do almost anything to our hair to stay current with today's trends. Hot curling, waving, weaving, perming and teasing are just a few of the stressful regimens that we subject our hair to on a daily basis.

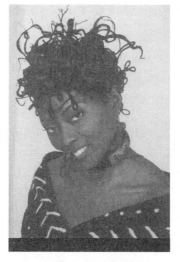

But hair is serious business and requires attention and care. And while "looking good" is a legitimate concern, a bigger one should be to truly understand our hair and its needs so it can remain healthy and vibrant.

Proper hair care really begins with how we view our hair. Historically, African Americans have been conditioned to view our hair as a problem, as a chore that we don't want to tackle. Our hair is a gift from "Mother Nature," not a curse. It has been placed on our heads to protect our brain from the elements, and its thick, wool-like texture ensures that we're well-protected.

African Americans have some of the most versatile hair in the world. We have the option of styling it straight, wavy, curly, naturally curly, matted, twisted or locked. This versatility and creative range are among the many factors that make us beautiful and unique. Ironically, though, this gift of versatility has become the catalyst of many black women's hair problems. Because they have so many options, black women tend to experiment more with hair products and styles, often

wearing ones that don't complement their hair texture.

For many young black women, having their hair relaxed for the first time is like moving from Africa to Europe in 30 minutes. The trip is a little hot and uncomfortable, but many think the environment is more conducive for maintaining their hair. After that first relaxer, some sisters are so overwhelmed with the ease in which they can manage

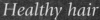

their hair that they never try anything else—and worse, they ignore the signals when it's time for a change. When we venture out and find something new or different that works for us, we may adopt it as part of our routine, but when that "new thing" no longer works, we usually return home and back to the basics. The same is true with our hair. In that instance, going home means returning to our hair's natural state.

On the other hand, natural styles may not necessarily be the best styling decision either. I have seen people allow their hair to lock and find that it became too dry. I will never forget one day I was riding the train to New York. Before I sat down I noticed there was something in the seat. It looked like a little hairy bud or caterpillar. I couldn't make out what the devil it was, and I didn't want to sit beside it until I was sure it wasn't moving. Finally I realized it was an abandoned, dried-out dreadlock. You see, wearing a natural style doesn't end all your hair problems. Locks, like relaxers, are not for everyone. Your hair needs nourishment and moisture no matter what. Without maintaining that moisture balance, locks could fall off like branches on Charlie Brown's Christmas tree.

When I speak at black colleges, some students confess that they feel pressured to wear natural hair styles. They actually fear that if they went to a straighter, more European style they would be deemed a sellout. The only parameter that should determine your choice of style is what your hair responds to positively. For example, when I wore my hair in a natural afro, I noticed excessive shedding while picking it out. But when I texturized my hair, I didn't experience shedding. This is because the chemical relaxer softens the hair and allows the cuticles to open and close more readily. This flexibility allows the hair to absorb more moisture, conditioning treatments and proteins. When our hair is in its natural curly state, the products do not penetrate as easily. When applied, most conditioners remain on top of the hair as

opposed to penetrating the hair shaft, resulting in dry hair and breakage. Chemically altered hair accepts moisture more readily, and moisture helps prevent hair breakage. This is why hair growth appears to increase among those clients who wear curly perms.

I have noticed that some natural hairstyles can make a person look older or more mature. In other instances, relaxed hairstyles can look too limp and detract from a person's overall youthful appearance. So there is a lot that one must consider when choosing hair textures, shapes and styles. It requires that we take the responsibility to understand our hair's individual needs and use that as a basis to decide our styling preferences.

STRUCTURE

To better understand the underlying causes of damaged hair, we must familiarize ourselves with our hair's structure.

Contrary to popular belief, hair is a living organism, and like skin, teeth and nails, the hair extracts its nourishment from the blood stream. This is why diet plays such an important role in the maintenance of healthy hair. Each hair strand is

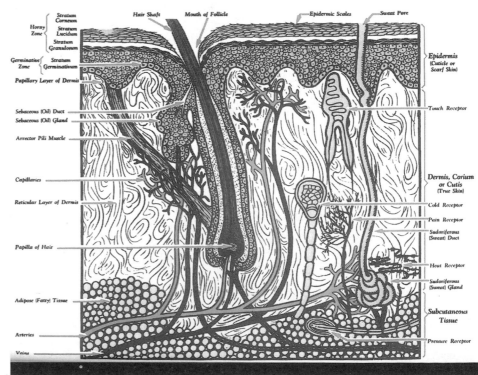

Diagram from Hair Structure and Chemistry Simplified

Living With Your Hair

Sebum also possesses powerful bacteria and fungi inhibitors that prevent the mass invasion of the skin and hair by these destructive organisms. When we consider the fact that every object the skin contacts provides more chance of attack from hostile bacteria and fungi, we realize just how much we depend on sebum for our survival. The skin would otherwise provide an ideal "home" for these tiny intruders, as it is warm, moist and supplied with ample nourishment. Sebum is slightly acid, has a protein content, and in many ways will benefit the hair in a manner imitated by commercially prepared conditioners.

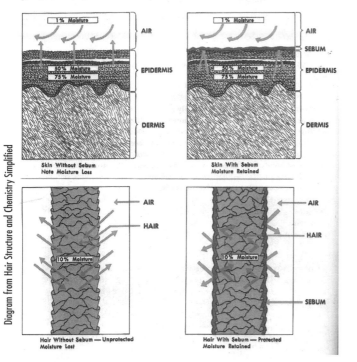

Diagram from Hair Structure and Chemistry Simplified

made up of three principal components. The first is the cuticle or outer-most layer. It acts as a protective shield to the hair shaft and is coated with a natural lubricant called sebum, which gives hair its natural sheen. When hair appears dull and dry, this means the sebum has been stripped from the hair shaft. This is usually the result of overprocessing, excessive heat or improper product usage.

The second layer of the hair strand is the cortex. The cortex determines the color, strength, elasticity and texture of the hair and accounts for 75 to 90 percent of the hair's bulk. If the cortex is damaged, the hair will appear fragile and weak and will break easily when touched. Deep conditioning and regular treatments are essential to maintaining and strengthening the cortex.

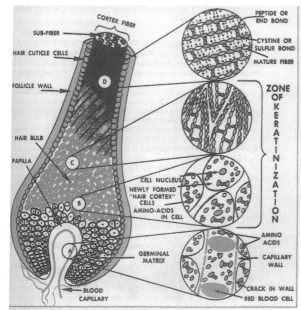

Diagrams from Hair Structure and Chemistry Simplified

A. Amino acids in blood circulation leave the capillaries thru minute cracks in vessel walls.

B. Hair cortex cells are constantly formed in the germinal matrix of the hair bulb. Selected amino acids (rich in sulfur) from A enter these new cells and are randomly scattered within cell contents.

C. In each cell (pushed up from B) amino acids are orientated into one direction. These amino acids are then joined together (by peptide or end bonds) in short strings of keratin. Cystine or sulfur cross bonds link adjacent keratin strings together. Cell nucleus and wall disappear. Hydrogen bonds assist crosslinkage as cortex loses moisture. (Not shown on diagram).

D. Hard Keratin from C results from complete coupling of keratin chains into a twisting complex structure. Hydrogen bonds are now present. These twisted bundles are called sub-fibers. The sub-fibers are also twisted around each other to form the cortex fiber.

A cross section of an entire hair fiber; formed by taking a series of photos which were assembled to create a composite picture, magnified 1400 times. Note especially the layers of the cuticle, the cortex and the medulla, all clearly defined. Of special interest are the thousands of pigment (color) granules which are so important in hair lightening. *Courtesy: Gillette Company Research Institute, Rockville, Maryland*

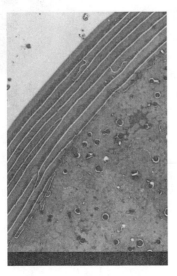

The third and final innermost layer of the hair is the medulla, also referred to as the marrow of the hair shaft. The medulla is frequently broken or entirely absent from the hair shaft. It is suspected that poor health and the use of certain drugs have a direct bearing on its absence or damaged condition. The exact function of the medulla remains a mystery. The hair does not appear to suffer from its absence.

♋ HAIR BREAKAGE, LOSS AND THINNING

"Madam C. J. Walker was a pioneer in the black hair care industry whose battle with alopecia inspired her to concoct a remedy to promote black hair growth. However, despite her efforts, more and more people of color are suffering from hair loss, and modern times demand different solutions."

According to Dr. Wanda Nelson, president of the National Beauty Culturist's League, "one of the major reasons for hair loss among women of color is that they rely too heavily on nonprofessionals to produce professional results as it relates to their hair."

There are many factors that come into play when discussing hair thinning, breakage and loss. Some factors are external, such as the weather, hair service and daily home hair care regimes. Other factors are internal and include: stress; medication; poor dieting; fluctuation in hormone levels from birth control pills; iron deficiency; pregnancy; menopause; hormone treatments; thyroid problems, and poor blood circulation. Whether external or internal, it's to our benefit to be aware of these factors and the role they play in determining the health of our hair.

There is a distinct difference between hair loss and hair breakage. Hair breakage is when the hair fractures on the ends or at any point throughout the length of the hair strand. Hair loss is when the hair comes out completely from the root of the hair follicle. We know that we are experiencing hair loss when we see a small white bulb at the end of the hair strand (this is the hair's root). In some instances we may not see the root at the end of the lost hair strand, but if the strand is the average length of hair remaining on your head, then it is still considered hair loss, not breakage.

Hair breakage is usually self-inflicted and is the result of improper hair care, either by ourselves or at the hands of an improperly trained hairstylist. Hair loss, on the other hand, is usually a result of a medical condition or something outside the hands of a stylist and should be referred to a reputable dermatologist or a medical physician for treatment.

Remember the old saying, "Two heads are better than one"? Well, when it comes to hair and scalp problems, three heads might be more sufficient, yours, the stylist's and a medical physician's. Everyone wants healthy, strong and shiny hair that is pleasing to touch, but

Common Types of Hair Loss (Exclusive of Hair Shaft Deformities)

Diffuse		Patterned	
Nonscarring	Scarring	Nonscarring	Scarring
Telogen effluvium (noninflammatory)[7,45]	Extensive radiodermatitis	Androgenetic alopecia	Discoid lupus erythematosus
Physiologic effluvium of the newborn	Total avulsion, burn	Alopecia areata	Pseudopelade
Postpartum	Leprosy	Traction/friction	Morphea
Post febrile	Extensive syphilitic gumma	Systemic lupus erythematosus	Epitheliomas
Severe infection		Tinea capitis	Focal trauma
Severe chronic illness		Trichotillomania	Dissecting cellulitis
Severe psychological stress		Secondary syphilis	Folliculitis decalvans
Postsurgical		Herpes zoster	Tinea capitis (kerion)
Hypothyroidism and other endocrinopathies		Folliculitis	Necrotic herpes zoster
Crash or liquid protein diets			Benign mucous membrane pemphigoid
Drugs: antikeratinizing, anticoagulant (especially heparin), antithyroid, anticonvulsant; hormones, heavy metals			Scalp tumors (e.g., cylindromas, metastatic carcinoma)
Early androgenetic alopecia (balding)			Ulerythema ophyrogenes
Anagen effluvium (noninflammatory)			
X-ray depilation			
Chemotherapy drugs			
Other potent toxic drugs (e.g., thallium)			
Anagen effluvium (inflammatory)			
Alopecia totalis and universalis			
Secondary and latent syphilis			
Systemic lupus erythematosus			

Diagram courtesy of Lippincott Williams & Wilkins

Living With Your Hair

only a few will go through the necessary channels to obtain and maintain it. Having healthy relationships with a professional hair designer, dermatologist and health care practitioner is the key. Whether we are experiencing hair breakage or hair loss, whether induced by genetics, health, environmental conditions or improper hair treatment, our hair needs to be properly evaluated and diagnosed so that we know how to properly repair it.

HAIR BREAKAGE

Trichoptilosis, also known as split ends, is among the most common cause of hair breakage and will result when the tip of the hair shaft is broken at the cortex. When the cortex is exposed, it becomes dry and the ends begin to fray or split, leaving the hair with a dull, ragged and thirsty appearance. Excessive use of chemicals such as no-lye relaxers and permanent color also rob the hair of its moisture and further promotes split ends.

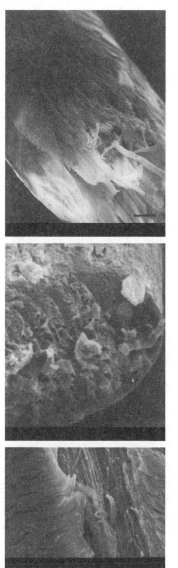

Photos courtesy of the Gillette Co.

To help avoid split ends, trim the hair every six to eight weeks or in conjunction with your touchups. When using steam or regular rollers, always apply endpapers to protect the hair strand and maintain proper moisture balance in the hair.

Traction is another major cause of hair breakage and occurs when the hair strand is pulled or rubbed against one another. This hair tension or friction is self-inflicted and can occur when you wear tight pony tails, hair pieces, barrettes, rollers, braids and weaves, or while brushing and combing the hair.

To reduce breakage from traction, avoid pulling the hair too tight around the hairlines. When opting to wear ponytails,

avoid rubber bands. If possible, wrap your own hair around the ponytail to hold it in place. Also, avoid sleeping with rollers or wearing accessories with metal clips.

HAIR LOSS

In the past two decades we have witnessed some of the greatest medical and scientific advances in the nation's history. Cures have been discovered for ailments that have baffled mankind for centuries. Just recently we witnessed a 77-year-old man walk on the moon, yet we have not figured out what causes baldness and hair loss or how to stop them. We don't even know what causes dandruff, for that matter. This assessment brings to light my concern regarding a scalp disorder prevalent predominantly among adult black women. This scalp condition is Follicular Degeneration Syndrome (FDS), also known as "Hot Comb Alopecia."

HOT COMB ALOPECIA

FDS, or Hot Comb Alopecia, normally occurs in the cranium or crown area of the head and can be described as a permanent deterioration of the hair sheath. The hair sheath is located beneath the scalp's surface and is what prevents hair products and other bacteria from seeping into the hair follicle and damaging the root of the hair strand. When suffering from FDS, the orifices of the hair sheath are permanently obliterated and the root is left vulnerable to hair products and other foreign debris, which will infect and destroy the hair follicle. When affected with FDS, the scalp will have a nude, shiny finish and a few strands or patches of hair emerging from beneath its surface.

For years it was believed that there was a direct correlation between FDS and the use of the hot comb. In 1968, examinations were conducted on 51 black women who had this form of alopecia. The belief was that the hot oil used for pressing was seeping into the crown area of the head, traumatizing the scalp and ultimately killing the hair bulb or root. All 51 women were pressing their hair at the time of the study, so this theory existed for two decades. In 1991, new experiments were conducted by Dr. Leon C. Sperling, one of the most interested dermatologists in the study of ethnic hair. Dr. Sperling studied 10 black women with this form of alopecia, using both vertical and transverse sections of scalp biopsy specimens.

All of the patients tested said that the condition was slowly progressive and described itching, slight tenderness and unusual sensations similar to pins and needles in the alopecic region. All had used a variety of hair care products and styling techniques over the years. While some used the hot comb before or during the early years of their condition, many of them discontinued hot comb usage years before the onset of the problem. Others had never used a hot comb. Dr. Sperling has also indicated that he has white clients with problems that are virtually identical. Now, approximately 30 years after the article was written about Hot Comb Alopecia, we are finding that most black women are using relaxers, but are still experiencing FDS. After his study, Dr. Sperling concluded that there is no exclusive link to the use of the hot comb and this form of alopecia.

There is currently no known cure for FDS. The two treatments often used are topical steroids and oral antibiotics. They are not guaranteed to make your hair grow back, but they help control or condense the affected area and retard further hair loss.

ANDROGENETIC ALOPECIA

Androgenetic is the most common type of alopecia in both men and women and accounts for 95 percent of all hair loss. Women with Androgenetic Alopecia will have scattered hair loss throughout the scalp. In men, however, the Androgenetic pattern loss usually begins with a receding hairline then expands to the crown area of the head.

Androgenetic Alopecia occurs when certain enzymes in the body convert male hormone testosterone and forms the hormone dihydrotestosterone, better known as (DHT). It is the DHT hormone that causes the hair shafts to narrow and produce progressively finer hairs. With each new growth cycle the hair strands become more transparent until eventually they stop emerging altogether.

While there is no known cure for Androgenetic Alopecia, there are several medical and natural treatments that are known to retard its progression. Medical treatments for women include Diane 35, a prescribed hormonal contraceptive tablet, and Spironolactone, commonly used to treat high blood pressure. Zinc, Saw palmetto extract, Green Tea, Vitamin B6 and Emu oil are among some of the natural treatments.

ALOPECIA AREATA

Areata is another popular form of alopecia and is identified as a bald spot on the scalp about the size of a quarter. People often panic about this type of alopecia and want to know why they lost their hair in that particular spot. This spot is also referred to as a nerve spot because it is believed to be caused by nervousness and stress. When the body is under severe stress, this sometimes triggers a reaction in the immune system that causes the white blood cells to attack the hair follicles as if they are fighting off a virus. This causes the hair to fall out. The good thing, however, is that it will grow back (often within six weeks to three months). The condition is known to recur and can effect children and young adults.

Treatments for Alopecia Areata are divided into two groups: patients with less than 50 percent hair loss and those with more than 50 percent hair loss. Treatment for less than 50 percent hair loss include:

- Cortocosteroid, lotion that is applied directly to the bald area, or cortocosteroid injections that are applied directly onto the bald area.

- Drithocreme, an anthralin ointment, is applied to the scalp.

- Retin A, a gel rubbed on the area of hair loss.

- Rogaine, effective on patch Alopecia Areata, used to fill in gaps until hair starts growing again.

- Zinc, in high doses.

Treatment for more than 50 percent hair loss include:

- Systematic Cortisone, taken intramuscularly or internally when the condition is spreading rapidly.

- Puva, a light sensitive drug that requires undergoing short exposure to long wave ultraviolet light. It should be used three times a week for six weeks.

TRAUMATIC ALOPECIA

This form of alopecia is self-inflicted, caused by excessive use of harsh chemicals such as relaxers, permanent coloring, curly perms and bleaches. Hair breakage is also caused by the misuse of such harsh hair chemicals, but unlike breakage—which occurs over time, and is eventually replaced—in the case of Traumatic Alopecia, the hair breaks all over at one time and will not grow back.

Traumatic Alopecia is also caused by excess tension on the hairline: wearing tight ponytails, braids and weaves. When we continuously pull the hair, we rip it out of the follicle, which inflames and eventually scars the scalp. Once the scalp is scarred, hair will not grow out of that follicle again. If you see bumps or any inflammation on the scalp it is time to change the hair design.

THINNING

Hair loss in both men and women is caused by a combination of genetic and hormonal factors. Testosterone, a hormone found predominately in men, is also produced in the adrenal gland of the woman and has a significant long-term damaging effect on the hair follicles. The estrogen in women is able to counteract Testosterone, which prolongs the thinning process until after menopause. This is why most women begin thinning around the age of 30, approximately 10 years later than when the average male pattern of balding sets in.

More than 85 percent of hair loss is heredity, but we speed up the process when we subject ourselves to physical and emotional stress and drug usage. Anti-arthritis drugs, beta blockers, blood thinners and even aspirin, when taken over a long period of time, will promote hair thinning. If you experience an unusual pattern of hair loss, see a medical physician or dermatologist who specializes in hair and scalp disorders. Your hair can tell a lot about your overall health.

According to Nioxin research laboratories in Atlanta, there has been a new discovery about thin, lifeless-looking hair and its link to an eight-legged bug called Demodex. This microscopic bug nestles inside the hair follicle and feeds off the sebum. In order to digest the sebum, the bug produces an enzyme called lipase, which seems to have an adverse effect on the strength and condition of our hair.

Although the scientific world has known about Demodex since the 1800's, Nioxin made the connection between Demodex and thinning hair in 1997. While conducting studies at Nioxin's Biotechnical clinic, researchers discovered "Demodex Folliculorum" on the scalps of 100 percent of men and women with thinning hair. For more information, contact the Nioxin Laboratory or a doctor who specializes in hair and scalp disorders.

BEAU LINES

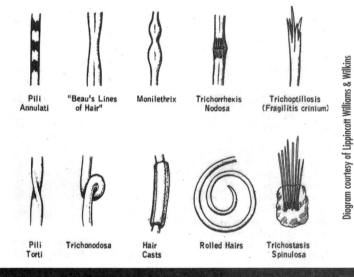

| Pili Annulati | "Beau's Lines of Hair" | Monilethrix | Trichorrhexis Nodosa | Trichoptillosis (Fragilitis crinium) |
| Pili Torti | Trichonodosa | Hair Casts | Rolled Hairs | Trichostasis Spinulosa |

Diagram courtesy of Lippincott Williams & Wilkins

Hair deformities can be detected when there is a significant change in the shape, strength or texture of the hair strand. Like hair loss and breakage, hair deformities may be hereditary or self-induced through the use of hair additions, braids, weaves, and repetitious designs. If your hair texture changes and becomes thin, grainy, soft or springy, more than likely some kind of abnormality has developed.

If we were to pull an abnormal hair strand out of the head and lay it on a piece of white paper, we would see peculiar irregularities. One common deformity is referred to as Beau lines. Beau lines are defined as an indentation within the hair shaft that occurs when the hair is locked in a permanent configuration for an extended period of time. Beau lines are evident throughout the strand, especially after the hair is braided or secured with a stitch of thread. Wherever the locking mechanism is fixated on the hair, it will decrease the diameter of the strand, causing the appearance of Beau lines.

◎◎ TRICHORRHEXIS

I want to address another hair deformity called Trichorrhexis. This is when the hair is severely fractured and shredded but has not yet broken off. Each strand holds the other together, and if examined under a microscope, they would look like the bristles of two paint brushes being pushed against one another. Unlike Trichoptilosis (split ends), in which the hair breaks on the ends, with Trichorrhexis, the hair can break at any point throughout the hair strand.

Trichorrhexis is mainly caused by excessive pulling of the hair and heat application. Oftentimes, hot irons are too hot and singe or fracture the hair. In many of these cases the hair does not fall out right away, but is vulnerable to breaking off the next time you style your hair.

◎◎ HEALTH AND HAIR

Although the hair root is living, we must remember that the hair has no self-repairing ability and little can be done to reverse the condition of damaged hair. Conditioning treatments and kutting off portions of damaged hair are among the most beneficial alternatives to restoring damaged hair. The reproduction of hair cells is dependent upon proper nourishment and oxygen. When the bloodstream provides the hair with nourishing elements, it grows long and strong. The average growth of healthy hair is a quarter inch

There are several additional remedies that have been known to strengthen the hair and reduce hair loss and breakage.

per month. If inadequately nourished, hair will become weak and hair loss eventually will occur. That's why good eating and exercise habits are so important.

A healthy diet is well balanced, rich in vitamins and minerals, abundant in fruits and green vegetables and generous in natural fluids. Two vital nutrients for healthy hair are vitamin B complex and vitamin C. Without these vitamins, hair growth will be minimal. When we are under extreme pressure our body will deplete its supply of vitamin B complex and vitamin C. Proper exercise will help the body release excess energy. Map out a vigorous but brief exercise routine and follow it daily. Also, take time out of each day to relax.

Another vitamin that is a tremendous benefit to the hair is vitamin A. This vitamin benefits the skin as well and relieves the scalp from itching and flaking. Vitamin E is an essential fatty acid and contributes to the sebaceous gland in producing sebum.

The following tips are also recommended:

- Avoid excessive quantities of salt.

- Take a teaspoonful of cod liver oil, enriched in vitamin A, on a daily basis.

- Avoid cigarette smoking.

- Avoid eating animal fats and hydrogenated fats.

- Avoid refined carbohydrates, i.e. white sugar and white flour.

- Maintain a basic diet, including foods that are naturally rich in vitamins, minerals and proteins.

Living good keeps us feeling good, and feeling good helps us to look good. Proper care of hair and skin surrounding it will result in one's total health and beauty for life. Check with a doctor that can tailor a personalized dietary plan for you.

❦ ADDITIONAL THINGS YOU CAN DO

There are several additional remedies that have been known to strengthen the hair and reduce hair loss and breakage.

- Biotin is a well-known B vitamin that helps to control dry scaly, scalp, depression, hair breakage and loss.

- Equisetum Arvense, also known as Horsetail Tea, is rich with silica and other minerals, and is essential for strong resilient hair.

- Standing on your head will help increase blood circulation. We recommend doing this exercise two to three times a week for 30 to 60 seconds. If the headstand seems a bit extreme, we suggest that you use a slant board.

❦ SLANT BOARD

Slant boards can be purchased or created by slanting a board on top of a chair. The purpose of the slant board is to reverse the body's gravity and to force blood, oxygen and nutrients through the capillaries to feed the hair roots.

For best results, while in a slanted position, massage your scalp with a hand-held vibrating massager for 5 to 15 minutes once or twice a day. When performed properly, finger massages can be very effective as well. Place both hands on the head, using all 10 fingertips, push the scalp toward the center of the head and massage in a circular motion. You might want to practice the flat-handed palm style. Both methods are relaxing and will not damage your hair.

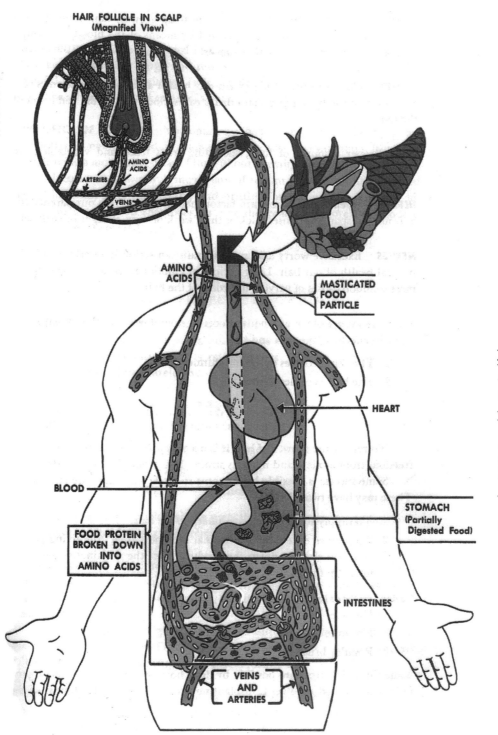

HAIR FOLLICLE IN SCALP
(Magnified View)

AMINO
ACIDS

ARTERIES

VEINS

AMINO
ACIDS

MASTICATED
FOOD
PARTICLE

HEART

BLOOD

STOMACH
(Partially
Digested Food)

FOOD PROTEIN
BROKEN DOWN
INTO
AMINO ACIDS

INTESTINES

VEINS
AND
ARTERIES

Diagram from Hair Structure and Chemistry Simplified

Nutrition and Hair

By Barry L. Fletcher

2

Hair is a cellularly active follicle, and just like the remaining cells and organs in the body, it needs vitamins, minerals and proteins to grow. Hair cells rely on the lymph or fluid portion of the system for their nourishment. As the blood circulates throughout the body, it transports and distributes proteins and nutrients to the hair cells through vessels known as capillaries. These capillaries then feed the nutrients directly to the root of the hair strand.

The World Health Organization estimates that herbs are the primary medicine for two thirds of the world's population, some four billion people. Amongst them are some of the healthiest populations in the world. Most U.S. physicians are trained to rely upon high-technology, laboratory-based medicine, but in the last 15 years, herbs studies made their way into the most prestigious medical journals. Today, there is a dramatic public interest and demand for healing herbs.

Scientists are taking a new look at the gamut of ancient healing remedies, and in the process, they are taking the guess work out of using nature's medicine. On the other hand, some people become so enamored with herbal healing that they reject mainstream medicine entirely. This is a serious mistake. Herbal healing can make a major contribution to human well-being, but many conditions require professional medical care. According to the Food and Drug Administration's present regulations, herbs cannot be patented and are not recognized as medicines. They are classified as a food supplement. They do not require pre-approval, but despite their proven safety and effectiveness, medicinal or healing claims are prohibited. Today, herbs are consumed in large amounts in this country. Since the late 60's, Americans have been changing their views about health care and investing their energy in preventing illness rather than treating it after the fact.

When correctly used, herbs promote the elimination of waste matter and toxins from the system by simple natural means; they support nature in its fight against disease.

"Today, a third of Americans take herbs, whereas probably more than 95 percent take pharmaceuticals," says Michael Castelman in his bibliography, "The Healing Herbs." I suspect those numbers will even out as more people use herbal medicines.

EPHEDRA

Ephedra is generally considered the world's oldest medicine, dating back 5,000 years. It's been used as a bronchial decongestant, to treat asthma, hay fever and nasal and chest congestions. A study in the American Journal of Clinical Nutrition reveals that its significant weight-loss promoting effects may also help smokers decrease nicotine cravings.

GUARANA

This herb from the Amazons increases mental alertness and fights fatigue.

WHITE WILLOW BARK

Has been used since 500 B.C. in China as an effective pain reliever. It's the natural source of the chemical that forms the basis for aspirin (Salicylic Acid). It helps to reduce fevers, soothes headaches and eases other pain and swelling.

BLADDERWRACK

This herb is used to ease obesity and it contains iodine, a nutrient that regulates the thyroid function.

GOTU KOLA

Improves circulation in the legs, which may prevent varicose veins, accelerates wound healing and helps longevity and problems of aging. The herb became popular internally and externally to help skin diseases.

Asia's ultimate tonic enhances memory, learning, productivity and the immune system. It also increases physical stamina while minimizing stress, reduces blood sugar levels and has excellent anti-viral properties.

BEE POLLEN

Bee Pollen is effective in combating fatigue and depression. It contains amounts of all the 22 nutrients needed by mankind.

ASTRAGALUS, LICORICE ROOT, GINGER ROOT, REHMANIA ROOT

These herbs are similar in nature and they are used to relieve stomach problems and reduce fevers and inflammations. They are also good for sore throats and coughs and can be used to help nausea, vomiting and motion sickness.

REISHI MUSHROOM

Listed No. 1 on ancient lists of Chinese medicines. Used primarily to strengthen the immune system. Helps stimulate liver activity and lowers stress, cleanses the blood and beautifies the skin.

Each hair strand is composed of nitrogen, oxygen, hydrogen, sulfur, carbon, water and protein. The composition of these various components vary depending on one's ethnicity, sex, age, genetic make up and overall health. Out of all these components, our health is the only one that we have a chance to influence and control. We achieve this by including proper vitamins, minerals and nutrients in our diet.

VITAMINS AND MINERALS

According to Dr. Lars Engstrand, the famous Swedish scientist and author of the book "Stop Hair Loss," most cases of hair loss are hormonal, nutritional or emotionally related. Dr. Engstrand points out that it is uncommon to see hair loss and balding among people from China, Japan, Spain and Alaska. These people usually have dark, thick, healthy hair, and they seem to grow older without graying as fast. Dr. Engstrand attributes this largely to their diet, and points out that Chinese cuisine is high in minerals, essential fatty acids, proteins, vitamins B and C and unsaturated fats — all important elements for healthy hair. He also indicates that the Japanese eat a lot of seafood, including seaweed, which is rich in iodine, one of the most important nutrients for healthy hair. According to Dr. Engstrand, the Italians procure their proteins, minerals and vitamins from seafood and fresh vegetables as well. Most importantly, Dr. Engstrand points out that all of these ethnicities experience balding and graying only after adopting American eating habits.

IODINE

Iodine is a trace mineral, which helps to manufacture thyroxin, an important element for healthy, strong thyroid glands. When the thyroid is healthy and functioning at its capacity, our metabolism is increased, which, in turn, improves the quality and growth of our hair. On the other hand, when our diet suffers from Iodine deficiency, this results in hair dryness, thinning and slow hair growth. Kelp (dried seaweed) is the richest natural source of iodine and is available in all health food stores in tablet or granulated form.

INCREASING GROWTH

As already indicated, some vitamins and minerals such as B vitamins, panthothenic acid, para-amino-benzoic acid, and folic acid are directly linked to the health of our hair, and they all seem to have anti-graying properties. When used in conjunction with Brewer's Yeast, these vitamins and minerals further darken the hair while improving its quality and increasing its growth.

Wheat germ and wheat germ oils are known to promote hair growth and are used extensively by fur and mink growers. When used as a dietary supplement, however, wheat germ should always be fresh.

Protein is also essential to hair growth but can be overconsumed.

Essentially, fatty acids such as vitamin F are believed to assist the sebaceous gland. The sebaceous gland produces sebum, which moisturizes the skin, scalp and hair. Vitamin F can be found in nuts, raw seeds and unsaturated vegetable oils. Vitamin A also can be used to combat dry, itchy, flaky skin and scalp. Cod-liver oil contains the richest source of natural vitamin A.

Protein is also essential to hair growth but can be overconsumed. Fifty grams a day will suffice and can be obtained in one potato or two swallows of milk. Be mindful, people who live in Asia, India and Mexico have thick, black hair, although they live on low-protein diets.

Lecithin and B vitamins, including choline and dinositol, protect the arteries from hardening. When the arteries are hardened, the blood supply to the scalp is restricted and hair growth is diminished. Smoking, overeating and high blood pressure may also impair blood circulation to the scalp.

According to Dr. Engstand, if we wish to optimize the health of our hair, we should supplement our diet daily with the following:

- Brewer's Yeast, powder or flakes - 2 to 3 tablespoons.

- Lecithin, Granules - 1 to 2 tablespoons.

- Vitamin E – One 400 to 1200 I.U. a day (before meals).

- Vitamin C (from a rose hips or other natural sources) - up to 1000MG.

  Note: In case of high blood pressure, consult your doctor for proper dosage of vitamin C.

- Vitamin B Complex, High Potency, natural - 1 to 3 tablets.

- Cod-liver oil, unfortified 1 TSDP.

- Vitamin A, natural - 25,000 USP.

- Kelp - up to 10 tablets.

- Bone Meal Tablets, For Minerals - 5 to 10 tablets.

- Cod-Pressed Vegetable Oil For Vitamin F - 1 to 2 tablespoons a day. This may be used on salads, cereals, etc. Olive oil and sesame seed oil are most likely to be cold pressed and non-rancid.

Unless otherwise indicated, food supplements should be taken with meals. Consult your medical physician regarding the amount of supplements you should take and how long you need to consume them before seeing results.

Going Natural: Breaking the Lyes

By Toya Watts, Managing Director, S.E.P.I.A., Washington, DC

Natural style options and advantages

Women choose to "go natural" for many reasons. Some cite religious practices, social and political movements or simply a desire to be a "down" sister. Sometimes, it's just a trendy here-today-gone-tomorrow fashion statement. Often expectant mothers heed the solid medical advice against using chemicals and allow their natural hair to flourish during pregnancy. There are as many reasons for the resurgence of natural hair as there are hairstyles.

For many years I had envisioned the endless afternoons of carefree child's play and the beauty of my plaits unraveling in the wind. Between touchups, I'd caress the sprouting tight wave pattern of my new hair growth. You see, in longing to feel the textured tresses I was blessed with from birth, I'd go for months without a touchup and became a master with the press-n-curl "the edges" technique. I did anything to keep my natural hair thriving under six to seven inches of relaxed hair. Then in angst and frustration, with pressure from impatient hairstylists, I'd throw up my hands and surrender my new growth once more to what had now become a way of life— styles, chemicals and burning scalp — the going price for vanity. All along I desired to experience, touch, see and wear my hair in its natural state.

I believe many women have this secret love affair with their natural hair. But through years of "burnreditchhothead afternoon" appointments, ending in straight, luxurious tresses, they have forgotten the splendor, feel and unique personalities of our natural hair. We have forgotten our hair and its sheer beauty, its versatility, the styling techniques and products, and the opportunities it allows us for nurturing and pampering ourselves. I admit it. I had just forgotten how or what to do with: "hair au naturel."

A PARTNER IN HAIR CARE

I wasn't giving up. My love for hair au naturel, a lean budget and growing intolerance for the six-to-eight-hour Saturday hair appointment sent me in search of hairstyling options. Luckily, I was working with a dear friend who was a very creative stylist and a proponent for ultimate versatility. She refused to overprocess my hair and retouch new growth every six weeks. Instead, she opted for 12 weeks or more. Finally, I had found a stylist who was a real partner in my hair care plan. She opted for setting my shoulder-length hair on rollers and smoothing the natural hair with a curling iron. Occasionally, she would gently blow-dry the roots, producing more body and the beginnings of a full head of healthy hair.

As the spring and summer months approached, my two to three inches of virgin hair became a bit more difficult to manage beneath four inches-plus of relaxed hair. Convenience then became the order of the hot, humid summer days. What is more convenient and versatile, with a more relaxed hair care regime, than braids? Or so I thought.

As you transition to braids, while making your way to natural hair, you trade several long six-to-eight hour appointments for maybe one daylong appointment every six to eight weeks. And you buy mounds of extra hair for braid extensions. Neck muscles and hair follicles often are strained from the extra hair on your head. You may even lose a few nights of sleep as you adjust to your temporary tresses. Braids also require careful maintenance, conditioning and washing to reduce residue and dirt. Over time, I found that braids could strain and reduce the natural hairline.

Choosing an experienced braid technician who will offer assistance beyond the initial hair appointment was the secret to my success. Braids are a beautiful option and a great temporary solution for growing natural hair without kutting. I wore casama braids for four months, then welcomed in the cooler months with a few extra inches of natural hair — and an appointment with a new hairstylist.

STYLIST OPTIONS

My stylist had moved to New York and recommended a friend to fill her slot. This new hairstylist happened to be Ethiopian and was one of the few I knew at the time who worked on such a range of hair textures. My braids were gone and I was on my way. It's important to choose a stylist who will tend to your particular needs and wants, and then work with you to maintain healthy hair.

During the winter months when humidity was not an issue, I visited the salon maybe every three weeks. Between those visits I would wash, condition and braid or twist my hair and then air dry. Sometimes I'd tuck my hair under hats or let it peep out from beneath other headgear. As my hair grew

longer, I finally started to experience what I had longed for: a healthy, luxurious, strong, shiny crown of natural-textured tresses. One day during the warmer months I missed my salon appointment and decided to administer my own home treatment. After washing and deep conditioning my hair, I stared into the mirror and noticed that my natural hair had grown so that now just two inches of relaxed hair hung limply on the ends of a vibrant, dark, kinky, coily mass. It had its own personality and was poised to come alive. I grabbed the scissors and gently clipped dozens of limp pieces from my crown and began my new life with "hair au naturel."

Natural products are best, no alcohol please!

Listed below are just a few satirical excerpts from my natural hair experience, ranging from public comments, societal attitudes and my rediscovery process.

My Facts About Natural Hair Care:

- You don't have to kut your hair off to go natural.

- Water is your natural moisturizer, so revel in the misty rain or fling your neck back under the shower and let your tresses...flow, coil, etc.

- Color is now a great option for your hair repertoire.

- You are in control of your natural wave pattern; it is yours and yours only, a one of a kind. It's like your fingerprint or your signature.

- You control the twist, turn, coil and curl of your hair with just a little water, a precious styling tool.

- Natural products are best, no alcohol please!

- Convenience is yours.

- The silk pillowcase is your friend.

- Maximum flexibility is also yours; if you want sleek, straight, smooth, it is still an option and not far out of reach.

- Natural hair is you on the job! In fact, you may receive more resistance from your brothers and sisters than any corporate world colleague. Don't be surprised and don't fret. Your beautiful tresses and unwavering confidence will break them in gently, and soon they will seek your advice and natural hair tips.

- Natural hair is sexy! And you and your lover will still enjoy running your fingers through it.

- Chemical-free hair can improve your health. Moving from inorganic harmful chemicals commonly absorbed through the scalp and skin to organic products — such as shea butter and herbs — can increase overall skin tone and elasticity.

- Chemical-free hair can reduce stress and in some instances, free you from endless hair appointments to enjoy your life, and especially Saturdays.

- Compared with popular chemical treatments, natural hairstyles can save you money over time.

- Natural hairstyles last longer.

- Natural is not wiry like a brillo pad; when clean, it is soft, supple and sensuous.

AN INTERVIEW WITH THE AUTHOR

Is going natural something every black woman should do?

No, hairstyles are personal and reflect each individual's sense of style, preference and mode. A woman should wear hairstyles that are most comfortable and complimentary for her. I personally recommend that women at least experiment and flirt with natural hairstyles as an option. For most of our lives, as women, we have struggled with our individual hair

textures to change or tame it. Now seems to be a great time to usher in natural hair, with the variety of hair care products available containing ingredients like shea butter, herbs and essential oils, and other nonalcohol and softening agents that are gentle and nourishing to natural and textured hair.

Do you think relaxing is a bad thing?

Chemically, I believe relaxing is bad for the hair. During the 15 years I relaxed my hair, I noticed my mane had thinned quite a bit. I believe the chemicals and relaxers are very harsh and damaging to the scalp and skin. I believe anything that burns like that could not be healthy in the long run. Again, for years I suffered the chemical irritants to maintain a luxurious flowing head of hair that I believed was more acceptable, convenient and easier to maintain than natural hair.

Have relaxers ever caused you problems?

The chemical in relaxers often irritated my scalp and skin when first applied, and I noticed my hair would cycle through various dry and brittle stages during my regular six to 10 week touchup cycle. As a result, I experienced more hair breakage and shedding when using relaxers.

Does your hair shed more now that it is natural versus when it was relaxed?

My hair-shedding pattern is very different, and overall I can say I experience less hair shedding with my natural hair. I believe my relaxed hair was more fragile and prone to breakage and split ends than my natural hair. With relaxed hair, the shedding occurred when the hair was dry or continuously exposed to heat products. I noticed a little hair shedding when styling with a large-tooth comb or during routine wash and comb out. Natural hair tends to be more tolerant of heat and dry weather, however, it also requires moisturizing and gentle treatment to prevent tangles and hair breakage.

Do you find that you have more dandruff now than when you started getting relaxers?

No, it's really about the same. I notice that my scalp is a bit drier than when I had a relaxer. Washing with a moisturizing shampoo and keeping the scalp properly nourished with a cream hairdress reduces my dry scalp and dandruff.

Can you tell the difference in over-the-counter versus professional, herbal, ethnic and European?

Yes, now more than ever I notice the difference in the quality of hair care products. There are several over-the-counter products that work well for natural hair, and for me it was worth the savings and convenience. However, I have not used many professional products specifically designed for natural hair. I'd love to try them. Most of the "professional" products are designed for use with chemically treated hair or they claim to be "recommended for all types" of hair. These products usually include some amount of alcohol or other ingredients that dry or make my natural hair coarse. Herbal formula products are far gentler and smell wonderful.

Do you think you will ever go back to a relaxer?

No. I wear my hair sleek and straight sometimes, and I love the versatility of being a quick-change artist with natural hair. One day I wear it silky straight, then a couple days later it's a textured 'fro; two days later, two-stranded twists. The possibilities are endless.

Do you feel sexier with a natural style?

Yes, I find it sexy that I can change my hairstyle, particularly the texture, to fit my mood with little damage and minimum effort.

Does it minimize our versatility?

The possibilities are endless, particularly when the weather is dry. During humid or rainy seasons I go with the flow of the weather and wear my hair in textured styles instead of sporting smooth straight hairstyles.

What is the difference mentally?

Mentally, I am confident, free and in control. I feel absolutely beautiful in all my chosen hairstyles. I feel like I have mastered the hair dilemma and found a place of comfort with myself since, in essence, I can totally surrender my hair to the environmental elements and still wear hairstyles that complement any style.

Which one is the easiest to take care of?

Both require proper maintenance. Relaxed hair requires more regular visits to a professional hair salon for touchups, trimming, conditioning and styling. To maintain my natural hair I visit a professional stylist every six to eight weeks for regular trimming and conditioning. Since my natural hair is not exposed to constant heat appliances, it is stronger, healthier and easier to manage with a home care beauty regime.

Which is the most expensive?

Relaxed hair is more expensive to maintain with the regular salon visits. I averaged about $45 to $65 per regular salon visit for regular maintenance of relaxed hair every two to three weeks. This is omitting the touchup, kut, color and other extras, which can raise the price to $85 and higher, particularly if you have long hair. The average price for maintaining my natural hair per salon visit every six to eight weeks is $35 to $45, without major extras like color.

Would you ever relax your daughter's hair?

Probably not, since I know how to nourish and style natural hair. I think most mothers relax their daughter's hair for a more manageable texture for themselves and their daughters who may want to start styling and maintaining their hair. However, if taught at an early age how to manage and style their natural hair and include proper products, more mothers may start to pass on relaxers.

How does pressing work for you?

I don't use a pressing comb. I use a hot curling iron to straighten and curl the hair when it is textured. It works well.

What do white folks think about relaxed hair versus natural?

Most white folks like and understand straight hair since it looks straight and similar to their hair. They are fascinated with the versatility of our hair in general. They seem to like and prefer what is comfortable for them: viewing black people with straight hair. Natural hairstyles will certainly separate the curious and despondent from those who sincerely appreciate and respect the diversity of African hair and culture. Corporate culture certainly has been reluctant to openly accept natural hairstyles — braids, twists — as a styling option for African Americans, and we are part to blame. When I worked for a top public relations firm, many of my black co-workers were more vocal about their discomfort with my "militant hairstyle" and issued words of caution at our appearing too black in the workplace. Surprisingly, my white colleagues overall were accepting and complimentary and quite frankly fascinated by the diversity of our hair. As we continue to change and create what is acceptable for ourselves, others will eventually follow our lead and accept us, too.

Could you grow your hair out using a relaxer?

I did not kut off my relaxed hair when I decided to let my natural hair grow. I followed a careful hair care regime with my hairstylist to minimize breakage and stress to the different textures. I did not apply any type of relaxer or light texturizer chemical treatment once I decided to go natural.

What kind of problems are you having now?

I would like to find more stylists who professionally care for natural hair from the initial growing-out stages to continued maintenance in hairstyling, hairkutting, and a variety of textures.

As we continue to change and create what is acceptable for ourselves, others will eventually follow our lead and accept us, too.

What's Hair Got To Do With It?

By Donna Britt—Columnist, Washington, D.C.

What hair

means to us.

Even when I was a little girl, one fact seemed obvious: Even if nothing else was working — if my clothes were wrinkled or my sneakers scuffed — if my hair looked good, I looked good, too.

Most sisters would agree. When your hair falls just right — when, through some miracle, you or your stylist manages to get each curl or wave to align just so with every other — you FEEL better too. And no woman on the planet needs the uplift that comes from having great-looking hair than a black woman.

That's because any sister who has beautiful hair and knows it has arrived at a hallowed place, indeed. For generations, black women were taught to hate the hair God gave them. Decade after decade, we learned to see the springy stuff on our heads as being "too" something or other — too knotty, too kinky, too thick, too hard to control, just too damn much. In a culture that often devalues black women's wider noses, fuller lips, lush behinds and myriad skin shades, having "troublesome" hair feels like the last straw.

I mean, really. How can a woman feel beautiful if she's convinced her hair is an irredeemable mess? How can she relax and celebrate all that she is — her intelligence, her sensuality, her tenderness — if she's convinced that one vital part of her is ugly? No wonder so many black women treat their hair the way they would treat any "problem" — by fighting it with all their might.

We have fought our hair with arsenals of harsh, ineptly applied chemicals. We've attacked it with smoking combs overheated in open flames, and with blazing hot curling rods. We've tried to tame it by smearing our scalps with every imaginable oil, cream and pomade.

The battle scars of our never-ending hair wars are impossible to miss: breakage, excessive dryness, inadequate growth, even balding. So when a sister somehow makes peace with her hair, when, through proper care and nutrition, she allows her crowning glory to become a glorious crown, indeed — she feels as great as she looks.

Most black women see that as a goal worth chasing. That's why no women spend more time, effort or a larger proportion of their income on their hair than black women. We know that no day feels worse than a really bad hair day.

I learned that when I was 12 years of age. Swathed in protective plastic, I sat in an aqua vinyl chair in Emma's Salon of Beauty in Gary, Ind., filled with the anticipation I always felt at the "beauty shop." I wondered: How gorgeous would I look when this painful process was done? What transformation would I see, once the beautician — whom Mom was paying eight whole dollars to wash, dry, oil, press and curl my shoulder-length hair — was finished?

Emma, my regular hairdresser, was away, but I knew her surrogate would make me beautiful. But how? Would I look sophisticated like the Ebony magazine model with the tower of cluster curls? Haughty like the helmet-haired Diana Ross? Cute like the girls in "Seventeen?"

The stakes were higher than usual because my best friend had accompanied me to the shop. I was hoping to impress Sharon, whose wavy, down-to-there hair required no beauticians, perms or hot combs to make it flow like the Nile down her back. I fantasized that my new, grown-up hairstyle would show Sharon how great we girls who didn't have "good" hair could look. When I felt my hair being brushed toward the crown of my head and then pinned into place, I happily realized I was getting an upsweep — an elegant, Audrey Hepburn 'do.

Finally, the beautician whirled my chair around for me to look at my hair. My super-straightened hair was plastered so flat against my scalp that I looked nearly bald — except for a Ping-Pong ball-sized topknot that made my head look as enormous as Tweety Pie's.

The walk across the room — past ogling fellow customers — was the longest I'd ever taken. Then I saw Sharon, red-faced and bulgy-eyed from her efforts to keep from laughing. When our eyes met, we both lost it, nearly falling on the floor giggling.

That time, at least, I could laugh. Nearly every woman has had moments when she confronted a stylist's "handiwork" and could barely keep from crying.

Like the time I got a perm guaranteed not to hurt my delicate hair. Weeks later, my stylist, examining my hair, excitedly called over three or four co-workers. "Look, you have to see this!" he exclaimed, pulling a small handful of my damaged hair out for their inspection. "See how EASILY it comes out!"

Clearly, the men and women to whom we entrust our precious hair sometimes make serious mistakes. Black hair is notoriously complex in structure; it comes in more types, textures and strengths — sometimes on a single head — than some merely competent hair professionals can handle. How often have we seen women who, disappointed by hairdresser after hairdresser, gave up and resorted to wigs, braids, scarves, hats or to just living with awful-looking hair?

Actually, less often than you'd think, hair has too much to do with how a woman sees herself, and with how she's seen by the world, for most women to throw in the shampoo towel.

Black women, especially, have the most versatile hair on earth, capable of being worn straight, nappy, wavy, curled, dreaded, twisted or darn-near-bald and STILL look amazing. It's also the most challenging hair to control and maintain. Truly, black hair can be a blessing — and a curse.

How many sisters do you know who haven't fled from an unexpected rainstorm so fast that you'd think the Blair Witch was pursuing her? How many haven't fielded veiled or blunt questions from white co-workers perplexed and fascinated by our hair's endless versatility?

What sister hasn't melted into a salon chair after a long week of working, cleaning, cooking and arranging things for others, grateful to finally have someone take care of HER? Who among us hasn't, at least once, had a stylist twirl her around to see in the mirror a vision whose perfect, gorgeous 'do made not just her day, but her whole week?

On the flip side, who hasn't sat, hour after hour, waiting to be seen by an overbooked stylist in a popular salon — even though she was ON TIME for her appointment?

No wonder some of us see the beauty salon as a haven as comfy as our grandma's kitchen, and others avoid it like a pot of month-old spaghetti. But salons, and our requirements of them, are changing — because WE are changing. Most African American women still straighten their hair either with chemicals or heat, and many look fabulous.

What's Hair Got To Do With It?

But impressive numbers are embracing heat-and-chemical-free afros, twists and locks. Our recent acceptance of our hair, as-is, signals a healthy adjustment in our self-esteem, challenging centuries-old notions that nappy, knotty and natural black girl hair can't be beautiful.

Yet the emergence of natural styles that suggest that ALL hair is "good" won't end our beauty shop addiction. A survivor of hot-comb burns, bad perms and 10 hours in a hair braider's chair, I graduated to locks two years ago. I felt like a caterpillar who'd shed at least a dozen false skins, and finally emerged — not as a butterfly, but as myself. I now have a long, versatile, entirely natural style that's all my own hair that I adore — and that I have professionally groomed every few weeks.

Sure I could maintain some version of the style myself at little cost. But why would I? My "loctician" or "locologist" lets me sit back and momentarily forget ringing phones, cranky kids, a perpetually messy house and an insistent career. I chill when she has done her magic and whirls me around; I love what I see: A relaxed woman with a style she loves, whose hair feels clean, shiny and healthy. And whose soul feels the same way.

Who's Relaxing— You or Your Hair?

By Barry L. Fletcher

The truth about lye verses no-lye relaxer and application methods.

✇ THE HISTORY OF RELAXERS

*I*t is a prevalent psychological theory that human beings yearn for the opposite of what we have. This is especially evident as it relates to our hair. Individuals with straight hair spend hours in the salon having it waved or curled, while those with naturally curly hair go through great lengths to have it straightened or relaxed.

The concept of using lye to straighten curly hair began in the 1920's. Hair products designed for coarse, curly textures were scarce or non-existent then, so black people created their method to soften and manage their hair. Using lye was an extreme measure, and the harshness of this process significantly limited its popularity. Eventually, conditioners and other products were added to the lye as a buffer; one of the most popular additions was petroleum. By the early 1940's, lye relaxers had grown in popularity, but their usage was still limited to entertainers, athletes and influential figures of that time. Ironically, most of them were men. Hair relaxers didn't become popular among black women until 1947, and didn't enter the mainstream market until approximately 10 years after that.

It was a black man by the name of George Johnson who first introduced and marketed the chemical hair relaxer as a professional product. Johnson was a chemist who began working with Fuller Brush Products in the early 1950's. By 1954, he left Fuller Products to develop his own product line, including a hair relaxer, which he introduced as a product to be sold only to professional cosmetologists. By 1969, Johnson Products Inc. achieved $10 million in sales, and by 1971, it became the first predominantly black-owned firm to be listed on a major stock exchange.

Hair relaxing and black hair care had become big business and suddenly the target of mainstream corporations, which wanted to capitalize on the growing success of this market. In the early 1980's, these corporations began directly marketing the chemical hair relaxer to general consumers. In addition, they produced the no-lye relaxer. The no-lye relaxer kit was introduced as a mild, safe, do-it-yourself relaxer that could be applied at home. The assumptions were that consumers believed that lye-based relaxers were unsafe and damaging to the hair and that they generally were unhappy with the chemical services provided by cosmetologist.

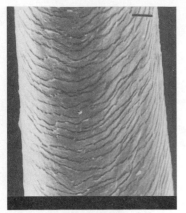
Healthy Hair Strand

After Lye Relaxer

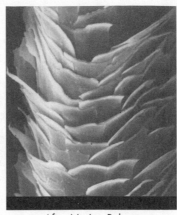
After No Lye Relaxer

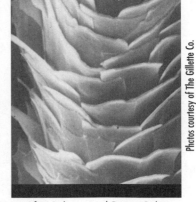
After Relaxer and Perm. Color

I always find it interesting that so many would claim sodium hydroxide relaxers to be damaging to the hair. Famous artists such as Nat King Cole, Duke Ellington, Sammy Davis Jr. and numerous others used sodium hydroxide (lye) relaxers more than 40 years ago and there was no evidence of damaging side effects from its usage. In fact, the majority of men who used relaxers then had strong, healthy hair. So why are we now suggesting that sodium hydroxide relaxers are damaging to the hair, when our relaxer products are far more advanced than they were 40 years ago?

I maintain that sodium hydroxide relaxers do not cause hair breakage. It is the improper application of the relaxer and poor follow-up procedures that cause breakage. When relaxers were first introduced, they had warning labels stating that excessive heat from blow dryers and Marcel irons should not be used on relaxed hair. In addition, cosmetologists were instructed to wet set the hair after the relaxer application. Numerous educational forums, workshops and seminars were made available to educate cosmetologists about proper chemical usage and application. But eventually these educational venues drastically diminished, leaving generations of cosmetologists misinformed and without the most basic guidelines to proper chemical hair treatment and applications.

The most common mistake made today when applying sodium hydroxide relaxers on female clients is in diagnosing the client's hair texture and calculating the appropriate smoothing time needed to successfully straighten the hair. Most manufacturers recommend that we allow eight minutes to apply the relaxer. The recommended time for smoothing the relaxer varies, however, according to the recipient's hair texture. If the hair texture is fine, then the smoothing process should not exceed five minutes. If the texture is regular, smoothing time should not exceed eight minutes and, if the hair is coarse and resistant, a 10-minute smoothing period is required. The total application procedure should never exceed 20 minutes. I personally suggest not exceeding 15

minutes. Most male relaxing services are kept under 10 minutes, which explains why men with relaxed hair have fewer problems with damage control.

BEAUTY—BIG BUSINESS

According to studies, African Americans purchase 37 percent of all beauty products sold in the United States but make up 12 percent of the population. In 1998 alone, over-the-counter health and beauty product sales totaled $1.6 billion in revenue. Relaxer kits were the No. 1 beauty product sold over the counter and represented $59 million in sales. Beauty has become big business. And while new hair relaxers and other products are entering the market every day, there is little or no emphasis on researching the companies that produce these goods or the long-term effect they have on our hair. Instead, manufacturers, both white and black, are more concerned with increasing their profit than with the welfare of the black consumer.

It is this greed and lack of concern for consumer health that fostered the Rio relaxer hair tragedy several years ago. The Rio hair relaxer was designed primarily for wavy, abundantly oily hair, but it was marketed to people with dry, excessively curly hair. Rio manufacturers claimed that the relaxer was chemical-free, but it registered on the acid side of the pH scale, which made it non-conducive for excessively dry, curly hair. Three hundred and fifty thousand packets were sold; 5,000 people filed claims.

Manufacturers should never be allowed to promote such claims. The sad part is that major publications will not educate consumers about this kind of information because they fear jeopardizing potential advertising dollars from these same manufacturers. So there is really no vehicle or visible outlet to retrieve critical information regarding the health of our hair. This is one of the reasons why I was compelled to write this book.

The hair care industry is at an all-time low. Publishing companies are selling consumers down the river in exchange for advertising dollars and manufacturers are turning their backs on the salon industry, marketing directly to the consumer. The beauty industry overall has evolved into a chemical waste dump, and in the process, black women are losing their hair. If you measure black women's hair from the turn of the century until now you will find that the average length of hair for an African American female was 10 to 12 inches. Now, the average length is four to six inches and is steadily decreasing.

We are experiencing a hair crisis within the black community, and it is not being addressed. In February 1998, I was invited to the American Health and Beauty Aid Institute's annual convention in Miami. The theme was "Maximizing Profitability." My goal was to discuss the current trends in the black hair industry. As a guest speaker on the panel, I tried to impress upon them that the trend was that black women are losing their hair. They didn't hear me though.

THE TRUTH ABOUT NO-LYE

I find it interesting that those who push no-lye relaxers do not educate the consumer about the effect the relaxers have on hair. The no-lye relaxer is the worst hair product to hit the shelves in my 20 years as a hairstylist. Remember, commercials are geared toward selling, and a lie can be perceived as the truth if eloquently told. The truth is, no-lye relaxers aren't as safe as they are promoted to be. In most

cases, it under-processes the hair, changes its texture and robs the hair of its moisture. Hair that has been repeatedly processed with no-lye relaxers becomes extremely dry and brittle. The scalp also will be excessively dry and deteriorated. The reason: consumers literally become relaxed— and careless—in their usage of no-lye relaxers because

they are under the misconception that the products are harmless to the hair and scalp. They do not take the additional care required to ensure the no-lye relaxer does not touch the scalp; they tend to keep it on the hair longer because it does not burn as fast, and because no-lye relaxers don't last as long as sodium hydroxide relaxers, consumers tend to apply the chemical more frequently. Instead of receiving touchups every six to eight weeks, as is the case with the lye relaxers, no-lye users may touchup every four to six weeks. In reality, some no-lye relaxers are higher on the pH scale than a super sodium hydroxide relaxer. The problems is, no-lye relaxers over-expose and under-process the hair. As a result, the long-term effects of no-lye usage tend to be much more damaging.

"No-lye" relaxers contain two main ingredients, carbonate and calcium hydroxide. Together they form guanidine hydroxide. Guanidine hydroxide has a high pH, ranging from 12 to 14, which is the same or higher on the pH scale than lye relaxers, but it does not produce equivalent results.

Relaxers containing lithium and potassium hydroxide are also marketed as "no-lye, no-mix" formula, and like lye relaxers or sodium hydroxide, they are high on the pH scale. They offer no real advantage over sodium hydroxide; they do not silken or straighten the hair like sodium, and with prolonged usage, the hair texture becomes dull, dry and grainy.

Two additional relaxer systems that qualify as "no lye" contain the ingredients tetramethy and ammonium bisulfate. They normally come in a gel and should be avoided at all costs. The pH is about 7 to 7.5. These ingredients do not straighten the hair at all, and have an extremely drying effect on the hair.

The chemical ingredients used in a no-lye relaxer are similar to the ammonium thioglycloate (thio) solution used in curl perms and has a similar effect on the hair. Thio has a high alkaline content, which has a tendency to drain the moisture from the cortex of the hair strand, causing it to become dry and porous. This is compounded with each new application. Eventually the hair begins to shed.

If you were to blow dry and hot iron hair that has been chemically processed with a curl, you would witness breaking and shedding within 48 hours. A chemically processed curl is only safe as long as it's maintained with activators and moisturizers. A no-lye relaxer is similar in this respect and requires that the hair be kept excessively moist — just like a curl perm. If you are using a no-lye relaxer, make sure that you keep an abundance of liquid oil or cream pomade on the hair. I recommend spraying a moisturizer or using a little activator on your hair the day before you shampoo it. I also suggest deep penetrating conditioning treatments, using a steam machine or a hot steam towel. Fortunately, you can switch over to a sodium lye-base relaxer. If you choose to switch, condition your hair at least three consecutive weeks before changing. I strongly recommend that a trained professional cosmetologist do the procedure.

KIDDIE KITS

The over-the-counter Kiddie Kits are simply no-lye relaxers marketed from a different angle. Again, I strongly recommend that you avoid no-lye relaxers. If you find that your child's hair is resistant and you are seeking more manageability, use a sodium lye-based relaxer. Leave it on just long enough to soften the hair, then set it to seal in the moisture. The off-the-scalp relaxer method would be best (see segment on relaxer methods). After setting the hair, you can follow up with braids, afro puffs or whatever style you want. An alternative is to dilute your relaxer with conditioners. This method would leave your child's hair in a much healthier state.

SODIUM HYDROXIDE — DISPELLING THE MYTH

The main active ingredient in lye relaxer is sodium hydroxide. This substance has a pH ranging from 12 to 14, and is made of inorganic active ingredients designed to permanently straighten naturally curly hair.

I often hear talk about relaxers being harmful. On the flip side, however, I know many women who would not have any hair if it were not for these relaxers. Sisters who have excessively curly or resistant hair and do not wish to wear it

in its natural state often resort to blow-drying, hot pressing and hot curling their hair. Using three consecutive heating elements is extremely stressful and damages the hair. Chemical relaxing softens the hair and allows it to accept conditioners and moisturizers more readily. When we follow up the relaxer application with a wet set or wrap, in essence we are sealing moisture in as opposed to blowing it out. This has a much healthier effect on the hair.

Sisters, sodium hydroxide relaxers are not your enemy and they do not have to cause discomfort if applied properly. If you experience any discomfort, it should be minimum. Personally, when it comes to lye relaxers versus no-lye relaxers, I would rather experience a little discomfort and know that my hair is being properly cared for, as opposed to experiencing temporary comfort while my hair is being destroyed.

I am hard on the no-lye relaxer because I know the damage it can cause. The average sister using this product believes she is doing the right thing and is not aware of the negative side effects until it is too late. The no-lye relaxer was introduced by mainstream companies to convince sisters that they do not need a professional cosmetologist and can apply their own chemical relaxer. Granted, many professional cosmetologists brought this upon themselves by rendering inferior services to black consumers for so long, but we all do not fit into the same category. There are many well-trained professional cosmetologists who will provide the quality care your hair needs and deserves.

TO RELAX, OR NOT TO RELAX?
THAT IS THE QUESTION

Many doctors, scientists and researchers have dispelled the notion that relaxers can cause birth defects during pregnancy.

As loving parents you want the best for your children. You want them to have clothing and shelter, get the best education, and develop a strong self-image. Most of all, you want them to be safe and healthy. Having healthy hair is part of that equation. In order to achieve this, you must learn your child's hair texture, understand its specific needs and respond accordingly, regardless of the child's age or gender.

Keep in mind that if your daughter needs a relaxer, whether she's 6 or 12, it will not harm the hair if properly applied. This is not to say that everyone should relax a child's hair at an early age. In most cases, a child's hair is strongest during the puberty stages. However, when we examine the average high school and junior high school student, a good portion of them have problem hair. Anytime you have children in junior high and high school wearing hair weaves, that should tell us that we are doing something wrong. Reversing this scenario may require us to relax the hair a little earlier, a little later or not at all. The point is, this is something that needs to be determined with the help and guidance of a trained professional cosmetologist.

There are vital signs that indicate whether the hair should be relaxed; for instance, if the hair is baby soft and will not hold a curl, then chances are it should not be relaxed; if the hair is very resistant but it has a lot of stretch and can hold a slight curl, you may use a light texturizer to reduce the frizz (look under texturizer for more information); if the hair is overly resistant and the child is in agony while having her hair shampooed, conditioned and styled; if there is excessive breakage when combing or brushing the hair; if it is excessively dry and brittle, then you should consider having the hair professionally relaxed using a sodium hydroxide relaxer. Sodium hydroxide relaxers can be diluted by simply adding and mixing a conditioner to its contents (i.e. B. F. Revitalizing conditioner).

Understanding proper chemical relaxer application procedures is critical to maintaining healthy hair. While most black women relax their hair for more manageability, style and control, it is important to bear in mind that hair does not have to be relaxed bone straight. Ideally, we should only relax up to 75 percent of our natural curl pattern. After the neutralizing process, only 50 percent of the sulfur bonds are going to reform the newly straightened condition. Therefore, after the relaxer procedure, only 35 percent of the hair actually should be transformed into a straighter position. This is enough relaxation for excessively curly hair to become manageable.

RELAXERS—CAUSE AND EFFECT

Hair relaxers contain active chemical ingredients that rearrange the curl shaped molecules in the cortex of the hair strand to create a permanently straightened molecular formation within the strand.

Longevity, manageability and flexibility are just a few of the advantages of chemical hair relaxing. Unlike pressed hair, relaxed hair will not revert to its natural state. Within six to eight weeks of using a relaxer, maybe longer depending on the hair texture, you should see a substantial amount of natural hair growth emerging from the root of the scalp. Chemical relaxers should be applied to this new growth to balance out the opposing hair textures and avoid breakage. When a chemical relaxer is properly applied and maintained, you will have more styling flexibility and the hair will grow. On the other hand, no matter how skillful you are in your relaxer application, excessive chemical relaxing does weaken the hair. Try to keep your relaxer applications to a minimum. Retouch applications should not exceed six to eight times a year for normal to resistant hair textures. Do not carelessly apply chemical relaxer or overlap onto previously relaxed hair because this may remove the hair's protective coating and cause it to dry and break.

In his article "Hair Loss and Baldness in Black Women," Dr. Cylburn E. Soden stated that the main cause of baldness among his patients is improperly applied chemical relaxers. He indicated that he sees an average of five patients a day and the chief hair complaints are dryness and breakage. Many of these patients are balding at the nape of the neck and in the crown and front area of the head. Almost without exception, the patients are using lye or no-lye relaxers, rinses or dyes. The products usually have been administered every four to six weeks over several years.

According to Dr. Soden, scalp fungal infection is also common among young black women and causes hair dryness, breakage and baldness. Most patients suffering from this problem range from 20 to 70 years in age and have received relaxers every four to six weeks over a period of 15 to 20 years or more. The women in the age range of

40 to 60 often have baldness in the crown and temporal area of the scalp. It is the chemical damage, perhaps from relaxers, perms or hair color that has harmed the structure of the hair and scalp. This eventually results in baldness.

Dr. Soden recognizes that there are strong correlations between relaxer usage and baldness, but he still does not label chemical hair relaxers as the direct cause of balding. He believes that hair texture is a major contributing factor and that prolonged usage of chemical relaxers compounds the problem.

Dr. Elise A. Olsen, author of the book "Disorder of Hair Growth," believes that hair breakage and loss can't be blamed on the relaxer itself. In many cases hair loss and breakage are a result of alopecia, which is a genetic problem. Dr. Olsen does acknowledge that chemical relaxers could aggravate these alopecia conditions and suggest that we either stop using the relaxer altogether, educate ourselves on proper relaxer applications or demand that superior relaxer products be put on the market.

Dr. Sperling, specialist in ethnic hair and disorders, dispels the theory that chemical relaxers cause scalp disorders such as Follicle Degeneration Syndrome (FDS). He points out that FDS starts in the hair sheath and works its way outward, and is therefore a genetic issue. He has numerous patients who experience FDS regardless of whether they use chemical relaxers. Dr. Sperling conducts seminars for other dermatologists. His articles are featured regularly in the National Institute of Health (NIH) publication and in dermatologist newsletters.

✑ RELAXING METHODS

There are four practical methods that are used when chemically relaxing the hair:

1. Full Relaxer

When a chemical relaxer is applied to natural or virgin hair for the first time, it is referred to as a full relaxer. Your hair should be thoroughly examined beforehand. If it is damaged or weak because of excessive braiding, weaving or heat application, the hair is not ready to be relaxed and should be treated instead with protein and moisturizing conditioners. Once the hair has regained its strength and moisture content, then you may consider the relaxer. A trained hair care professional can advise you properly.

2. Retouch

About six to eight weeks after using a relaxer, new hair growth will emerge. The point at which the new growth meets the previously relaxed hair is referred to as the demarcation line and is extremely sensitive to tension, heat and chemical application. The purpose of relaxing or retouching the new hair growth is to smooth out the demarcation line and balance the opposing hair textures. This process relieves the tension from the hair and prevents potential breakage. Bear in mind that during the retouching process, the chemical relaxer should be applied to the new growth only.

Some practitioners (so-called professionals) believe that it's okay to pull the relaxer to the end of the hair during each touchup application. This is referred to as overlapping, and is not only unnecessary, but if applied excessively, leads to overprocessing, which damages the hair. Some cosmetologist try to justify overlapping by claiming that relaxed hair eventually reverts to its natural wavy state. A sodium hydroxide relaxer permanently straightens the hair. It will not revert. If you have always been using a no-lye product, some reverting could occur. If so, a corrective relaxer may need to be applied by a trained, professional cosmetologist.

3. Texturizing Relaxer

Texturizing is a simple procedure in which the relaxer is combed through the hair with a wide-tooth comb then left on the hair for five minutes or less. This process is designed to simply soften the texture by elongating the hair's natural curl or wave pattern.

4. Off-the-Scalp Application

Off-the-scalp application is an excellent alternative to no-lye relaxers because the lye relaxer does not come in contact with the scalp at all.

Off-the-scalp application involves applying the relaxer one and a half inches away from the scalp, as opposed to three-fourths of an inch away as in a regular full relaxer application. This minimizes the chances of the relaxer touching the scalp, relieving concerns about burning and irritation. The only time the relaxer touches the scalp or skin during this technique is during the end of the process when you are smoothing the relaxer around the outer parameter of the hairline. This method is highly recommended for children.

THE RELAXER APPLICATION

Chemical hair relaxing is a very skillful procedure and should be performed by a trained, professional cosmetologist. If you choose not to seek professional assistance, then you should fully understand the proper procedures involved in the relaxing process.

Again, I am not encouraging you to apply your own relaxer, but I am supplying this information for those sisters who insist on relaxing their hair at home and for those consumers who wish to empower themselves with the information needed to protect the health of their hair. Let's get started:

Step One: Preparing for the Relaxer

There are some very basic precautions necessary before applying a relaxer. First, thoroughly examine the scalp and hair. If the scalp is suffering from minor abrasions or infections, or if the hair is limp, brittle and dry because of excessive bleaching, frosting, tipping or permanent color usage, do not relax the hair at this time (see the manufacturer's instructions on the container). I recommend strengthening the hair and healing the scalp before applying the relaxer.

After you have thoroughly examined the hair and scalp, comb the hair free of tangles. If you have oil, grease or gel buildup, then shampoo and condition the hair. Wait at least two to three days before applying the relaxer. Never apply a relaxer the same day you shampoo and condition it.

Step two: Gathering Your Tools

There are a couple of tools that you will need to complete your relaxer application. I suggest a tint-colored brush rather than a comb because it allows you to apply the relaxer more precisely and expeditiously. Some practitioners elect to use the comb. I suggest using the tool that allows you to work most effectively. Following is a list of tools you will need to gather before starting your relaxing process:

1. Clean towels.

2. Protective gloves.

3. Clean combs.

4. Tint-color brush.

5. Timer.

6. Base, there are two types: menthol, which has a cool soothing effect, or any mineral oil and petroleum-based product.

Step Three: Analyzing the Hair Texture

Analyzing the hair texture and choosing the correct relaxer strength is a critical step. I recommend that you conduct a strand test to determine the hair's elasticity and moisture content. Take several strands of hair and hold them straight up from the head. Run your fingers down the hair strand, starting from the end of the strand and working your way toward the scalp. If the hair texture feels smooth, this means it has elasticity and will not readily accept moisture. In this case, the hair will be more resistant to the chemical relaxer, so you may want to choose a regular to super strength. If the hair strand feels rough, this means it is very porous, has little elasticity and will readily accept moisture. In this case, you may want to choose a milder strength relaxer (refer to the maintenance diagram for details).

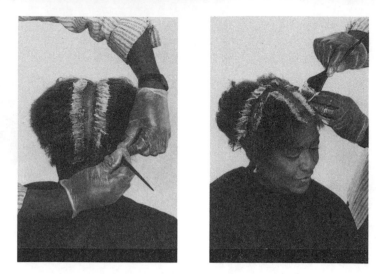 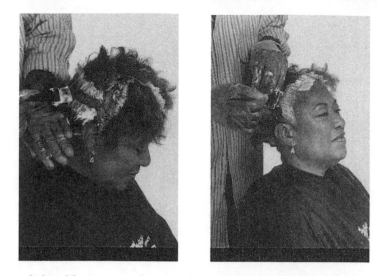

A general guideline is used to assess the overall texture of the hair. If you have very soft, thin or delicate hair, select a mild relaxer. If you have normal to resistant hair, select a regular relaxer. If you have excessively curly and resistant hair then select a super relaxer.

Step Four: Basing the Scalp

Basing the scalp protects it from the caustic reaction of the chemical application. Distribute the emollient evenly onto the scalp. Try to keep the base off the roots of the hair because it may retard the chemical relaxing process. You may also apply some of the base to the ends of the hair to protect it from overprocessing.

Step Five: Applying the Relaxer

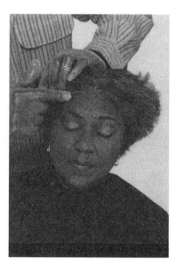

Once you have selected the appropriate relaxer strength, place the container nearby. This will allow you to work more efficiently throughout the process. Carefully read the manufacturer's instructions. Caution should be used at all times. (Keep the relaxer out of children's reach. If accidentally swallowed, seek immediate medical attention.)

Part the hair into four even sections. When parting, be careful not to scrape the surface of the scalp with your comb. Any scalp irritation may promote scarring after the relaxing process. Before you begin your application, set your timer. The application process should take no more than five to six minutes to complete. Keep in mind that the relaxer should be applied approximately a quarter inch away from the scalp

and should never touch its surface. If you are applying an off-the-scalp relaxer, the chemical should be applied one and a half inches away from the scalp, and if you are working with virgin hair, the relaxer should be applied a half inch away from the scalp and two inches away from the ends of the hair. Keep the relaxer off of your ears and away from your eyes, nose and mouth.

Apply the relaxer along the outer parameters of each section. Concentrate on completing one section at a time, beginning with the back area. Part each section into smaller subsections, beginning at the crown area and working your way down toward the nape. Apply a generous amount of relaxer on both sides of each subsection, starting with the front. Once applied, direct the hair toward the front of the head and apply a generous amount of relaxer to the backside of the subsection. Continue this pattern until the relaxer is applied throughout the entire section. If you are working with thick hair texture, subsections should be small. If you are working with fine hair texture, subsections should be larger.

If you are applying a full relaxer, upon the completion of each section, the relaxer should be combed through to the ends of the hair. If you are applying a retouch, however, the relaxer should be applied to the roots of the hair only, and should never overlap previously relaxed hair. Again, be conscious of keeping the relaxer away from the scalp as you move down the section and into the nape area. I recommend putting a conditioner on the previously relaxed hair, prior to a retouch, to protect the hair from possible overlapping.

After the relaxer has been applied throughout the entire head, then proceed to apply the relaxer around the hairline. Not only is the hairline the most sensitive part of the scalp, it also possesses the most delicate portion of the hair and therefore should always be the last section applied in the relaxing process. Avoid touching the forehead. Use the comb to smooth out and remove the four parts from the hair so that they do not become permanent impressions. Now you are ready for the smoothing process.

Step Six: Smoothing The Relaxer

Applying the relaxer initiates the relaxing process. It is the smoothing process, however, that allows us to achieve our end result. First, set your timer. If you are working with fine hair texture, allow five minutes for smoothing time. If the hair is a medium texture, allow eight minutes for smoothing and 10 minutes if the hair texture is coarse and resistant. Smoothing time should never exceed 10 minutes.

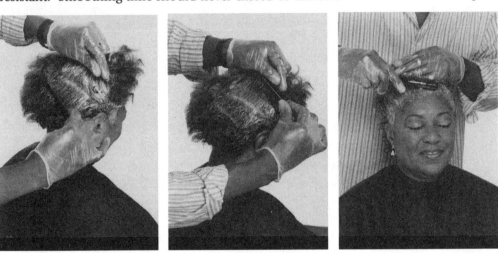

Use the back of your rat-tail comb to smooth each section of the hair. Complete one section at a time. Start at the nape area and motion the hair in either direction from top to bottom, or reverse. Continue this process until you complete the entire back section of the head. Repeat this process for the front section as well, and be sure to apply a little tension every now and then to aid the chemical processing. Utilizing your thumb to smooth the hair also aids the processing. The heat from your hands actually softens the hair and speeds its reaction to the chemical. Make certain that the relaxer covers all hollow spots of the head. Depending on how much time you have left, you may allow the relaxer to set on the hair. When the timer goes off it is time to remove the relaxer. Keep in mind, while you are in the process of relaxing, if your scalp gets overly irritated or

you find that the hair is relaxing faster than you anticipated, then rinse the relaxer out as fast as possible.

Step Seven: Rinsing the Relaxer

The process of rinsing the hair is very important. Avoid using water that is too cold or too hot. If it's too cold, it will leave a strong residue on the hair and the relaxer will not rinse out adequately. If it's too hot, it could irritate the scalp. The water should be lukewarm. Also, make certain the water pressure is strong. This will ensure that the chemical is completely rinsed from the hair and scalp. Any manipulation of the hair or scalp should be light. When massaging the scalp, use the cushion part of your fingertips, not the nails. The hair and scalp are at their most delicate state directly after a relaxer application, therefore, any rubbing or scratching may cause irritation. Rinse the hair until the water runs clear and keep a towel over your eyes and face to avoid any contact with the chemical. Check thoroughly to make sure there is no chemical residue left on the hair or scalp. Pay special attention to the neck, crown, nape and frontal areas.

Step Eight: Neutralizing the Hair

Once the hair is thoroughly rinsed, you are ready to apply the neutralizing shampoo. The neutralizing shampoo stabilizes the relaxer, removes it from the hair and fixates the hair into a straight configuration. Use a mild cream neutralizing shampoo and apply it twice. On the second shampoo, apply evenly and let it set for three minutes, then shampoo with lukewarm water.

Step Nine: Conditioning the Hair

Any time we apply chemicals to the hair, we run the risk of drying it out. For this reason it is important to follow all chemical applications with a moisturizing or conditioning treatment. If the hair is shedding after a relaxer has been applied, it will need a protein treatment, followed by a moisturizing conditioner.

Distribute the conditioner evenly throughout the hair and then either place the head under a heated cap or dryer for 10 to 15 minutes. Next, place the head under a steam treatment machine without a plastic cap for 10 to 15 minutes. If you are at home, you can wrap your hair in a hot steamed towel and leave it on for 10 to 15 minutes. Any of the three methods will require you to rinse the hair thoroughly upon completion. If the hair feels a little weak after the relaxer application, you may want to use a leave-in conditioner as well.

After the hair is relaxed we tend to want to further straighten it via blow-drying, pressing and hot curling. This is far too much heat to apply on the hair directly after relaxer application; it places unnecessary strain on the hair. One way to ensure that our hair receives proper moisture and conditioning after a relaxer application is to wet set and style the hair using alcohol-free conditioning setting lotion with built-in conditioners and humectants. Wet styles such as setting, wrapping and sculpturing allow you to dry the hair while sealing in the moisture. Blow-drying the hair, on the other hand, blows the moisture out of the hair. There is a difference between locking moisture in and blowing it out. When working with excessively dry and curly hair textures, you want to stay clear of the latter.

Black women are in constant search of innovative methods to soften their hair, while avoiding harsh chemical applications. There have been numerous products and methods introduced over the years that have tried to fill this void. The most recent attempts include Copa, a natural curl release system, and Willie Morrow's Aqua Supreme relaxer, a new system that claims to contain 90 percent less harsh chemicals than the average sodium-hydroxide relaxer.

The Copa system claims to be 96 percent natural, containing food starch, fruit acid, Vitamins C and E, mineral salts and preservatives. I am like most consumers, skeptical of new inventions. I haven't tried the Copa relaxer system, so I cannot endorse it. Based on its acidity content, however, it appears to be for wavy or naturally oily hair types.

I did have the opportunity to test Willie Morrow's Aqua Supreme relaxer system. Aqua Supreme uses thermo-trai-act-o-mene, a new technology that formulates active alkaline agents, penetrates the membranes of the hair and softens the hair without dissolving its outer layer. When tested, it did soften my hair and left a lot of its natural curl pattern. However, I didn't experience the same longevity as I do with the other sodium hydroxide relaxers.

Copa products are based in Irvine, Calif. Willie Morrow products are based in San Diego.

Hair Crisis 6

By Cheryl Lynn Hendrickson, freelance editor, New York, NY

Poor planning can lead to bad decisions.

*I*n my experience, where there are four or more "sisters" gathered on any given occasion, at some point the topic of hair will surface. What to do with it? How to style it? How to keep it? Where to buy it? How to maintain it? How we lost it? Can somebody please recommend a reliable stylist?

For six consecutive years, I enjoyed the fringe benefits of a healthy head of hair — and needless to say, six years without hair issues for a black woman is a blessing. During this time I listened to my family and friends cry out in desperation for solutions to their "hair drama." And I embarrassingly admit that I listened with a distant ear. My hair program seemed to be working for me, so my attitude was, "What is all the fuss about?" The rules were simple: Don't apply too much heat to the hair. If the hair is dry, give it moisture. When the ends split, kut them. When you see too much breakage, get a touchup, and throw in a deep conditioner every other month as a bonus."

What I didn't understand then was that responding to our hair problems after they've occurred does not constitute maintenance. That's hair-crisis management, and it eventually catches up with us. It caught up with me in the summer of 1998. For six months, I had been trying to secure a meeting with a very influential client. After months of plugging away, the client finally agreed to meet with me, but insisted that we meet on Thursday of that week. The problem: It was Wednesday afternoon. I had three inches of new growth in my hair, little available cash and no credit on my credit cards, and to top it off, we were approaching a holiday weekend.

Over the years, I have developed a terrible habit of waiting until the last minute to get my touchups. It seemed as though I got a thrill from seeing how much new growth could sprout before my hair would begin to break. When the breakage began, I would then test my latest persuasion techniques on my stylist —kick, scream, beg and plead for her to squeeze me into her schedule, then make my mad dash to the hair salon. I knew how difficult it had been to meet with this client, so I confirmed and immediately called my stylist, confident that with a little persuasion, somehow, some way, she'd squeeze me in. "No way Cheryl. I can't do it," she said. What do you mean you can't do it?" "I can't do it. It's a holiday weekend. I just lost two operators. I'm here alone, and I'm so backed up that I had to call my girlfriend in Virginia and ask her to come to New York to help me shampoo." I was devastated, and I sympathized all of one minute. Then, all I could think about was that "the most important business meeting in my career is about to take place in less than 24 hours and I looked a mess! What was I going to do?

I have girlfriends who relax their hair at home. However, years of experience in the hair care industry has exposed me to the serious repercussions of a poorly applied chemical relaxer. Quite frankly, after witnessing some of these hair tragedies, I vowed never to apply my own relaxer, or even allow an inexperienced, nonlicensed cosmetologist to apply it. So that was not an option. But the question remained, "What am I going to do?" I called a girlfriend for advice. "Go to the Dominicans," she said. "The Dominicans?" "Yeah, I'm telling you. They're fast, cheap and I know this sounds crazy—but I heard that they make your hair grow."

For years, I heard rumors that "the Dominicans" owned hair salons that were located primarily in the Manhattan and Bronx areas of New York. The word on the street is that they are inexpensive, work fast and you don't have to schedule an appointment. My girlfriend went on, "I'm telling you. I got a touchup, a color, a deep conditioner and a kut for $40!" "$40?" Normally, I'd be very skeptical about such a deal. Why are they charging so little? Where are they kutting their costs? On product quality? The service? The expertise? But I was desperate. The thought of being able to walk right in, get a touchup, a rinse, trim and pocket an extra $60 (I normally spend $100) sounded good, real good. "What the hell." I thought. One time can't hurt. I was in.

But I was still skeptical, so I called the shop first, just to confirm that all my girlfriend had said was true. The person who answered the phone spoke little English, but we seemed to agree on the touchup, walk-in and $40 fee, and that was good enough for me.

Now, aside from my hair-crisis management syndrome, I am a stickler about hair care, especially when it involves my own. My girlfriend knows this so she made certain to give me strict instructions. "Ask to speak to Doris," she said. "Doris is the owner. Tell her that I recommended you." The confidence in her voice made me feel secure. So I jumped in my car and headed uptown.

Just as I suspected, the place was jumping. No one greeted me when I walked in, so I made my way to the back of the salon where I spotted a group of workers gathered at the shampoo bowl. Per my girlfriend's instructions, I introduced myself and asked if I could see Doris, the owner. "Touchup mommy,?" one of the women asked. "Yes—but can I speak to...?" "What kind of relaxer do you use, mommy?" another woman asked. "Whoa, whoa, slow down," I thought to myself. "Take it easy." "Actually, I was told to ask for Doris," I repeated calmly. One of them pointed to a woman behind me who was talking on a pay phone.

She was about five feet tall, had huge rollers in her hair and bedroom slippers on her feet. She was smoking a cigarette and appeared to be engaged in a rather animated discussion. "That's Doris," said one woman. By this time the two others were examining my hair and talking in Spanish.

Then one of them said to me (speaking in English), "$50." Now of course $50 for a touchup is quite responsible. However, my girlfriend received a touch up, trim, rinse and conditioner for $40 bucks, so the $50 quote made me feel slighted. "There must be a mistake," I responded. "I confirmed with someone on the phone before I came, and they quoted me a cost of $40."

I noticed that Doris had hung up the phone and was approaching us. "Finally," I thought to myself, "Doris to the rescue." "Hi. My name is Cheryl. I was recommended by..." "Fifty dollars," she said, kutting me off. I paused. "I was told it would be $40," I responded. "Look at this mommy!" she said, raising her voice and flicking my hair. "You have a lot of hair, and we have to pull the relaxer all the way through." My red flag flew up. She calls herself a trained cosmetologist and she plans to pull the relaxer all the way through to the ends of my hair? Sure, a "trained cosmetologist" knows that relaxers should never be applied all the way to the ends of the hair unless he/she is applying it to virgin hair, performing a corrective relaxer (which is a rare and deliberate procedure), or plans to overprocess and damage the client's hair.

"Excuse me," I interrupted. "You only need to apply it to the new growth." Then the real drama began. "I know how to do my job!" she said. This seems to be a favorite line among cosmetologists, especially when they are on the defensive.

Hair Crisis

Then came the second favorite. "I've been doing hair for 20 years!," she said. "Yeah, and you've probably been messing up some heads for 20 years," I thought to myself. But I remained calm, trying not to draw any more attention to myself. And I certainly did not want to squabble over $10.

At this point, I realized that for me to expect a traditional first-time hair consultation was a pretty lofty goal. So I took a deep breath and reminded myself that I was in a bind, that my options were relatively nonexistent and that I needed to just "go with the flow." I followed one of the women over to a lonely chair in the corner where the relaxers were being applied. "What relaxer do you use, mommy?" she asked. "Mizani." I responded. She looked puzzled. "Spell it," she said. "M-I-Z-A-N-I," I said slowly. She still looked puzzled. She reached into her pocketbook, pulled out a piece of scrap paper and a pen, and asked me to write it. I cooperated. "We don't have it," she said. "OK, what about Affirm?" "We don't have it." "What about Optimum?" "No mommy." "Let me try it another way," I thought. "What do you have?" She named several relaxers of which Cream of Nature seemed to be the most familiar. So I figured I'd better play it safe.

All sorts of thoughts began racing through my head as I sat in the lonely corner, awaiting my chemical relaxer application. "What am I doing here? How did I get into this predicament? Is my girlfriend out of her freakin' mind? Just when you think you know a person! I could kick myself for not making my appointment ahead of time. This is my fault. I should know better, I should have been more prepared. Why do I always wait until the last minute?"

The woman returned from the back room with a jar of relaxer and a pair of latex gloves. Something was telling me that she thought she would be applying that chemical relaxer without basing my scalp first. "Please don't do this to me," I thought. "I've already created enough of a scene in here today." She slipped on the gloves. "Please don't." She dipped the comb into the jar. "Wait a minute!" I said. "Aren't you going to base my scalp?"

"You want me to base your scalp?" she asked. "Yeah," I thought, "a little protection would be nice, since you're about to apply a half jar of lye onto my head!" It amazes me when cosmetologists make certain that they put on their latex gloves to protect their skin from the chemical relaxer, but won't apply base to their client's scalp to protect his or her skin. I don't understand that. At this point, there was a lot of talking going on. I couldn't understand any of it. But I had a strong feeling that I was the headliner.

It was obvious that she was annoyed by my basic request. She marched to the back of the room and returned with an economy size jar of Petroleum Jelly to base my scalp. "Why not just bring out some lard and a big bucket of chicken grease?" I thought to myself. I was really beginning to lose my patience, and I guess it showed, because a customer sitting across from me felt a need to console me. "Don't worry honey, be patient. I've been coming here for seven years. You'll get used to it. I usually base my scalp at home before I get here." I felt like I was in the twilight zone. And if that wasn't enough, I looked up and saw that the operator had slapped some petroleum jelly around the front edges of my hairline and the nape of my neck ONLY, and was convinced that she had successfully completed the basing process. Now, unless she ONLY planned to relax the outer edges of my hairline, I didn't know what good her version of base application was going to do either of us.

Finally, I was through being diplomatic. I was worn out by the communication barrier and outraged by the lack of expertise and professionalism. I recognized the health of my hair was in jeopardy and diplomacy was no longer a priority. I excused myself, reached for the "base" and began to properly apply it throughout my scalp.

I felt the tension rising. Suddenly I was reminded of why so many women, particularly black women, develop a "do it yourself attitude" when it comes to taking care of their hair. Many of us complain that we'd rather save our money and do our own hair because we feel we can do a better job. I've heard some rationalize that they would rather mess up their own hair than to pay for someone else to mess it up. At that point sitting in that chair I was tempted to support this position, but I couldn't help but question its rationale. The ultimate goal is for us to enjoy the benefits of having beautiful, healthy hair. And if our hair is as important to us as we say it is, then we are the ones who are ultimately responsible for finding reputable, experienced and qualified cosmetologists.

Yes, I was angry, and in my anger I blamed my girlfriend for recommending that salon to me. In my anger, I blamed the stylists for their poor work. But ultimately, I couldn't help but think of all the ways that I could have prevented that scenario. Too many of us have become complacent consumers, always ready with the excuse, "It's hard to find a good stylist." The reality is it's hard to find a good attorney, a good accountant, dentist, or doctor — why should finding a good cosmetologist be any different? The bottom line is that we put forth an effort for those things that are important enough for us to use and we protect the things we value. If, for instance, we discovered we needed open heart surgery, we wouldn't just walk into any doctor's office, stretch out on the table and ask that doctor to operate. We would request a consultation, ask questions, get referrals, check their credentials, check out the facilities, etc. Why not employ the same level of intensity when seeking a salon and cosmetologist?

I reflected on all of this as I watched the woman incorrectly apply my chemical relaxer. Halfway into the application, my scalp began to burn and the only two working sinks in the place were occupied. I was whisked away to a cold back room apparently reserved for emergencies, at which point they rinsed out my relaxer with cold water. As I sat shivering in my chair, I remembered something a friend of mine shared with me during her recent hair crisis. Hoping to save a few bucks, she had switched from her regular cosmetologist. Within two months, her shoulder length hair was completely broken to its roots after one incorrectly applied chemical relaxer. I recalled her looking at me with tears in her eyes, and a few lonely strands of hair left on her head, and saying, "If someone said to me right now, 'Give me $1,000 and you can have all of your hair back,' I'd do it in a heartbeat.'"

I thought that was profound. Just how many times have we been tempted to skimp when it comes to our hair? And how often have we decided that buying that new outfit or those new shoes was more important? The next time we question how much money we should spend on our hair, we need to ask ourselves, "If we lost it all, how much would we be willing to pay to have it back?" Then maybe we would understand how much our hair is truly worth to us.

I fought back my tears as I sat under the scorching hot dryer praying that the soreness in my scalp would subside. I didn't know how much damage had been done, but I prayed that if I could have another chance that I would never neglect or subject my hair to this kind of abuse again. It was at that moment that I realized how much my hair really meant to me.

A healthy head of hair is one of the most attractive and beautiful gifts that a woman can possess.

Three weeks after the relaxer application, my hair began to experience dryness and severe breakage. Eventually, I had to kut off three to four inches. I have since returned to my regular stylist, who helped nurse my hair back to health. Now not a day passes without me thanking God for the health of my hair.

So when the question is posed, "What's hair got to do with it?" My response is, "Everything." A healthy head of hair is one of the most attractive and beautiful gifts that a woman can possess. It expresses our sensuality, it is an extension of who we are, and it makes a statement to the world about us. We owe it to ourselves to make certain our statement is a strong and healthy one.

Hair Crisis

Just a Man's View

By Bruce Wendell Branch, minister, journalist and author

A longtime obsession over long hair.

For me and most of the guys I've known over the years, hair is the sexiest part of a woman. It can make or break a beautiful woman. It can make an average woman gorgeous. It can make a beautiful woman extremely eye-catching. A lot of people will tell you well-buffed bodies, attractive lips, hips, breasts or legs make a woman, but hair supersedes all that, especially if it is nicely meshed with some bright round eyes (my preference is hazel), textured skin and sexy lips. The kind of hair most men like — and I'm a preacher, and black ministers and other black professionals have developed this notion about women and hair — is long and flowing. We like it bright and shinny. We like it wavy and curly. There is nothing like a woman with good-looking hair to catch your attention.

One of the first things I noticed about my wife was her hair. Most of the women I dated seriously before I got married had nice hair. Nobody is going to tell you, but good hair, or a nice hairstyle gives a woman a leg up in the relationship game. It will keep her husband hanging on her arm. It will allow her to get away with all kinds of shenanigans with her mate. Good-looking hair has that kind of power.

Now we just don't want long hair for the sake of long hair. I tolerate braids, and on a lot of women, I think braids would be right up there with that long, flowing hair that I've been discussing. It doesn't matter (nor, for that matter, can most guys tell) whether it's your hair.

Professional weaves can serve the cause because most guys, including me, won't be able to tell the difference. I am not a hairdresser, but I've always wondered why women get these shaggy-looking manes that scatter over their face. Or, if they have nice, long hair, they rush to the beautician to kut it, or worse yet, don't keep it clean. Long hair is sexy, but dirty long hair with dandruff is unbecoming. It's a turnoff.

My man Barry told me to keep it real. For women to catch a man's attention, he says, they have to understand how men think. Well, a major turnoff for me personally are the African American women who become bleached blondes. It looks whorish. It says to a guy that you are promiscuous and that's why you are wearing that style.

Now I have talked a lot about that sexy long hair but haven't mentioned short hair. For the most part, I don't like it, but I have seen some attractive kuts on a few women. Styles, for example, popularized by the likes of Toni Braxton and Jada Pinkett-Smith. They have the right faces for the style. Still, I think both of those sexy women would be even sexier if they wore longer hair. But hey, who am I to complain? If their significant others like it, so be it. A short hairkut symbolizes power in a woman. It says that she is aggressive, that she's about business.

Who am I to complain?

When I see a woman with a short hairkut — and I know a lot of women do it for style as well as convenience — I think modern diva. I put on my male armor because I know I'm getting ready to do battle. To me, that short hairkut says, "Let me get on top and I plan to stay on top." That short hairkut symbolizes that frustration with sexism and racism in the United States.

Women who wear that kut are often lawyers, doctors, single mothers who have been jilted by jive-time dudes and survived, women who are saying to anybody who will listen, "I can do whatever I want, when I want." I don't think a submissive woman would wear that haircut.

To a smaller degree, I see braids the same way. Thank Susan Taylor of Essence. That's power, brother. It says, "If you mess with me, you better come strong with your game because I ain't about no mess."

Still, I dislike short hairkuts. I am in the tank for long hair. When you get right down to it, hair makes the woman more than anything else, including clothes. It's her identity. It's her signature for life. It's her way of saying, "Make room for Ms. Thang." It's her way of saying, "I'm the most beautiful creature on the planet because I got hair, long, flowing, bright, shiny, creatively styled hair."

So the next time you go to the salon, think before you let the stylist kut your hair. But if a woman insists on getting a short hairkut, who am I, or any man, to stop her. I just hope, for all our sakes, she doesn't dye it blonde.

Just a man's view.

Don't Sew It – Grow It

By Barry L. Fletcher

How to grow up to six inches of hair a year.

To grow your hair to its maximum length, you must assume complete responsibility for its health and condition. This means knowing your hair texture and selecting the appropriate styles, shampoos, conditioners and maintenance products to accommodate it.

Anyone who is serious about maximizing the length of their hair should have the guidance and counseling of a professional stylist and a dermatologist. I am a strong believer that two heads are better than one. And when it comes to our hair, three heads are better than two. But being honest about your stylist's strengths and limitations is the key. Some cosmetologists may be good at kutting and styling, yet they lack the skills and patience to successfully guide you in growing your hair. That's why it's always wise to have several stylists with whom you are comfortable; and you should tailor each of them around your hair's specific needs.

DIET AND NUTRITION

Hair is a cellularly active follicle, and just like the body's other cells and organs, it needs vitamins, minerals and proteins to grow. The bulk of the body's cells, including the hair cells, rely on the lymph or fluid portion of the system for their nourishment. As the blood circulates through the body, it transports and distributes proteins and nutrients through vessels known as capillaries. These capillaries then feed the nutrients directly to the root of the hair strand. This is why any abnormal condition in the blood such as anemia or leukemia has a severe effect on hair growth.

HEALTH

Excessive tension and emotional stress are the most common obstructions to hair growth. Among others are drug use, genetics, poor diet and aging. As we age, all of our body processes slow down, including our reflexes, our ability to heal, our thought patterns, our memory, and our hair growth. To aid our hair growth, first we must minimize the pollutants poisoning our system and robbing the hair propella of its natural nourishment. This can be achieved through proper diet and exercise.

Increasing blood circulation with scalp massaging and hot towel treatments help eliminate waste. Administering a hot towel treatment involves damping a towel with hot water, then wrapping it around the head for 15 to 20 minutes, or until it cools, then repeat the process three to four times.

Additional methods used to aid in hair growth — although they're more severe — include drug hormone treatments and surgical hair transplanting. (For more information, refer to Nutrition and Hair and Holistically Healing Hair.)

SALON VISIT

The number of times you visit the salon is relative to each individual and is largely determined by the condition of your hair. If your hair is flourishing under your care, then you may want to consider visiting a hair salon once a month or every six to eight weeks for your chemical service. If your hair is healthy under your supervision but you still enjoy being pampered in a salon, a bi-weekly visit will suffice, provided you shampoo and condition your own hair the week in between your visit to the salon. If your hair is damaged, I suggest weekly visits to the salon. Once the hair is healthy again, you can change your schedule back to bi-weekly visits. If budgeting is a concern, it may be a good idea to work out a monthly payment plan with your salon.

When growing the hair out, allow your chemical services to be applied by a trained professional, even if you have been successful at applying your own chemicals in the past. It's almost impossible to apply your own relaxer without overlapping onto previously relaxed hair. This eventually causes your ends to split. Whatever damage we initiate at the root area of the hair eventually manifests down to the end of the hair.

STYLING REMEDIES

When the hair is healthy it will grow an average of one-fourth to one-half an inch per month. This should be your goal when growing your hair. You should trim the ends approximately one-fourth of an inch every six to eight weeks to avoid split ends and breakage. Over a two-month period, you would have accumulated approximately one inch of new growth, which still leaves you with an excess of three-fourths of an inch of new hair growth after your hair has been trimmed.

Natural styling remedies, such as twisting, coiling and braiding are excellent ways to expedite hair growth. When opting for such natural styles, you may not have to trim the hair at all. Once you have achieved your desired hair length, you have the option of returning to your relaxed style or remaining natural.

If you avoid applying excessive heat to your hair and properly shampoo, condition and wet set it weekly, it will grow at a maximum speed — and remain healthy while doing so.

Blow-drying and hot-curling strips the hair of its moisture. Hot curling should only be used within the first three days after shampooing. When drying the hair, use a hooded dryer instead of a blow dryer. A hooded dryer will allow you to mold, wrap, sculpt, or set your hair after shampooing, in addition to sealing in moisture. Use moderate heat only; extreme heat damages the scalp.

After the hair becomes soiled, don't use the curling iron. Instead, put a little setting lotion on each strand from its root to its ends. Roll the hair, using magnetic or mesh rollers — whichever is more convenient — then sit under the dryer for 5 to 10 minutes. When preparing for bed, remove the rollers and place a hair net over the curl pattern. In the morning, comb out the curls and style your hair.

If your hair is straight, it can be wrapped and tied down with a satin or silk wrap scarf. Sometimes it is necessary to pin

Don't Sew It — Grow It

curl the wrap with plastic clips. If your hair is limp, then dampen it with a conditioning setting lotion. Then sit under a dryer for 5 to 10 minutes.

Do not be afraid to try different drying techniques while growing your hair. After shampooing and conditioning your hair, use a moisturized enriched setting lotion and allow your hair to dry naturally. You may even want to braid the hair while the setting lotion is on it, then sit under a hooded dryer or allow it to air dry. Once the hair is dry, finger comb it to create a nice texture. There are various techniques that can be used to dry the hair. You should choose a technique that seals in the hair's moisture. Once the hair is dry, massage in a light liquid moisturizer (see Moisture Therapy).

SHAMPOOING

People fail to realize that a lot of hair is loss because of poor shampooing techniques and poor shampoos. When growing the hair out, keep in mind that normal to dry hair requires conditioning shampoos and deep-penetrating moisturizing conditioners. Fine or oily hair textures require cleansing or clarifying shampoos, followed by protein conditioners.

Avoid shampooing the hair too vigorously and too frequently. And when shampooing and conditioning, make certain that the hair is thoroughly rinsed to ensure that all the conditioner is washed away. Shampooing and conditioning require careful administering. After the shampoo, do not rub or rough up the hair with a towel as if you are waxing your car. In addition, when shampooing the scalp, massage with the cushion part of your fingertips, not your fingernails. And be certain to rinse the hair thoroughly with lukewarm water.

CONFUSION ABOUT DANDRUFF

There seems to be a lot of confusion about what causes dandruff and whether it promotes hair growth. There is a special row of cells located at the base of the scalp that are constantly reproducing. As new cells are formed, they push the older cells up toward the scalp's surface. This process normally takes about 30 days. When the younger cells grow faster than usual, the older cells are pushed upward at a faster rate and begin to accumulate on the scalp. This cellular accumulation is what we refer to as dandruff.

There are two types of dandruff — dry and oily. Oily dandruff can be treated by lifting the dandruff with a small-tooth comb before shampooing the hair, then mixing a teaspoonful of witch hazel in with the shampoo. Use an anti-dandruff shampoo. After shampooing, saturate a cotton ball with a skin and scalp antiseptic and blot the scalp.

As with oily dandruff, you should use a small-tooth comb to lift dry dandruff off the scalp before shampooing and conditioning. Cotton blot the scalp with witch hazel, then follow up with a liquid moisturizer. Additional treatments, which eliminate dandruff and promote hair growth, include massaging your neck and scalp, elevating your feet while in bed, eating well, exercising and even making love. If excessive dandruff persists, see your dermatologist. It's possible there may be an immune disorder.

FOR GOOD OR FOR BAD

Growing your hair out is a process. Everything you do will either promote or discourage your hair's growth. So everything is relative. During your daily maintenance regimen, avoid brushing the hair while it is wet. If you must use a brush at all, use one with widely spaced plastic bristles and soft cushion tips. Always use a wide-tooth comb; they are safe and easy on the scalp. And remember, use the cushioned part of the finger for massaging and shampooing the hair and scalp. It's less abrasive.

Anything that stimulates blood circulation helps promote hair growth. This is why hair grows more in warmer climates and during the spring and summer months (heat exposure increases blood circulation).

I also encourage using a hand vibrator to stimulate extra blood, nutrients, oxygen and hormones to the hair follicles. Hand vibrators can be used twice a day, once in the morning and once before bed.

Keep in mind that there is no scientific evidence that supports the idea that hair can be reconstructed with a conditioner once it has been damaged. But conditioners are important when growing the hair out because they protect and strengthen the hair and help prevent additional damage. Following is a good homemade conditioner for growing your hair out: Combine one-fourth ounce of peppermint oil, one-fourth ounce of Barry Fletcher's Liquid Moisture and one egg white. Mix thoroughly. Once mixed, apply evenly throughout your hair and scalp and sit under a heat cap or a warm dryer for 20 minutes.

I have found that placing a client under the steamer with a deep penetrating conditioner or hot oil treatment will help the hair and scalp maintain a healthy moisture level. Cod-liver oil tablets also keep the scalp and skin moist. And vitamin B complex preserves the hair and promotes growth.

HAIR GROWTH AND HORMONES

Female hormones contribute greatly to healthy hair growth. During pregnancy, a woman produces more hormones, which is why her hair grows faster and healthier during this time. Women usually discover by the fourth or fifth month of pregnancy that most of their hair problems disappear. The hair is healthier and more abundant. After pregnancy, some women experience a temporary hair loss while the body's hormones readjust to their normal level.

Lately, even some women who aren't pregnant are using prenatal vitamins to help promote hair growth (see your doctor for more information). If you follow the guidelines mentioned here, you should witness up to six inches of hair growth in one year.

Systemic Illness and Hair Loss

By Dr. Sandra Gilman-Baldie, Madison, AL

Hyperglycemia

(diabetes),

Hypoglycemia

(low blood sugar)

and hair loss.

In this age of technological advancement, profusion of ideas and overload of information, it is amazing that the seemingly simple act of maintaining a healthy head of hair is still elusive for some. Sure, we have been bombarded with products and fancy styling techniques, but we have reaped a crop of hair damage and hair loss. Simply put, in our quest for greater fulfillment in other areas, our time-saving methods have robbed us of the ability to care for ourselves physically.

Hair is a very resilient fiber judging from its ability to survive the abuse to which it has been subjected even at the hands of some hair care professionals. Hair that is physically damaged by chemical and mechanical means will be replaced by new growth. However, hair that is damaged by nutritional imbalance will have to be corrected from within. The growth of hair and its cycle depend largely on the right combination of nutrients. Thus, it is influenced by the internal environment of the body in addition to the external forces determined by styling methods and climatic conditions.

WHAT IS HAIR

One dictionary definition of hair describes it as "the natural covering of the human head." It is known that one of the major purposes of hair is for the conservation of body heat, but the human body can survive even with a loss of hair. This is so because the body's defense mechanism recognizes, by order of priority, that the vital organs need to be preserved for the continuity of human life and that hair, as an appendage, is not an absolute necessity. Because of this, loss of hair or a change in the hair's texture is a first indicator when something goes wrong systemically.

Understanding the cycle of the hair follicle will help us to understand why this takes place. From the time of formation, each hair follicle undergoes repeated cycles of active growth and rest. So the development of hair takes place through cellular growth and division, a process called keratinization, whereby living and growing tissues and cells are converted into a tough, lifeless, insoluble structure. Each hair follicle has a growth cycle of its own. Any interruption in this biological process will give rise to hair loss.

HAIR LOSS

Abnormal hair loss must always be investigated and particular attention must be given to abnormal hair loss in children, as some rare, childhood disorders do manifest themselves this way. There are different reasons for hair loss, such as hereditary factors or traumas, such as mechanical damage, pressure and friction. Systemic illness as a cause is usually overlooked. There are a number of conditions that are known to be associated with hair loss: cancer, thyroid imbalance, tuberculosis, syphilis, hepatic diseases, lupus erythematosus, diabetes and low blood sugar. Physiological changes of the body will affect the hair growth cycle because the hair, functions on the same rhythm as the body, so cellular growth and division are affected by metabolic disturbances.

NUTRITIONAL CAUSES

Proteins are the body's building blocks. Practically all of our muscles, organs, glands, ligaments, nails, skin and hair are composed of protein. In order to preserve the structural integrity of these units, the supply must be kept constant. Proteins serve as enzymes and hormones and every process of the body depends on them. So a body deficient in protein will suffer excessive hair loss. Along with protein, hair needs a correct balance of vitamins, minerals and essential fatty acids to be healthy.

HYPERGLYCEMA (DIABETES) AND HYPOGLYCEMIA (LOW BLOOD SUGAR)

In my book "Could this Be Your Hair Loss Problem? Diabetes and Low Blood Sugar and Their Effects on Hair Loss," I went into detail on how these two conditions may result in hair loss.

There are two main types of diabetes:

(1) INSULIN DEPENDENT DIABETES MELLITUS, known as type 1 or juvenile onset diabetes. This type of diabetes is sometimes caused by viral infections. It is an autoimmune disorder that attacks pancreatic beta cells destroying them, so that insulin secretions halt. The person usually contracts this at an early age and needs insulin injections to live.

(2) NON-INSULIN DEPENDENT DIABETES MELLITUS, or type 2 diabetes is often called adult onset diabetes. In this case cells lose insulin receptors and cannot respond to insulin, or the pancreas does not make enough insulin and much of the insulin that is made goes into the fat cells. The blood sugar then goes up as the pancreas cannot make enough insulin to cope. This type is usually hereditary, but may also be caused by a lifestyle of overeating and underexercising.

So diabetes mellitus really is a disorder of carbohydrate, protein and fat metabolism resulting from an insufficiency in the production of, or utilization of insulin. What are some of the symptoms? There is an increased volume of urine, increased thirst, itching, hunger, weight loss or gain, weakness, dry skin and diffuse hair loss and, in some cases, alopecia areata. Without treatment the condition only worsens. We need to recognize the implications of hair loss where diseases are concerned. Many people do not relate hair loss to systemic diseases. Often it is blamed on something used by the hairdresser or simply "stress" so they try to solve it with the topical preparations that abound on the store shelves. Though these sources must certainly be considered, hair loss should not be attributed to those causes alone. It is always wise to investigate further.

The condition HYPOGLYCEMIA has received no more than a scant reference in textbooks.

In 1922, two Canadian scientists, Frederick Grant Banting and Charles Herbert Best, conducted experiments which culminated in the isolation of insulin. They discovered that some people, were unable to produce insulin in their bodies and developed diabetes. However, doctors using this hormone quickly learned the consequence of an insulin overdose. Physicians using the drug noticed that a slight overdose would send their patients into shock. By investigation, it was discovered that there were people whose bodies were producing excessive amounts of insulin. This

came to be known as hyperinsulinism, which means that the pancreas is overresponsive to sugar. Thus, these people existed in a state of insulin shock constantly. Over time, practitioners gradually came to identify some of the contributing factors responsible for this condition.

Disturbed sugar metabolism leads to disturbance in other areas. In the case of diabetics, they are lacking in the process by which the body derives a substantial part of its vitamin supply. They are unable to convert carotene from fruits and vegetables into vitamin A. A poor diet in vitamin A, among other things, affects the hair and the skin. It is essential for the growth and maintenance of the epithelial layers, which also include the lining of the gut and the respiratory tract, formation of teeth enamel and growth of hair and nails. The skin becomes dry and flaky, oil glands become plugged with keratin and the lining of the respiratory tract loses its layer of fine hair and mucus, which protect the lungs from infection. The appearance of hair and skin depends on the health of cells that are born daily. Hair and skin are made up mostly of protein. Deficiencies lead to their breakdown. Added to this, oil glands are found alongside each hair follicle to keep it lubricated and moisturized. This is to minimize breakage and loss, so the hair suffers further when there is metabolic mismanagement of fats and cholesterol. Hypoglycemia presents its own reasons for hair loss. Those affected more or less exist in a state of insulin shock daily, so a chemical imbalance is always evident which also effects the process of keratinization.

CONCLUSION

We need to recognize the implications of hair loss and our lifestyle in this day and age. A trichologist will recognize which conditions can be traced to a change in the biogenesis of the hair follicle. Care must be taken to determine the origin, whether from systemic cause or local disorder, so that the patient may be referred to the correct specialist. Accurate dietary and medical histories are important in the assessment. So hair has proven to be more than just "the natural covering of the human head." Serious thought needs to be given about where we choose to go from here. What are we sowing now as far as our health is concerned, or will baldheadedness be the new trend of the 21st century?

Chakras - Centers of Energy

SEVEN - CROWN
   Gland - Pineal
   Musical note - B
   Color - Violet/White

SIX - BROW/THIRD EYE
   Gland - Pituitary
   Musical note - A
   Color - Blue/Purple

FIVE - THROAT
   Gland - Thyroid
   Musical note - G
   Color - Blue

FOUR - HEART
   Gland - Thymus
   Musical note - F
   Color - Green

THREE - SOLAR PLEXUS
   Gland - Pancreas
   Musical note - E
   Color - Yellow

TWO - SACRAL/BELLY
   Gland -Reproductive organs
   Musical note - D
   Color - Orange

ONE - ROOT
   Gland - Adrenal
   Musical note - C
   Color - Red

Energy and Hair

By Ollie Goodlow, M.D., LAC, Laurel, MD

By Ollie Goodlow, M.D., LAC, Laurel, MD

The seventh chakra is on the crown of the head.

The human body can be thought of as a complex energy network. The heart is the center of this network. Energy flows through the heart cells, keeping them in a harmonious beat. This understanding of the body as a complex energy network has been with us for a long time. Historical notes of the Chinese refer to the energy network running through the body as meridians. The Indians called the merger of these energy channels "chakras," which are located along the spinal column and are related to major organ systems. To understand the concept of an energy network, think of the channels or meridians as rivers. These rivers represent lines of energy. When the rivers flow freely, they are considered balanced. Disruption of the flow of the rivers may be caused by obstruction, draining empty or flooding. Where the rivers merge, they form a confluence, which is called "chakra" or "wheel of energy."

The chakra energy centers are important to maintaining health. There are seven major energy centers that contribute to the human aura.

Why is this important for human hair?

If you do not keep the energy flowing freely within your body, "disease" develops. The location of the seventh chakra happens to be on the crown of the head. This is the most common location of hair loss for women. Stress — which can disrupt the flow of energy within the body — and post-menopausal changes may be linked to the hair loss at the seven chakra centers.

How do I keep my body's energy in harmony?

- *Meditation.* By taking time to stop the noise inside your head, your mind can take a break from the constant thoughts. It is through deep relaxation that the body is able to bring its energy back into balance. Your own inner rhythm will develop.

- *Creative visualization.* This is an excellent way to affect your energy flow. Taking time to visualize the seven chakra centers can assist in balancing the energy. Making a mind/body connection can have a great impact on your physical well-being.

- *Acupuncture or energy medicine.* Using acupuncture needles to move energy allows your internal pharmacy to help balance your flow of energy.

Healing is the restoration of balance to an organism or a situation. The word heal means to "make whole," and it is believed that all diseases — whether caused by germ, injury or stress — are the result of an "imbalance" that then fragments the organism and destroys its natural resonant affinity.

When Your Menstruation Pauses

11

By Barry L. Fletcher

A woman's concerns may intensify between the ages of 40 and 55.

More than 30 million baby boomers are gradually losing their hair for hormonal, genetic and hereditary reasons. A woman's concerns may intensify as she goes through the menopausal stage, which usually arrives sometime between the ages of 40 and 55.

Black women must factor in all the things they are doing or have done to their hair and scalp up to this point. This may explain why some panic. It is unfortunate that more than 50 percent of the women we service in the salon — be it natural or chemically altered hair — experience some form of shedding during this phase of their life. The thought of losing your hair can be distressing, but especially to those who do not easily accept the idea of aging.

Let me save you some anguish! Do not look for sympathy from your insurance company, doctor or personal trainer because they are not going to give a darn. You would be better off talking to a hairdresser, trichologist or nutritionist.

And be careful. Some hormone-replacement medications contain testosterone, which can promote hair-thinning.

Clinical nutritionist Robert Erdmann, Ph.D, maintains that soy and wild yam endoplex and stinging nettles will help raise your natural estrogen level and help prevent the dehydration of testosterone, which causes the hair follicle to shrink and contributes to hair loss. Some dermatologists suggest 10 to 50 milligrams of vitamin B and five milligrams of zinc. Although researchers have used these daily supplements to stop shedding in animals, most often genes are the blame. Consult your medical doctor if you are on medication. There are more than 300 medications that could thin your hair or cause it to shed.

No dermatologist has been able to explain to me how minozidil opens up sodium and potassium channels, stimulating degenerating follicles to produce new, finer hair and stopping other follicles from degenerating. It's a mystery to me, but for now it's marketed to men and women.

Gracefully Gray

By Barry L. Fletcher

Gray hair

brings a new

perspective.

Each hair strand is birthed in the bulb or root area of the hair, and is gray in its original state. As the strand develops and moves up the hair follicle, it collects all of its properties, including pigment, which is responsible for the hair's color that we see once it emerges from the scalp.

As we age, the pigment cells die off, leaving more of the hair's original gray coloration exposed. This transition begins during middle age and takes anywhere from eight to 20 years before pigmentation is completely gone and the hair is all gray or white.

The predominant question most people have regarding gray hair is whether to cover it up or allow it to be exposed. Some decide to wear highlights until the gray grows completely in, others use a semi-permanent color to disguise the gray. The health of your hair, and whether it is natural or chemically altered, should be carefully considered when determining how to make a complimentary transition. Your hairdresser can help you with alternatives.

Gray hair brings with it a new set of rules and concerns. The lack of pigmentation in the hair causes it to become coarse, dry, resistant and porous. It also has less elasticity and tends to scorch easily and show burn marks. It is best to avoid applying excessive heat to the hair or using hot tools.

Gray hair can also be spongy, dingy, ashy and subject to discoloration. It is usually just as strong as your naturally colored hair, but it is more delicate and sensitive to the environment. Gray has a tendency to absorb smoke and film from cigarettes and other sediments in the atmosphere that leave a yellowish cast on the hair. Any contact with chemicals such as hair relaxers, chlorine from the pool or salt from the beach will promote discoloration in the gray hair. Fortunately, there are ways to clean gray hair. Here is one: use a bluing shampoo to wash your hair; mix in one ounce of vinegar or a tablespoon of peroxide in your clarifying shampoo.

It is not clear what causes premature graying. Generally speaking, however, genetics could play a major part. We do know that graying results when the mechanism that produces pigmentation shuts down or switches off. The good news is that scientists may soon be able to restore this mechanism (and essentially, turn it on again).

Investigations indicate that there are cases in which people with gray hair discover that their natural hair color returned. Dr. Ted Daly, director of Pediatric Dermatology at Nassau County Medical Center in New York, says, "This does not happen often, but the fact that it happens at all seems to suggest that aging does not distract the body's ability to produce hair pigment, it just turns it off. The reason is unclear, however, since it does, it may mean that there is a way to turn it back on."

Studies also indicate that there may be a link to adult illnesses such as eczema, adult hay fever and asthma and men who gray prematurely. Another treatment on the horizon includes liposomes. These small molecules are applied to the skin and selectively deliver a combination of gene pigments and proteins to the hair follicle.

Pigment granules vary in diameter, volume and the way in which they cluster or spread evenly throughout the cortex of the hair strand. These three properties, when combined, determine the hair's natural shade or hair color. There are only four natural hair pigment colors: black, brown, yellow and red. It is the unique mixture of these four colors that provide the infinite range of color variation found in human hair.

There appears to be no relationship between skin pigment and hair pigment except that both have a melanin content exceeding 90 percent. In some people there is a complete lack of pigment in the hair, skin and eyes. This deficiency is known as albinism. When subjected to this condition, avoid bright sunlight.

Gray hair is not always synonymous with old age, but the reason the majority of people elect to cover it is because they want to look younger. Those who prefer natural remedies to darken their gray should try vitamin B Complex's, pantothenic acid, para-aminobenzoic acid and folic acid. These vitamins have been known to contain anti-graying properties. Utilizing vitamins in conjunction with brewers yeast can also help to reduce graying.

On the upside, gray represents wisdom and maturity, and that is nothing to be ashamed of. It's something to be proud of and to cherish. Salt-n-pepper hair has always had a compelling effect because of the light and dark color contrast and how they work equally together. So if someone says to you, "My sister, it is all WET (working equally together)," know that it is all good.

Graying Gracefully

By Doris Hill, retiree and longtime Barry Fletcher client

You've heard the saying, "Your hair is your crowning glory!" At least that's what we were told back in the good old days, starting back when the care of your hair was in your mother's hands and you got a head full of plaits — 99 to 100 of them, all tied down with ribbons, berets or those colorful rubber bands. You were told that was the only way to get your hair to grow.

When you became a teenager and Ma wasn't looking, the plaits turned into a ponytail. The hot comb helped to make the hair longer, depending on how successfully the braiding stage had ended. Then, sometimes, with scissors and a bold hand, you simply would create your own do! Those were the years when you wanted to look cute. Besides, you thought you were in control. After all, "It's My Hair!" So you would spend hours combing, twisting and preening to look the best with what your birth right had provided.

Then came the twenties, and oh boy, the styles were the thing, whether it was the "flower girl," with tints of who knows what, or "Miss Prissy blue nose," with hair straight and sleek. During the thirtysomething years, you became more serious and the styles often imitated those of the first lady…Mamie Bangs, Jackie Page-Boy or a Nancy Poof.

By the time 40 rolled around you began to gain confidence and design your own style. Finally, you knew what looked good and what felt right for you. Then, lo and behold! the gray strands arrive one by one. What to do! You start with a rinse, but soon that isn't enough. You go for the tint, and that doesn't last. Before you know it, you are asking your stylist for something that will last longer. The answer, the real bomb: semi-permanent or permanent hair color. And wham! You've just been snared in a hair trap, because each time you get the treatment, it's a different color or shade that gets over-layered with different base colors, because all coloring is not equal. Sometimes you end up with orange, green, red or black hair color (the sins of going to more than one salon). It's seldom the color you truly want, the one that looks more natural, back to the way it once was. How do I know so much? Because once, I was caught in that trap.

It started with a shock to the nervous system. There was an unexpected death of a loved one, gone at the young age of 43. My hair stood on edge. It felt like straw. Fortunately, I had an understanding and caring beautician who nurtured my hair back to health. It came back with gentle shampoos, hot oil treatments, conditioners, and neck and shoulder massages. Before long, I noticed the silver threads beginning to appear. At first, the glistening gray strands were striking. But within six months to a year the gray was starting to overwhelm me and I was ready to let the rinses begin.

It started with shimmering lights. That soon coated the strands and the hair began to look blue, then purple. I switched to a slate color that calmed the gray. That was great for a while, but after a few times of that color, I got the growing-old blues and just wanted the gray to go away. Vanity, vanity! Let's face it, gray hair won't go away. But that doesn't stop us from trying. Soon I went for the tint (a medium brown, sometimes ash brown) and that worked for a while. Of course it didn't last. The next thing was a semi-permanent color; (I was told it lasted through four to six shampoos, but not for me. My hair grew fast.) After a few years of coloring my hair, my scalp started to rebel. My hair started to thin and my scalp began to itch. The style that I liked no longer worked for me and finally I screamed, "I want out, out of this trap. The vanity trap!"

Now I have learned the secret is to start early in the game, to begin preparing to accept the aging process and to gray gracefully with the crowning glory that God has given you. That saying was right all along. Your hair is your crowning glory. And you can live with it and look good.

Small World
Careful or Careless?

By Barry L. Fletcher

Protecting your

child's hair.

Children have their own ideas about how they want their hair to look. Some prefer relaxed hair, some favor more natural styles and others want extensions. Whatever their preference, as parents, it is your responsibility to understand your child's hair texture and to make decisions that promote the health of their hair.

I suggest seeking counsel from a trained, professional cosmetologist, particularly one who enjoys working with young people. Together, the two of you can develop a healthy maintenance program for your daughter's hair.

✍ TO RELAX OR NOT TO RELAX?

Deciding to relax your child's hair is a serious decision. The consequences of making a hasty decision can be devastating, especially if the relaxer is improperly applied. A bad relaxer application can have short- and long-term damaging effects, ranging from minor scalp burns to severe hair breakage.

If you are confused about the best time to apply your child's first chemical relaxer, consider this rule of thumb: When she reaches puberty or receives her first menstrual cycle, this signifies the beginning of a mature head of hair, and is the best time to apply a virgin relaxer.

✍ FIRST-TIME RELAXING

When opting to chemically relax your daughter's hair, I suggest again that you seek assistance from a trained, professional cosmetologist. But if you choose to apply her relaxer at home, use the "off-the-scalp" technique. As noted in Chapter 5, when using an off-the-scalp technique, the chemical is applied one and a half inches away from the scalp. Off-the-scalp application minimizes the chances of the relaxer making contact with the scalp and, therefore, relieves concerns regarding scalp burning and irritation. The only time the relaxer touches the scalp or skin during this technique is when it is being smoothed around the outer parameter of the hairline. Relaxers should be applied quickly around the edges of the hairline and quickly smoothed at the root area to create a textured effect. Remove the relaxer quickly to avoid any skin irritation. This method is highly recommended for children.

TEXTURING

Hair texturing is very similar to the hair relaxing process, except when texturing, the chemical relaxer is not left on the hair as long. The relaxer is combed through the hair with a wide-tooth comb and left on the hair for five minutes or less. This process is designed simply to soften the hair texture by elongating its natural curl or wave pattern. Therefore, the hair remains close to its natural texture and is less likely to experience breakage. Texturing is an excellent option for children, because it provides manageability while allowing hair to maintain its natural body, thickness and texture.

RETOUCHING

When to apply the retouch application will vary according to the individual's hair texture and growth rate. Generally speaking, unless the hair is excessively curly, your daughter's retouch should be applied no more than four times a year. Although her hair may appear to be thick and strong, a child's hair and scalp are more delicate than we realize. This needs to be considered when choosing our relaxer application procedures.

OVERLAPPING

Remember, no overlapping, or applying chemical on top of previously relaxed portions of the hair. It remains one of the most common causes of hair breakage. Chemical should be applied to new growth only (see "Who's Relaxing, You or Your Hair?").

PRESS-AND-CURL

The pressing-and-curl for your daughter's hair is an excellent way to enjoy manageability and control without introducing the hair to premature harsh chemical applications. Press-and-

curl is versatile because it offers your child the option of wearing her hair smooth and straight, as well as natural or braided.

Traditionally, the pressing comb has been the preferred tool for straightening naturally curly hair. Today, however, more people are utilizing flat irons to press the hair straight. The flat iron looks very similar to the curling iron and uses two flat heated surfaces to press the hair straight. Small portions of the hair are placed in between the iron. The iron is then closed onto the hair and pulled towards the hair's ends until they are silky and straight. Flat irons are healthier styling tools because they do not have teeth and will not tangle and yank the hair.

It is no secret that pressing-and-curling can be challenging and time consuming. One of the ways to make creative use of this time is to plan a Happy Hair Day. Put one day aside to focus solely on pressing, curling, grooming and styling your daughter's hair. Create a festive atmosphere, play good music, enjoy a home movie, prepare tasty food and snacks and utilize this quality time to bond with your child.

SEVEN STEPS TO GROOMING YOUR CHILD'S HAIR:

Step One

Part your child's hair into quarters, two sections in the front and two in the back.

Step Two

Spray each part of the hair lightly with moisturizing detangling setting lotion.

Step Three

Comb and detangle each section until all four are tangle-free.

Step Four

For tender-headed children, braid the hair and leave overnight, or braid and place under a hooded dryer for approximately 35 to 40 minutes.

Step Five

To avoid tangles, after the hair is dry, blow-dry each section of the hair and press one section at a time.

Step Six

Use a soft bristle brush to smooth hair toward the crown of the head. When you are able to gather all hair together in one hand, use a fabric coated elastic band (with or without the balls) to secure the ponytail.

Step Seven

For dry styling, take small sections of the hair and spiral curl the ponytail. For wet styling, use perm rods to roll the hair in a spiral motion. Then put the hair in a ponytail.

FLAT TWIST

Another styling option is the flat twist, which can be styled either wet or dry. To create the flat twist, part a section of the hair using a small-toothed rattail comb. The hair should be parted in the direction of the twist. If you are right-handed, hold the hair in the left hand, twist it around the tail of the comb while twisting the comb in the same direction, then secure the hair with bobby pins or a twisted knot. You may opt to leave the hair straight in the back, wet set, or spiral curl. A wet set also may be pulled into a ponytail. Another option would be to relax the hair and kut it into a short style.

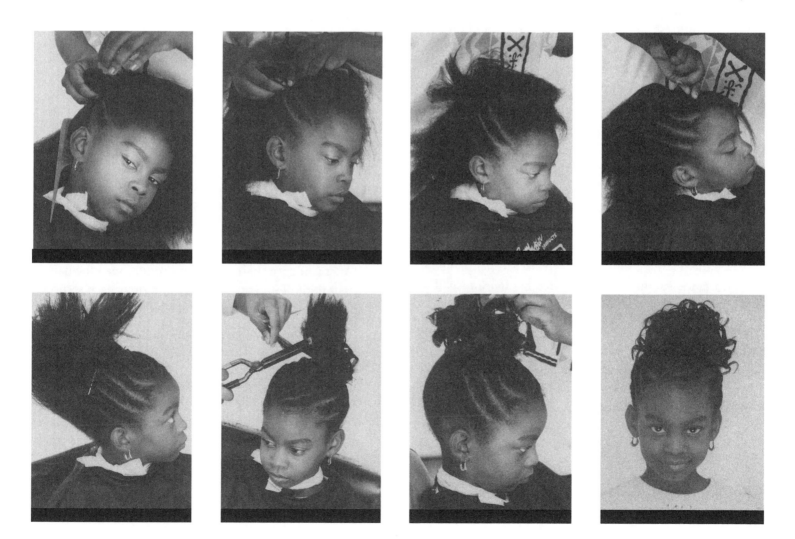

CAREFUL

Roller setting best complements relaxed hair and can be styled in a way that retains your child's youthful appearance.

Hair should be set using large rollers and a moisturizing setting lotion. Once the hair is dry, condition it using a hair and scalp vitamin-enriched emollient. Brush the hair and style into your desired look. Twist sets, ponytails and short bobs are the current popular styling choices for children.

Children today are enjoying a diverse collection of hairstyles, including press-and-curls, relaxers, locs, braids and twists. Caring for their hair, therefore, requires much of the same attention and care used for adults, with one major exception: a child's hair will always require a little extra tender, love and care, especially when it is chemically relaxed.

CARELESS

I have a friend who applied a relaxer to her 4-year-old daughter's hair. She claimed her daughter's hair was unruly and unmanageable and began retouching it once every three to four months. Although my friend based the scalp before applying the relaxer, she was very careless with her applications and follow-up maintenance procedures. She overlapped when applying the relaxer, applied a fresh relaxer to her daughter's hair during the summer months, styled her hair in small tight braids and placed tight rubber bands at the roots of each.

Her daughter is now 10, and the entire front temples of her hair are no more than three inches long and completely damaged; and the remaining four to five inches of her hair is sparse, dull, lifeless, damaged and split. Ironically, my friend is the one who created Happy Hair Day, and for the last six months she has been sharing valuable time with her daughter, conditioning, treating and restoring her daughter's hair back

to its healthy texture. It's hard to imagine the aesthetic need for a relaxer for a toddler, but my friend says she just recently applied a lye-based relaxer to her 1-year-old daughter's hair, using the "off-the-scalp" technique. She says it's working like a charm.

Key Points to Remember

- Use extra protection when applying all chemicals to the hair.

- Use hair mannequins to practice relaxer applications. Mannequins can be purchased at your local beauty supply store.

- Remember, while no-lye relaxers are mild on the scalp, they dry out the hair when used repeatedly. Opt for lye relaxers and use the "off the scalp" technique.

- Always make certain you thoroughly rinse chemicals from the hair.

- Use quality shampoos and conditioners. Cheap shampoos and conditioners revert relaxers and roughen hair textures.

- Avoid brushing hair while it is wet. Instead, use wide-toothed or detangling combs to separate the hair.

- Shampoo the hair using a special aromatic shampoo containing Pine Tar.

- Use a mentholated conditioner to soften, strengthen and detangle the hair. If extra conditioning is required, then provide your child with a hot oil treatment.

- After you have shampooed and conditioned the hair, part it into four equal sections and spray each section lightly, using a moisturizing setting, detangling lotion.

- When pressing, make certain that the hair is completely dry. Pressing wet hair can promote scalp burning.

Remember, a healthy beginning lays the foundation for one's healthy hair future, and as parents, the future of your child's hair is in your hands.

My Search For Self

14

By Rashida Johnson, student, Syracuse University, Syracuse, NY

Understanding

my roots.

air consciousness in my life began with a biweekly ritual that my father initiated. Every two weeks I could depend on his reminder, "Rashida, your hair needs to be washed."

Throughout childhood, until I was about 11 years old, my father had designated himself as my hair caretaker. He recognized hair as a special possession, never to be neglected. So I would kneel, bending over the bathtub rim, my head under running water, while my father began the initial rinse. He would shampoo it with loving care, rinse it and condition it, extending positive vibrations.

Sometimes when he was finished, with my head dripping wet, he would look at my hair, observing it in its state of bushyfrizz with curly tendrils randomly sticking out. We would both face the mirror and he would suggest with sincere admiration, "You should wear it like that." I would cringe at my reflection. In disbelief, I would think, "He must be joking." But understanding my father's daring artistic style and perspective, I knew he was serious. "My hair is in a frizzy bush, I can't wear my hair like this." And to no avail, I struggled to convince myself, "No, he can't be serious."

Perhaps, to my father, hair should make a fashion statement. I'm sure that's what I internalized, then later demonstrated.

My mother will tell you how proud my father was as my hair keeper and how he treasured our ritualistic bond. After he washed it, she was in charge of the next step. She would part it and comb it, blow dry it, brush it, grease it and braid it tight. My hair was very thick and long. Taming it was an arduous process. Sitting in one spot for two hours required concentration. I learned discipline and luckily, for my mother, I wasn't tenderheaded.

I remember making style requests, "Mommy, can you put it in a bun with two curls on the side?" I was also quite candid when expressing my disapproval. "I don't like when you put it in two braids and tie it on to" — "a ponytail on the side is prettier" — "can you leave some hair out in the back?" I was very particular about the appearance of my hair. Even at a young age, I always wanted to be stylish.

When I was in the fourth grade, an indelible memory took its place in my hair experience. On a bright Saturday afternoon I dashed outside to play, neglecting to brush my hair. My mother saw me and I thought I had committed a sin. She loudly admonished, "Girl, what are you doing outside without your hair combed?" I rushed inside to save myself from further humiliation. She continued without a pause, "Your hair is your crowning glory! Don't you ever go outside with your hair looking like that!" I was so embarrassed, but it was understood, my negligence was shameful. Easing the wrath, she later explained that every woman should take care of her hair, that a woman should never leave her home with rollers in her hair, and if you are unable to do your hair on a particular day, it should be covered with a scarf. A woman's hair carries her image. These were pearls given to her by her father. I appreciated being endowed with such wisdom, and I think it was at that moment that I became especially conscious of my hair as a representation of me.

As I moved into my adolescent years, hairstyles took on new meanings. They symbolized maturity and teenage sophistication. Throughout junior high, my entire circle of friends wore permed hair. Because I didn't have one, I felt singled out. Even though people complimented me on my creative hairstyles, I still declared myself an outcast among my peers. Wanting to include me, they didn't hesitate to invite me into the Dark and Lovely club. Persuading me further within our collective identity, they suggested, "Rashida, you have good hair, you should get a mild relaxer—your hair won't get so frizzy." My hair was always frizzy and out of control. "Bangs standing to attention," my mother would say. It wasn't Barbie hair, but it wasn't coarse hair either. It was in between and undecided. A mild relaxer would eliminate the bushyfriz and I'd be protected from treacherous D.C. humidity. With my hair relaxed, I could wear an asymetric hairkut! But I needed permission from Daddy. I began asking him if I could get a relaxer. He answered without hesitation, "You don't need a relaxer; your hair is beautiful." "But I can't do anything with it; it's always frizzy!" He wasn't understanding my adolescent dilemmas. I heard "no" again in his silent response. Discussion dismissed.

I turned to hair gels and afro sheen to shield my hair from humidity. My hairstyle selection was limited. If my hair was going to look groomed, I had two basic choices, a french braid or a bun.

For my eighth-grade graduation, I got my hair kut — nothing drastic — and a press-and-curl. The weather turned on me. My hair "went back." The press-and-curl just wasn't kutting it.

During high school, my hair was long, a few inches below my shoulder. I rarely wore it out. It was thick and often overwhelming, always braided or wrapped in a bun. Meanwhile, my friends wore fly hairkuts. So, I began the campaign again.

"Daddy, can I please get a perm?" "No, you're not putting chemicals in your hair. You'll mess your hair up. I don't understand why your mother put chemicals in her hair. She had beautiful hair."

Being an obedient daughter, I did not want to challenge my father's orders. Again, I acquiesced.

One day, my father took me to Hecht's, a department store, to get my hair done. I was so excited! He wanted me to get it kut, but no relaxer. I'm sure he made that clear to the receptionist without my knowing. "It's not in a style. Why don't you get it kut like Anita Baker's?" he told me. Of course I liked that style on Anita Baker. It looked nice on my mother, too, but it wasn't for me. A little too matronly for a teenager, I thought.

At the store I eagerly awaited my turn, hoping for transformation into a fly girl. I really wanted to look older—not necessarily older—just my age. I stood shorter and smaller than all of my friends. People always thought I was three years younger than my age. A new hairstyle would add maturity and that coveted teenage sophistication. I depended on this hairkut.

Finally, it was time to approach the chair. The stylist asked, "What are you getting done to your hair?" "I want an asymmetric hairkut," I replied.

She unbraided my hair and began the process. "You have a lot of hair. It's so long." "I know," I added, a sigh of exhaustion for all the hours I devoted to my hair.

After washing it and blow drying it, she commented again with apprehension, "Your hair is so long, are you sure your daddy's going to let me kut it?"

My Search For Self

"Yeah, he wants me to get it kut like Anita Baker." "Really?," she gasped in disbelief. "Are you sure he won't get mad?" "I'm sure."

I tried to convince her. Still unsure, she kut it sparingly. I really didn't understand why it was a big deal and why people valued and praised and envied long hair so much. To me, long hair was overrated. After about an hour and a half, the process was complete. The final result stunning. The transformation successful.

My hair always looked nice a few hours after leaving the salon. The next day was a different story. No trace of that fly girl who left the store yesterday, and not a penny in sight for a return visit.

I couldn't afford to visit a hairstylist to maintain my hairkut, so it grew out. And my parents weren't looking to finance monthly visits, so I didn't dare mention biweekly ones.

Surprisingly, in preparation for my sweet 16th birthday party, my mother treated me to a signature Barry Fletcher kut. I was so excited to sit in his Louis Vutton chair. He shaped up my asymmetric kut, no relaxer included. I relied on press-and-curl to give me that straight silky look. My hair crowned me queen. I sported my look with confidence as host of the party. There was no telling me I wasn't the "hostess with the mostess."

I had no personal income, no relaxer and thick long hair. Creativity saved me. I enjoyed becoming acquainted with my hair. Experimenting with it filled my hours after school. I observed in the mirror, "This looks good; this doesn't look good." Experimenting pacified me for a little while longer.

Finally, as I was moving toward my 17th birthday, my father caved in. "Daddy, please, can I put a relaxer in my hair?" Hesitantly, he answered, "Go ahead, Rashida." And he sighed.

I heard his disappointment, and for a second, I was stifled. But thoughts of my hair being in a manageable hairstyle, in a fly kut that would maintain its shape days after visiting a stylist, that thought evoked celebration.

I rushed to the store to buy a relaxer. "I can do it myself. I've watched my aunts and my cousins. The directions will tell me all I need to know."

I looked at all the different relaxers. I was most familiar with Dark and Lovely, but I chose a different, more exotic brand: Hawaiian Silky. I bought a mild relaxer as my friends had advised. I stood in the bathroom eagerly anticipating the change. I read the directions carefully. I had heard stories about getting burned by relaxers. My goal was to avoid the pain. Fearing chemical damage that my father warned me about, I let the relaxer set in my hair for only a few minutes. After rinsing it out, I noticed the difference.

I started to wear my hair out more often. It wasn't kut in a style, just long and straight, but I felt older and ready for D.C. humidity! Not long after the change, a wave of afrocentricity forged its way into black culture. Many young women felt a need to announce self-love for their natural roots. My senior year in high school, newer friends who had joined the circle began wearing naturals and kept their hair braided. Avoiding perms was the move. But I wasn't ready to go back. Besides, it wasn't that I disliked my hair like some sisters, I just wanted to be able to manage my hair and I wanted versatility. I enjoyed not having frizzy hair so I continued to wear it long.

But then long hair was getting to be a hassle. Of course everyone else seemed to like it. The high regard people had for long hair became sickening. I equated the sentiment with self-hate and displaced love for European characteristics. At the mall, in the supermarket, at a party, my hair attracted attention. Guys, especially, would express their approval and interest by first making a statement about my hair. "You have pretty hair; it's so long." Frustrated and disgusted by their obsession, I answered with spite, "Yeah well, I'm kutting it." "Don't kut your hair," was usually the answer. I considered chopping off a few inches.

The summer before I entered college, I asked my cousin to kut my hair into a bob. She didn't have professional training, and I should have predicted my hair would come out slightly lopsided. By this time I wasn't trying to wear an asymmetric hairkut anymore. At least I was rid of some of the hassle and I had attained a fresh look for my new academic endeavor.

Stepping onto the Howard University campus opened my world of hair and possibilities. I saw a range of hairstyles on display, from dreadlocks to braids to short naturals to afros, permed hair kut in bobs, long permed hair, naturally curly hair. The style diversity moved me. I wanted a daring new look. Immediately I forged a path to Avant Garde Hair Gallery. I knew exactly what I wanted. I took my place in Barry's Louis Vutton chair.

"I want you to kut my hair like Jody Wately's." I had always liked Jody's eclectic style. "You want kind of a pageboy/ pixiekut?" "Yeah."

As he started the chopping process, my peripheral vision witnessed several inches of hair cascading to the floor. His swift kut caused a little anxiety, but I trusted his skill. When he finished and handed me the mirror for inspection, I was pleased and eager to show off my new look. I rushed to tell my friends, "Girl, my hair is so short you can roll it with rice."

When they saw me, my friends were shocked, probably for several reasons. My new hairstyle drastically changed my appearance. It complemented my features and made a statement to the world, "Short hair is sheik! Forget all you brothers who love long hair so much." Few women were bold enough to kut their hair so short at the time. I was expressing that boldness my father instilled in me.

In fact, people were now complimenting my courage. Quite often people would comment, "That's a nice hairkut." Women would stop me on the street and ask, "Where did you get your hair kut?" I knew I had one of the flyest hairstyles, and I wore it with confidence and attitude.

Before I had my hair kut, I decided to maintain the new style with my hair in its natural state. My father's admonishing voice replayed in my head so I had refused to get a touchup and settled for a press-and-curl instead. I realized very soon that I wouldn't be able to achieve the desired look without a relaxer. So that my hair would lay straight in a "wrapped" look, I had to submit to the chemical.

Eventually, the afrocentric wave carried me and I went back to a natural. But I kept my hair short, proudly emulating the militant style of Black Panthers and other revolutionaries. My neoafro personified my philosophy and reinvigorated love for the African Diaspora. Photographs of my parents donning their classic afros affirmed my hair statement: I'm black and I'm proud!

Being surrounded by other women who wore naturals encouraged me to care for my natural roots. A man who roamed campus passed out business cards to several of us who belonged to the "Happy to be Nappy" club. They read: THANK YOU for not straightening your hair. Signed an AFRICANAmerican. His subtle approach was a gift of significant encouragement. The message was understood. I felt that my self-proclaimed status as a maverick was recognized and appreciated.

During my natural phase I even considered growing dreadlocks. My boyfriend at the time wore dreadlocks mostly because he chose to uphold the word of the Holy Book. "Jah commands that we not shave our hair," he would tell me. Pointing the word out to me in the Bible convinced me that growing dreadlocks would be a highly righteous act. I considered locking my hair more seriously. On several occasions, I discussed this decision with close friends who wore naturals and who could foresee the ramifications. They too, acknowledged those words in the Old Testament. They also were pulled by Western influence and deterred by our natural inclination to change as maturing young women. None of us were prepared to make the required commitment, yet I struggled with the decision. If I kut my hair should I consider myself unrighteous? A sinner?

Finally, after months of deliberation, we convinced each other that growing dreadlocks might be more appropriate as we entered our forties, when we were more settled and less concerned with being trendsetters. At our moment of youthful contemplation, all of us knew that we needed the freedom to be versatile.

After about a year and a half of keeping a natural, I returned to a relaxer. I wasn't feeling feminine enough. I wanted my chic short hairkut back. Natural-haired friends discouraged me from doing the "European thing." I did it anyway. Only this time I went to a different stylist. Big mistake. I ended up getting a really bad hairkut. The hairkut disappointed me so much that my entire attitude changed. I didn't walk around

with that confidence I had the first time I had my hair kut. After three weeks, I decided to let the relaxer grow out. Besides, wearing a natural was a more economically sound choice for a broke student.

I let my hair grow out this time. I figured that a little more length would give me that femininity I so desired. As it grew longer, I would twist it, let it remain twisted overnight, then untwist it and wear it in a curly bush the next day. By this time I had nurtured the necessary confidence to wear my hair with nuances of unleashed energy. I knew that this hairstyle required attitude that challenged any contenders. However, maintaining this hairstyle became tiresome. I had to spend four hours twisting it. I didn't have that kind of time every night, nor did I have the patience. I began to wear African head wraps consistently. Every day I chose to cover my hair. I had always admired the Muslim sisters for covering their hair as a gesture of modesty. And after finally understanding hair as a mystical and sensual attribute, I decided to make that practice my own without converting to Islam. With my hair covered I felt as if I were preserving my energy, protecting myself from the negative vibrations and confusion that find their entrance into our soul through the hair's natural magnetism. More and more, covering my hair became a very spiritual practice and humbling experience.

Many students would ask, "Why do you keep your hair covered?" "For modesty," I would answer.

"I've never seen your hair," they would state, curiosity boiling in their veins. "Are you Muslim?" "No, but I feel I should protect my hair."

Throughout this phase I answered such questions with dignity.

The days when I revealed my hair were few. On one particular morning when I decided to let my hair "breath," I entered the classroom wearing a winter hat instead of my usual head wrap. I sat down next to a classmate who had become sort of a study buddy. Immediately he noticed the unusual headgear. Hesitantly I began to peel off the hat. His intense stare felt uncomfortable. He looked at me, ogling, anticipating the moment as if I were denuding myself. I was shy and nervous. I continued to pull the hat off slowly. He

continued to stare, patiently awaiting the unveiling. When I finally pulled the hat off, he was still staring. I felt naked and vulnerable. Never has it been clearer to me that within our hair we possess electrifying prowess.

After nine months, graduation was no longer an abstract suggestion. My hair had a place on my list of anxieties. I acknowledged that I would be leaving an academically progressive environment that supported my search for self.

I would be entering the corporate world, a world that showed no mercy for the ideas of a young revolutionary/nonconformist. A more politically correct — and less time-consuming — style was in order. Thoughts of the corporate world challenged my hair consciousness. If I go back to a relaxer will I be a sellout? Will I be mistaken for a woman who has given up her convictions and revolutionary philosophy? I traversed the terrain of choices. The weight of the decision overwhelmed me. Angst added to my confusion. I turned to my mother. Surely she could give me sound advice. She was an active revolutionary turned career woman. She would understand my perspective and the importance of this decision. And she did. With only a few assuring words, the answer was clear. "Rashida, it's not about your hair. There are people with afros and dreadlocks who ain't about nothin'! It's really all about what you are doing. It's not about your hair."

And this was coming from a woman who at my same age was wearing her afro proudly, donning her African head wrap. Now she has a relaxer and does more work in the community than a lot of women I know. I was convinced. My commitment to the African American community has nothing to do with my hairstyle and everything to do with my actions. She inspired me to free myself from judgments made on my outward appearance and to challenge others with my service to "the cause."

I went back to a relaxer and my Jody Wately kut, which had recently become recognized as a Halle Berry kut. I allowed myself to change because that is me, always expressing a new perspective. My hair consciousness embraced my versatility, my chameleonesque manner. My hair is an extension of me, and what I do is an extension of my philosophies.

Holistically Healing Hair

15

By Dr. Akmal Talib Muwwakkil, Ph.D, C.C.N., Oriental Therapist—
The Energy Institute of The Art, Inc., Washington, DC

There is a link between the chemicals in food and the chemicals on hair.

When I was growing up, I can remember watching my aunt and other women cover their hair with wigs or hair pieces to limit their hair-combing or to hide hair loss, especially after the hair had been damaged by a "permanent." I also remember the girls in school who had long straight hair and the girls who were teased because of their short, perm-damaged hair. On the other hand, women like my mother would put some water, hair grease and maybe conditioner on their hair and go about their business. These women rarely suffered from hair loss. It was only when women started using perms with harsh chemicals that they began to experience hair loss, split ends and even baldness.

Nowadays, it is apparent that there is a link between the chemicals in the foods eaten and the chemicals used on the hair and hair loss. Today's women are on the go much more than the women of my mother's generation, so many do not take time to eat the right food, let alone to manage their hair without the help of sprays, dyes or other chemicals. Other women have returned to wearing short naturals, braids or dreadlocks, giving up the hairstyles that required those damaging chemicals. But even so, many are still finding that their hair is thinning and falling out.

Why? The main reason is that their bodies have been so polluted with toxins that their organs have been impaired. The organs (kidney, spleen, and liver) are failing to provide nourishment to the body so it can enrich the hair. In order for the hair to be healthy, several body functions — i.e., digestion, absorption, elimination, storage of essences, and the usage of enzymes — must operate in harmony. When nutrients are not absorbed through the organs, the body suffers from malnutrition. Many women in the United States who are experiencing hair loss are malnourished. The diets of women in many other countries are more nutritionally balanced, with fresh fruits, vegetables, seeds, grains and little meat products. Not only do these women have beautiful, shiny hair, but they also have fewer female issues. Rarely do they experience hair loss, because their organs are being nourished and in turn are providing nutrients to the hair. What is more interesting is that women from other cultures usually do not have problems with hair loss until they come to the United States. Once they are introduced to U.S. food, which is laced with all types of chemical additives, they begin to have problems not only with their hair, but their skin (acne, blemishes, blotches) and other organs.

Additives in food create toxins in the body and are a major contributor to organ dysfunction. For instance, the B vitamin, Biotin, which is needed to maintain healthy hair and skin, is normally contained in large quantities in the intestinal flora. The intestinal flora aids in the production of the healthy bacteria that live in the colon to promote healthy bowel functions. Biotin is absorbed from the colon and assists hair growth, luster, color and aids the sebaceous glands in creating healthy skin. Biotin is also used by the body to disintegrate fats, synthesize amino acids and assist the pancreas in converting carbohydrates and sugars into nutritional energy. Some of the best natural sources of Biotin are Brewer's yeast, brown rice, calf liver, egg yolk, nuts, barley, oatmeal, mushrooms, soy products and black-eyed peas.

There are many other mineral and vitamin deficiencies that can cause hair loss. Vitamin A strengthens the body's immune system, but it also stimulates healthy hair growth. A deficiency of vitamin A can cause hair loss or dandruff, whereas an overdose of vitamin A could result in hair loss and dry skin. Although it is safer to take vitamin A in the form of Carotene, consumption of vitamin A should not exceed 5,000 International Units during any period of time unless supervised by a knowledgeable health practitioner. Care must be taken when using vitamin A because it is a fatsoluble vitamin that stays stored in the liver and can build up to a toxic level.

The hair needs a constant supply of blood and oxygen to maintain its growth and color. However, when the blood supply does not contain oxygen carrying nutrients such as Folic Acid, vitamins B6 and B12, then the hair loses its shine and luster; it becomes thin and eventually falls out. If these three B vitamins are deficient at the same time, then a woman may develop a low hematcrit level (volume of blood in the blood cell) or anemia. These women tend to be susceptible to deficiencies of iron, B vitamins, copper, zinc and vitamin C. In general, women are more susceptible to anemia than men because of the blood lost during childbearing years. Many women do not eat foods or take supplemental vitamins to replenish nutrients lost while menstruating or while pregnant, so they wind up suffering from blood deficiency.

Sweets, like chocolate, which has a high concentration of sugar and caffeine, provide the body with quick energy to help it operate at its optimal rate, in the absence of the blood and nutrients normally present in the body. Refined sugar causes the blood to turn acidic as opposed to alkaline, thus reducing its ability to maintain nutrients and provide nourishment to the body. Refined sugars are "empty" calories that provide no nutritional value. In fact, they strip the body of nutrients like the B vitamins, according to Dr. Donald Lepore ND, DN, NMD., in his book The Ultimate Healing System—The Illustrated Guide to Muscle Testing and Nutrition. Dr. Lepore notes that sugar destroys phosphorus in the body. Phosphorus balances calcium, synthesizes lecithin to enhance the brain cells, stimulates hair growth and maintains the blood's pH (alkaline and acid) balance. Symptoms of phosphorus deficiency include memory loss, hair loss, neurological disorders, respiratory imbalances, gum and teeth problems, insanity, arthritis, cataracts and sexual dysfunction. Foods that are high in phosphorus are rice, bran, wheat germ, pumpkin, squash, safflower and sunflower seeds. Dr. Lepore also suggests that too much sugar can cause oxidation, causing cancer.

When sugar or alcohol — a derivative of sugar — is ingested, it interferes with the liver's ability to synthesize B vitamins. As previously stated, the small intestine is where the nutrients

The hair needs a constant supply of blood and oxygen to maintain its growth and color.

are absorbed that the hair needs for its nourishment. In medicine, the liver is the general of the body. It makes sure everything runs smoothly and stores the blood before it travels throughout the body and into the uterus during

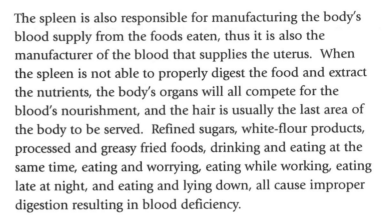
menstruation. If sugar or alcohol irritates the liver then the smooth flow of blood and Qi (energy) will not occur, and it can lead to PMS, anger, frustration, anxiety and nervousness — which results in hair loss. When dealing with hair loss because of alcohol's influence on the liver, it would be beneficial for the person to stop drinking any alcohol and start a liver detoxification program that will renew the liver, which in turn, will rejuvenate the whole body, especially the hair.

In his book Healing With Whole Foods, Paul Pitchford states, "Hair is the one indicator of blood quality. In Oriental medicine, hair is said to be an extension of the blood and, therefore, is influenced by the health of the spleen, pancreas and kidneys." He goes on to say that "Hair loss and prematurely gray hair can be treated by improving blood quality and strengthening the spleen, pancreas and kidneys." This points to the nutrients lost through excessive consumption of sugar and salt, which are directly linked to the spleen (sugar) and kidneys (salt). In Oriental medicine the spleen is energetically connected to the stomach; this pair of organs initiate food digestion. When there is a disorder of the spleen or stomach, digestion is inhibited and the body will continue to produce waste, causing malnutrition of the cells and organs, including the skin and hair. The spleen and stomach have different roles in Oriental medicine than they do in Western medicine. In Oriental medicine their duties include formulating blood, turning food into nutrients, producing the body's Qi transporting fluids — Qi and blood — through the body, and discharging waste byproducts. If any of these processes fail, the body will not be nourished and neither will the hair, resulting in possible hair loss.

When the spleen or stomach is deficient, blood and nutrients are not distributed around the body, causing malnutrition that is manifested as weight gain, skin disorders, hair loss, premature gray hair, abdominal distention and constipation. If the abdomen is distended, the colon is not absorbing nutrients from the food, waste is accumulating in the blood stream and, as a result, is poisoning the hair shaft. Whether the hair just grays or falls out depends on the toxicity of the blood stream. At any rate, the process can be reversed by correcting the digestion process.

The spleen is also responsible for manufacturing the body's blood supply from the foods eaten, thus it is also the manufacturer of the blood that supplies the uterus. When the spleen is not able to properly digest the food and extract the nutrients, the body's organs will all compete for the blood's nourishment, and the hair is usually the last area of the body to be served. Refined sugars, white-flour products, processed and greasy fried foods, drinking and eating at the same time, eating and worrying, eating while working, eating late at night, and eating and lying down, all cause improper digestion resulting in blood deficiency.

Oriental medicine, which has been practiced by many for more than 5,000 years, consists of acupuncture, herbs, bodywork and Qigong (energy). Although often referred to as traditional Chinese medicine, it is still practiced throughout Asia. In Oriental medicine, the kidneys rule over the scalp hair, reproduction, aging, growth, development, the bones, marrow, brain marrow and a person's overall constitution. The kidneys have a direct effect on the color, texture and strength of the hair and its ability to grow. Weak kidneys in a family's bloodline can cause hair loss, because kidney essence is deficient and is not able to properly nourish the scalp hair. In addition, weak kidneys are a common cause of women's reproductive disorders, which include infertility, menstrual issues or menopausal imbalances such as hot flashes, and short term memory loss. Other signs of kidney imbalances are lower back pain, salt cravings and dental problems. All women lose a portion of their essence during menstruation, but excessive sexual activity, frequent childbirths and overwork can further deplete kidney essence. The kidneys maintain and nourish all of the organs in the body, but signs of kidney deficiency mainly manifest in the color of the scalp hair (graying). The kidneys must be balanced in order for women's reproductive systems to be healthy and for women to have healthy hair.

Women need to eat foods that harmonize the spleen and nourish the kidneys so that the body can acquire post heaven Qi, blood and energy, as well as vital essences (fertility). In order for women to fortify their kidneys, they should eat kelp. Kelp is powdered seaweed that can be sprinkled on the food instead of salt. It contains a multitude of minerals, vitamins and trace minerals that the body needs. It is especially good for balancing the thyroid gland because of its high iodine content. Other supplements used to balance the spleen and kidney are spirulina, which is a microalgae that has a high concentration of iron; amino acids; RNA and DNA; chlorophyll and B vitamins. Chlorella is another type of algae that is high in DNA and RNA. It cleanses the blood stream as it nourishes the kidneys and balances the spleen.

The thyroid is another part of the body system that plays an intricate part in the hair's growth, luster and thickness. When the thyroid is out of balance, women will experience hair loss, premature graying and weight gain. The thyroid produces thyroxine and trilodothyronine, which are two hormones that maintain the body's energy levels, promote skeletal growth and sexual development and contribute to the health of the hair and skin. When the thyroid is in an excessive state known as hyperthyroidism a woman will experience heart palpitations, restlessness, nervousness and insomnia. The opposite condition, hypothyroidism, contributes to the loss of head hair, weight gain, tiredness and scaly skin. One way to balance the thyroid naturally is to increase the amount of iodine rich foods in the diet. Fish, seafood and seaweed are all high sources of iodine. Kelp, Dulse, Higiky, walcame, Spirulina and Chlorella are also good sources of natural iodine, and they can be eaten with food, taken as a supplement in tablet form, or mixed in juice. Chicken (as long as it comes from an organic source), apricots, dates and prunes also contain large amounts of iodine.

Emotions can also disrupt the digestive process. According to Oriental medicine, worry, anxiety and excessive thinking affect the spleen and stomach and inhibit the digestive process. Because the spleen and stomach control the beginning stages of digestion, if they are not balanced, their function of transporting and transforming of food into nutrients will result in malabsorption of nutrients, causing blood deficiency and waste buildup in the colon. This leads to Biotin deficiency and can result in hair loss. Worrying effects the nervous system, which in turn affects the liver's ability to regulate the smooth flow of Qi and blood.

The key factors that determine whether the hair is healthy are: (1) Whether the person consumes overprocessed, devitalized foods that are not providing nutrients to the hair, and (2) whether the chemicals used on the hair are robbing it of whatever nutrients that are received from the body. The end result is that a woman can choose to change her lifestyle, eat healthy, take dietary supplements and stay away from hair chemicals, or she can wear wigs for the rest of her life, because she is going bald. That doesn't seem like such a difficult choice, now does it? Be well!

Hair is Sexual

16

By Barry L. Fletcher

Appreciating

its seductive

powers.

Dearly beloved, your hair has entered into a mode we call sexuality; it's a powerful thing, sex. It is the activity that sparks all creation and the force that sustains humanity. It is impossible to understand the importance of human hair without appreciating its role as a sexual object. Beautiful, healthy hair has always been a symbol of sexual prowess, and its texture, color, length, scent and softness have been used as potent weapons and sexual armor. To caress someone's hair, to play with it, or to run your hands through it, consciously or unconsciously, may be seen as a sexual act. As a hairdresser, I can really appreciate the site of strong, healthy hair. In fact, in so many ways, I am always prompted to touch it, caress it, fondle it, love it.

I have always found loose, natural-looking hair more sexy than the artificial, fixed styles that hairstylists often create. I never understand why hairdressers try to fix women's hair so perfectly. It is not the style or the perfection of a woman's hair that makes it sexually compelling; it's the health, radiance and freedom of hair that men find so magnetic.

Sex is the most powerful force on Earth, and hair is a symbol of its expression. In fact, hair is the only sexual characteristic that can be openly displayed or flaunted in public. I can tell a lot about a woman by the way in which she cares for her hair. It tells me whether she is flirtatious, introverted, extroverted, aggressive, conservative, seeks attention or prefers to be left alone. On the other hand, sometimes a woman's hair sends the wrong message to a brother. It may be saying she's a freak of the week, when in reality she's a happily married woman. Therefore, it is important to understand the role your hair plays as a sexual object so that you can convey the proper image or expression.

hair, beards and mustaches contribute to the appearance of male dominance and aggression. Traditionally, warriors have grown elaborate mustaches and beards even when they knew that beards offered an all-too-convenient hand-hold for their enemy. The association between a man's strength and his hair is also reflected in the biblical parable of Samson and Delilah. Samson was considered the strongest man during his time, and the secret to his power rested in his hair. When Delilah revealed Samson's secret to his enemies, they kut off Samson's hair and took away his strength. Hair is such an important symbol of strength and masculinity that men create false hair headdresses and hair pieces to compensate for their loss.

Hormones are known to have a tremendous effect on hair growth and hair loss. Men produce hormones called androgen, and women produce hormones called estrogen. Estrogen is largely responsible for healthy hair growth. When these sexual hormones are out of balance they have an enormous effect on the hair's condition and loss. This is why women experience changes in their hair during and after puberty, pregnancy and menopause. The strong correlation between hair and sexuality explains why there is such fear surrounding its loss.

During pregnancy most couples find themselves growing closer together as the primary sexual characteristics of the woman are enhanced: Her physical being is more beautiful; her skin is more radiant; her breasts grow larger; her body softens and becomes more curvaceous, and her hair is more abundant and healthy. All of these changes are designed by nature to entice the male to show the woman increased attention, greater tenderness and more affection.

Studies confirm that the very anticipation of having sex, as well as engaging in the actual activity, has a positive effect on the growth of our hair. Likewise, the lack of sexual activity may contribute to its loss. As a rule, whatever stimulates circulation in the bloodstream promotes the growth of the hair. Hair receives all its vital nutrients from the bloodstream, so when blood circulation is stimulated, this facilitates the transportation of nutrients to the hair cells. Heat and exercise also stimulate blood circulation and promote hair growth. This is why hair tends to grow faster in

Hair entices a man's imagination. Looking at a woman's hair is like three-play — it comes before the foreplay. When a man looks at a woman's hair he is making a conscious or subconscious assessment of how her body hair looks when she's nude. Many men find the navel and bikini area, eyelashes and even eyebrows to be sexy. Personally, I find women with hairy legs to be enticing.

The sexual attraction of hair is so powerful that Americans spend billions of dollars a year to take care of it. Religious sectors demand that we conceal it, and select government establishments require that we remove it. Nuns, Orthodox Jews and Muslim women cover their hair in public to conceal their sexuality. Uniformed services and military regimes enforce short hair codes to encourage collective identity and discourage sexual, individualized expression.

Hair is not only an expression of sexuality in women, it is also a symbol of power, aggression and virility in men. Body

warm climates and with increased activity. Exposure to a cold climate and lack of exercise on the other hand, slows its growth.

Your hair is a symbolic, powerful and erotically charged body part. Not to mention your most important fashion accessory. So ask yourself, What is my relationship with my hair? Sexual beauty is in the eye of the beholder, and your hair beholds your strongest impression. I believe in using a woman's hair to exploit her natural sexual characteristics and reflect her personality and lifestyle. Exhibiting these qualities is the ultimate expression of my craftsmanship. Sex is not always about feeling; sometimes it's about appearance — hair sex — get the connection? Show more affection.

Sexual beauty is in the eye of the beholder, and your hair beholds your strongest impression.

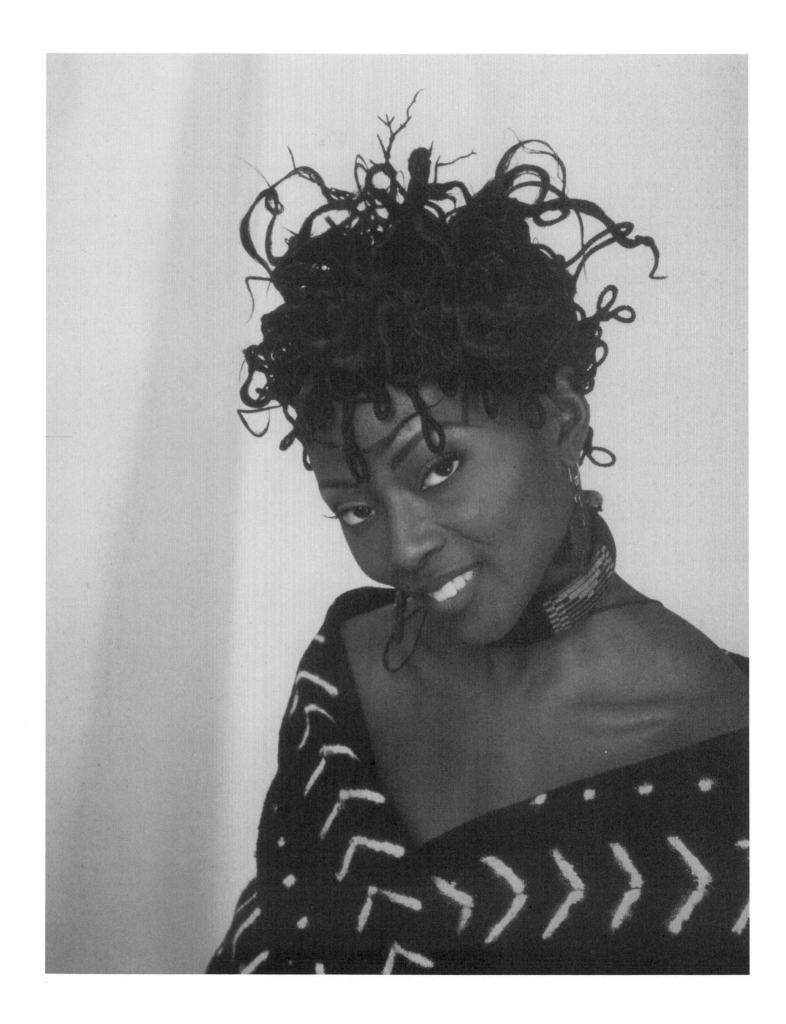

Black Hair

17

By Bruce Britt, freelance writer, Sherman Oaks, CA

The Problem is

Poor Self-Esteem.

In 1993, I was assigned to do a magazine story on hair trends for black men. The premise was simple enough: interview hairstylists in my Los Angeles neighborhood and report the findings. When I phoned a San Fernando Valley barber to ask what hairstyles were popular with its clientele, the proprietor matter-of-factly replied: "Balds." Her answer seemed so far-fetched that I did a double take. Until recently, baldness was considered a dreaded male malady, a humiliating cancer of the scalp. It seemed inconceivable that scores of young brothers were mowing their majestic fades in pursuit of the Mr. Clean look. Asked to explain this curious craze, the salon owner uttered a single name: "Michael Jordan."

The above anecdote may seem irrelevant in a book about black women's hair, but it illustrates an important point, a point best summed up by an old saying: To thine own self be true. Before Jordan's explosive arrival on the sports scene, baldness was shameful. But in the wake of his triumphant NBA reign, hairlessness was transformed into a symbol of power and self-assuredness. As the 1990's progressed, it wasn't unusual to see white, Latino and Asian kids sporting shaved pates. Even brothers with wavy "good" hair were opting to be like Mike. Which brings us to you. Like the formidable Mr. Jordan, are you courageous enough to celebrate your uniqueness? Are you creative and confident enough to turn your perceived shortcomings into assets? Sure, I could regale you with details about my taste in women's hair, but the opinions of strangers are beside the point. It's your personal style that sets you apart, and personal style is totally dictated by you. Being a fashion follower is difficult, frustrating and costly in more ways than one, and this is especially true of black women and their hair. Permit me to explain.

The book you are reading poses an intriguing question: Why are black women losing their hair? I would argue that the answer is poor self-esteem. In their attempt to conform to arbitrary fashion trends, many sisters have burned, bleached, permed, toxified and otherwise abused their delicate crowns. By the time the average African American woman reaches age 30, her hair has seen 60 years of combat. Some of you have paid dearly for your folly, having lost some of the hair you so diligently tried to enhance - hair that probably didn't require much enhancing in the first place.

Ask yourself what is so hideous and unacceptable about black hair that sisters worldwide are compelled to subject their locks to constant treatments and experiments? Abusing your hair in the name of fashion is tantamount to Michelangelo applying lacquer to the Sistine Chapel; it's an insult to something that's already perfect. Contrary to advertisers' outlandish claims, attractiveness doesn't come in a bottle or from a hairstylist's chair. If that were true, women the world over wouldn't have to cajole their men into noticing and complimenting their neat, new $100 hairstyles. Beauty is simplicity. It sounds clichéd, but clichés endure for a reason; they possess powerful kernels of truth.

Beauty is simplicity.

For black women, simplicity means a variety of things: graceful, cascading dreads or afros of various lengths. Long straight hair is fine, too, just so long as you're not compromising your hair's health too much to achieve the desired result. Weaves are modern marvels; they offer length and volume without resorting to harmful chemicals. Personally speaking, I must confess distaste for hairstyles that are too refined. Like many men, I don't care for hair that's excessively manicured, sculpted or processed. The salon look makes most women look so self-conscious and untouchable, it's almost impossible to imagine them in the throes of sexual ecstasy. And for guys, it's all about sex. Why do you think the porno mags feature women with professional mused hair? The pornographers know something many women don't: wildness can be tremendously alluring.

I have always gravitated toward women with personal style. One of my first crushes was Gloria, a girl who attended my elementary school in my hometown of Gary, Ind. Even as a kid, Gloria exuded a fierce black pride that was manifest in her artfully hand-picked afro. Years later in the mid-80's, I spoke to a friend who attended college with Gloria. He said that she totally shaved her head her senior year. I had to laugh. Gloria was still asserting her independence in bold and interesting ways.

My first girlfriend, Michelle, was no less enigmatic. A gangly young woman with an almost psychedelic sense of personal style, Michelle was 16 years old when I first encountered her at a bus stop in Gary. Her hair was a fashionable mess, and she wore a blue jean jacket to which she had stenciled a massive, acrylic eyeball. That bus stop encounter remains one of the great epiphanies of my life. It was like a gong had sounded in my hormone-addled head. Wild and creative, Michelle came off like some untamed pony that guaranteed a fun ride.

Michelle and Gloria are great examples of personal style, but you can easily find public examples. Oprah Winfrey, Lisa Nicole Carson, Erykah Badu and Macy Gray are just a few sisters who exude tremendous confidence and personal style. Whoopi Goldberg is one of the triumphant living examples of self-awareness. When she surfaced in the mid-80's, Whoopi's dreadlocked style seemed amusingly bohemian. Now, 15 years hence, Whoopi has remained true to her dreadlocked aesthetic, though it's been a hard-won battle. I vividly recall the controversy over reports that the popular actress wore blue contact lenses. Many black people were incensed that a black woman would alter her bold African features in favor of a more Eurocentric look, but the controversy was ridiculous on many levels. Anyone with a smattering of experience will tell you that black people come in all shapes, sizes and colors. In my travels, I have actually encountered naturally blue-eyed black people. Whoopi's fashion statement didn't necessarily suggest an identity crisis; it may have just been a predilection for the color blue.

Whoopi did what all of us should do; she followed her heart and paid no attention to the gossip. She continues to thrive in one of the world's most cutthroat professions, and she's dated some of Hollywood's most eligible bachelors. Radiant and self-assured, Whoopi Goldberg seems remarkably comfortable in that tawny skin of hers. How comfortable are you in yours?

For some, the thought of cultivating a personal style may sound difficult, but it doesn't have to be. Speaking from experience, the key to style is honesty and self-awareness. When I started writing nearly 20 years ago, everything I wrote felt contrived. In my struggle to find my voice I studied other writers I admired, hoping to find a crucial common thread. I discovered that the true masters were those who shared something of themselves in their writing.

Towards my goal of developing my own writing style, I made a list of everything I was. I tried to be as honest as possible. One by one, the adjectives flew: sarcastic, sensitive, philosophical, agnostic, skeptical, compassionate and black. Everything I thought I was, and everything I'd ever been told I was, made the list. The resulting inventory marked a turning point. Instead of trying to mimic the "irreverent" writing styles of others, I cultivated my own kinder, gentler technique; it felt right. Nearly 20 years later, I'm still at it, so I must be on to something.

What applies to writing is equally true of your looks. Developing your own style depends on how honest you are with yourself. Make your own list and don't be modest. If you're overweight put it on the list. Got an angular face? Jot it down. You may have hair so kinky a lawn rake couldn't negotiate it. You may have even lost some of your hair. It doesn't matter. Put it on the list.

Once your list is complete, contemplate how to best express yourself. If you're shy and reserved, then you may opt for a more modest hairstyle. If you've got an angular face, then a similarly angular hairstyle might complement your features. Perhaps you've already suffered some hair loss, in which case you might consider a close-cropped hairdo that calls attention away from your head. If short hair strikes you as being too masculine, then compensate with a feminizing dash of subtly applied makeup. Personal beauty is an ongoing process of discovery, addition and elimination. It is a constant, fascinating search for the real you.

One of the most interesting things about the Black American experience is watching the world emulate your every move. No matter what black people create, the rest of the world eventually tries to co-opt it. I like to think that non-blacks are fascinated and astounded by our passion, infectious enthusiasm and insistent creativity. Though we rank as one of the world's most despised and misunderstood peoples, the world has always beaten a path to our door. We have more power than we possibly could imagine. Make your own power by creating your own style. To thine own self be true.

Developing your own style depends on how honest you are with yourself.

To thine own self be true.

Hair 2000 and Beyond

Barry L. Fletcher

DAY

"Freedom"...It's all in the kut!

DAY

EVENING

*A*llow me to suggest a few predictions for the new millennium. We will witness a modern evolution in hair designs inspired by the changing aspect of our lives. Since change is inevitable, we should direct change rather than have it direct us. The future brings about a question of perspective, both figuratively and literally, as it relates to hair. Forging beyond the surface dimensions of hairstyles is a new viewpoint called "freedom." This freedom is compliments of the Kut—The New (K2 Kut).

Your hairkut is the ultimate fashion dictator. For it is an outside force—whereas style comes from within. As your hairkut changes, so does style. "It is all in the Kut." You may ask just how do I get this newly found freedom with a hairkut? Sister, you simply have to wear the kut. First of all, the word kut, as in hairkut, will be spelled with a "K," which reflects the beginning of the year 2000. It will take on a whole new meaning to black women; it will mean freedom. Therefore, my sisters, you have to reevaluate your kut and style selection. Take the time to visualize the hair design after the curls have fallen out, or if the hair is without curls at all. Curls should be used to soften the texture, and curling irons should be limited to the first three days after you shampoo your hair and apply a conditioning treatment. Setting, sculpting, wrapping and allowing your hair to dry naturally is still the best way to dry your kut. The blow dryer should be used for fast drying only. This concept of wearing the kut can be a great benefit to black women,

EVENING

because it will free them from the elaborate dressing of the hair. The world has changed, so has the lives of many black women. Women no longer want to spend hours every week sitting in a salon in rollers under a hot dryer. They want hair that will compliment a more active lifestyle: rushing off to work in the morning or taking the children to school, then feeling confident enough to go out in the evening without worrying about their hair.

EASY

With a good kut, women will find that they can easily look after their own hair in the six to eight intervening weeks. Again, I will refer to my slogan, "It is all in the Kut." But my philosophy is that a good kut cannot succeed with hair that's in bad condition. I want to encourage women worldwide to regard their hair as a precious asset, requiring specialized, gentle, tender loving care. This is the adage behind the development of Barry Fletcher's Products, a complete line of moisture-enriched maintenance products.

RESTFUL

A good maintenance regiment is the passport to healthy hair. Healthy hair should be your No. 1 priority. There is nothing more flattering than to have your hair tailored to your bone structure, lifestyle, or personality — or that special occasion.

As a cosmetological entrepreneur entering the new millennium, I realize that I have to train myself more about trichology, hair and scalp maladies, hair loss, and hair breakage. It is important that we build a correlation with physicians, dermatologists, endocrinologists, and trichologists

to aid in identifying disorders and refer them to the proper professional(s). I know some of you are saying to yourself, it is hard enough to find a hairdresser who can get me in and out of the salon. Well, let me put one more thing on your mind: kutting craftsmanship is at an all-time premium, with emphasis placed on color. The new era of hair designing has moved away from fixed and untouchable hair. The objective is to get the consumers more involved with our creativity by exposing them to healthy hair care techniques. You should not have to depend on a stylist to keep up your look, only your kut, chemicals and color. There are lots to choose from in terms of low-maintenance, restful hair kuts that will represent you properly for the year 2000 and beyond. Color can be used to spice up

ELOQUENT

your personalized hairkut. I predict that the new color revolution will be televised to inspire, suggest, and impose design ideas. The experienced designer who keeps in focus with hair and fashion will be guided into the future with color that will be used for textured effects.

FREE

Color is the flavor of life. You will develop a new way of seeing lights, darks, and shadows. Did you know that color becomes texture when you break up the flat color with variations of light and shadow colors? Color next to color, color overlaying color, and

Hair 2000 and Beyond

ROGRESSIVE   LOW MAINTENANCE

color defining color will actually change the way your eyes perceive it and unveil a new and exciting vision for the future. The revolutionary hair and fashion ramifications are new and innovative ways to cross-breed color to represent texture. The technique is simply highlighting, tri-lighting, and two-lighting, mixed with low-lighting, shadowing and dark frosting.

Awaited by everyone with curiosity and expectations, the new millennium hair-dressing intelligence will be tested. We have to be retrained to detect hair and scalp disorders, learn the elements of designing, the dynamics of making someone feel good about themselves, and more effective communication skills. We must take hairdressing beyond the norm, to give you a better feeling about yourself while spending less time on your hair. The most personal decision is about the choices you

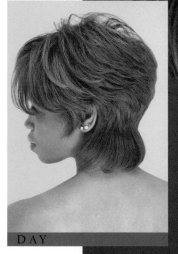

DAY

EVENING

Color is the *flavor of life*

make to create an image to represent you. Your hair will encompass at least 51 percent of your image. As you know, a hairkut could provoke fascination and — dread in your search for freedom.

COVER GIRL

Trusting the Eyes and Hands of the Man

Barry L. Fletcher

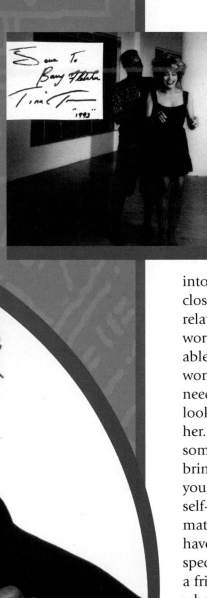

Perhaps it is only natural for a woman to become attached to a man who handles and manipulates her hair. After all, a woman's hair is an erogenous zone, a symbol of power, her most important fashion accessory.

A male hair designer is allowed the opportunity to gain unique insight into a woman's nature. It is an often close and sometimes sensual relationship. When it works, the designer is able to connect with a woman's unconscious needs and give her the look that's just right for her. Anytime you find someone who can bring out the best in you, especially in this self-absorbed, materialistic world, you have found not just a special technician, but a friend --someone who can fulfill a basic human need, the need to feel special.

The male stylist has an advantage here. When someone can define the image you are trying to project -- they see you as you want to be seen -- you have established a special relationship. We know that any relationship between a male and female can have its own dynamic energy. But the relationship between the male stylist and female client has its own provocative allure.

The Man, the Mission, and the Relationship

Getting your hair done can be a very sensual experience. Shampooing the hair, for instance, involves massaging the head and neck. Kutting the hair can also be sensual. In most cases, I kut to bring out a shape that will reveal some inner sensuality, self-esteem, and confidence. Just running your hands through a woman's hair can be a sensual act. More than just a conduit for women's escapism, I feel that part of my job is to educate women and make them feel more beautiful. I am responsible for easing their tension and providing a relaxing atmosphere. I treat all of my clients the same. I truly love the response that I get from them. I enjoy what I do and I devote myself to it.

I can tell a lot about a woman by designing her hair. I can tell if she is confident, introverted, selfish, down-and-out, or feeling like she is on top of the world. There's always a little mystery and intrigue between a male hair designer and his female client. The question usually revolves around what a woman wants from a male hair designer. Sometimes that is more than the hair care services we render. Because of the closeness between a client and her male stylist, a "client crush" can develop. Let's face it, a lot of female hair designers are technically more proficient in many areas than their male counterparts. Yet, most male stylists have boatloads of clients. There must be more to it than talent.

I have had a lot of women tell me that they would never let a female stylist kut their hair. Many women believe that a man can better assess what is best for them. They believe that a male designer can bring out a more flattering style. We also exert a kind of therapeutic influence. Like a psychiatrist or psychologist, we can be captive listeners. I hear quite

a few stories. Most of them are very interesting. There are some clients who feel they can tell me anything and are confident that it will not go any further. I also get to see women in their most vulnerable states — without makeup and with their hair in its worst condition. This alone puts me in an intimate and confidential position with the ladies. It warrants trust.

In essence, a hair designer's role is to maximize a client's good features and minimize her flaws. A designer should change his client's identity, if need be, and expose her to different aesthetic ideas. Women seem willing to trust a male hair designer with their image because a man is willing to explore some of their fantasies. Usually, a client wants what she does not have. On the other hand, it is important that she have a hair designer who will not be afraid to burst her bubble. Honesty helps clients realize who they really are and what they can and cannot have.

So, who holds the power in this complex relationship? There should be a balance of power between the client and stylist. Some women like to tell you what to do; others like to hear what you think is best for them. You have the shears; she has the money. I don't think any woman wants to be pushed around or disrespected. But it is up to the client to determine how much power she'll relinquish, and that "power" should never be abused.

I have learned a lot since I opened the first Avant Garde Hair Gallery in 1984. I started with one chair and a staff of two in the same community I grew up in – a tiny suburb outside of Washington, D.C., called Seat Pleasant, Maryland. Today, Avant Garde has grown to eight chairs and I have a staff of 16. The shop was rated by Essence magazine as "one of the Top 5 Salons in the USA." Avant Garde is now franchised in St. Croix.

In the beginning, many of my clients were neighbors or the mothers and sisters of friends -- just regular folks willing to give me a chance. I appreciated that chance. Over the years, some famous folks caught on to what I

Trusting the Eyes and Hands of the Man

My reaction to winning a spot on the World Hair Olympics Team

was doing, and they too gave me a chance. Tina Turner, Maya Angelou, Donnie Simpson, Carol Moseley-Braun, Toni Braxton, Chaka Kahn, Eartha Kitt, Halle Berry, and Iman have all been clients of mine. I was even flown to Minnesota by Prince to create an album cover for Chaka.

Over the years, I managed to win a few awards in national and international competitions. My first biggie came in 1985, when I won a Rolls Royce in the "New York Beauty Classic." Four years later, I won the Oscar De Elegance award in Brussels, Belgium. And in 1994, I represented the United States in the "World Hair Olympics" in London, becoming the first African American selected to the team using a black model.

From these competitions, I nurtured my desire to teach. Now, my training classes and seminars are regularly sold out. I have attracted stylists from across the nation, as well as from Canada, England, France, and the Caribbean. In 1997, I was privileged to receive an honorary doctorate from the National Beauty Culturists' League for my innovative educational methods and dedication to the industry.

I truly have been blessed. My current love is Barry Fletcher Products, Inc., which develops and distributes a variety of moisture-enriched hair care products. In conjunction with my product line, I have created training videos, styling books and professional tools for a complete educational package.

TEAM AVANT GARDE

Vidal Sassoon

World Hair
Olympics Silver
Medal

As I stated earlier, I have learned a lot since I first started out in this business. I can still remember being 25, creative, but rambunctious, hoping to get somewhere in a hurry. I had just received my master barber's license and had decided to pursue a career in cosmetology. I had tried my hand at drumming - kicking it with local go-go bands. I had tried setting up a makeshift boxing gym in my basement. I even assembled computers. But cosmetology, I finally decided, would be my future.

When you're young, you don't always know what you need to know. In the beginning of my career, I dressed provocatively. But I eventually discovered that my way of dressing did nothing to advance my career. I learned that you attract people who are attracted to you. As I grew professionally, I began to dress in business suits every day. At the very least, a shirt and tie. Almost immediately, middle class professional women became the dominant group on my client list. Business attire became the standard dress code of my salon.

Most of the stylists at Avant Garde Hair Gallery are men, and we are very serious about the business. Our image is masculine and powerful. We have become the trendsetters of the industry and are better known nationally as "The Hair Gangsters." When you think of gangsters, you might not summon the most positive image. But you sure don't think of gangsters as anything less than manly.

Before the 1970s, the male hair designer was a rare breed. The few who occupied the field were stereotypically viewed as effeminate. This steered your average male away from the field, and many black women did not find the prospect of a male stylist attractive. Then there was the era of the afro, and the male hair designer was really small in number. But as time wore on -- and as the black beauty industry became more prominent and salons took on a sleeker, more sophisticated look -- more men entered the field. And they were masculine. They were interested in helping a woman express her beauty.

Today's male designer is a new breed. In order for him to be successful, he must learn to communicate well with people. He has to understand the importance of professionalism, practice good grooming and perfect his craft.

It is clear that one's hairstyle influences one's image. Therefore, a hair designer has a whole lot of power. There are many women who are more than willing to trust a male stylist with their "crown of glory." They are willing to put a new twist on the old saying, "Only your hairdresser knows for sure."

Moisture Therapy

Barry L. Fletcher

Unlocking the mystery to healthy hair lies in one of the most basic, natural elements known to humankind - water. The human body is comprised of 70% water, therefore, hair, a cellularly active follicle, relies on water and moisture as key elements for its existence. The elasticity of hair, or the ability for hair to stretch, is largely determined by the moisture content. A healthy strand of hair consists of approximately 5 to 10 percent moisture, which allows excessively curly hair to stretch 1/16 of an inch. This is an important factor to consider because the constant application of pressure to hair by blow drying, braiding, or simply combing can cause damage. If our hair does not have the proper moisture and elasticity present, it will not be flexible enough to withstand the pressure of daily grooming and styling. The result is hair breakage. There are many mysteries surrounding moisture and hair. The following guide will serve to unlock those mysteries and unveil the secrets underlying the Moisture Therapy Hair Care System.

HAIR MAINTENANCE

Avoid heavy hair oils such as grease when responding to hair dryness. Most people do not understand the correct treatment for dry hair. Rather than applying moisture, they apply grease, but there is a distinct difference between the two. There are four basic forms of hair oil: (1) grease, which has a heavy consistency and lays on top of the hair strand; (2) liquid oil, which has a light consistency that penetrates the hair strand; (3) lotion, which has a tendency to weigh the hair down because the form of the substance tends to lead to over use and; (4) cream pomade, which is a mixture of oil, moisture and penetrating ingredients.

Consider getting moisture from your hair care products

Barry Fletcher's Glo-N-Grow Light Pomade Hairdress is a vitamin-enriched hair treatment that moistens the scalp to promote hair growth. It gives protection and super shine for hot curling, pressing and blow drying.

When dealing with dryness, opt for cream pomades or light hair oils with moisturizing components. The ultimate in light hair oils is Barry Fletcher's Liquid Moisture. The name is indicative of its very nature. Liquid Moisture is an all-natural, unisex hair and body oil composed of Jojoba oil and vitamin B protein oil, with a unisex moisturizing fragrance. It can be used for the hair, skin, and scalp. This will help the cuticles lay flat on the hair strand and lock in moisture. Liquid Moisture is better known as a mild "aphrodisiac."

To determine if a hair oil has moisturizing or penetrating ingredients, perform a penetration test. It's simple: rub the oil on the back of your hand, if it penetrates the skin, it has absorbing capabilities. But if it leaves a shiny finish and appears to rest on the surface of the skin, it will have the same effect on your hair. Such lack of penetration can clog the pores of the scalp, collecting dust, dirt and pollution, and resulting in buildup. A nightly hair care regime for fuller hair: dry set hair, remove rollers and cover with a light hair net (pin curls are optional). For straighter looks, wrap the hair with a Barry Fletcher (BF) Silky Head Wrap scarf. For the ultimate in sleeping pretty, use the U-shaped BF sleep neat pillow. It comes with a silky-finish pillow case that helps maintain the hairstyle while sleeping.

STYLING

Wet styles such as roller sets, wraps and sculptures (waves, molded hair) allow the hair to seal in moisture and are key allies to maintaining moisture in the hair. These are healthy alternatives to blow-drying and hot curling that you may want to add to your styling

Moisture Therapy

repertoire. These styling methods are more effective when the Moisture Silk Alcohol Free Wrap Set Lotion is applied to the hair. The setting lotion is a thick moisture-enriched lotion with built-in humectants that deliver maximum style, control, body and sheen. This non-flaking formula helps to restore the moisture balance in all textures of hair, with its five-in-one usage: (1) wet and dry set, sculpt, wrap and blow-dry; (2) adds softness, body and sheen; (3) activator moisturizer; (4) holds curls longer; and (5) silkens, conditions and detangles hair.

The Moisture Silk Plus Alcohol Free Concentrated Wrap Set Lotion creates a firmer set. This revolutionary conditioning styling lotion delivers maximum style, control, body and sheen. It penetrates the hair shaft to seal porous hair and split ends for a beautiful hold. Moisture Silk Plus will restore the moisture balance in all textures of hair, from naturally straight to chemically relaxed. It will leave the hair clean without a dull film.

To add the finishing touches to any style use Memory Mist holding spray. Memory Mist also has a five-in-one usage: (1) humidity resistant, (2) gives curl memory; (3) seals in moisture; (4) holds styles longer, and (5) leaves hair soft and shiny. Memory Mist is fast-drying and lacquer-free. It's a perfect finish to creative hair designing. It's developed to direct, control and hold curls and hairstyles, and is designed without a sticky, gummy feel.

BRAIDING AND WEAVING

When wearing braid extensions or weaves, use clean human hair, not synthetic hair -- it's healthier. Synthetic hair works like a sponge and depletes the moisture in natural hair. The Social Security Mentholating Shampoo is an exclusive formula that leaves the hair and scalp healthy and tingly clean. It is designed specifically to eliminate flaking and itching associated with dandruff. It is beneficial to hair that has been environmentally stressed, because it stimulates blood circulation, which promotes faster

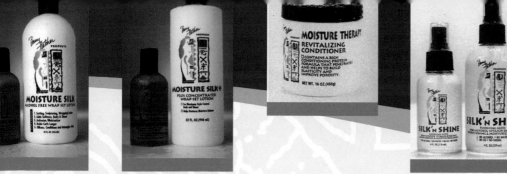

growth. This shampoo contains an active ingredient, pine tar, which has been used for centuries to soothe the problem scalp. It has a special blend of natural herbal extracts, nettles, and chamomile for their astringent

qualities. Panthenol is added to help prevent split ends.
Major Moisture Deep Penetrating Conditioner is formulated with natural peppermint oil to gently refresh and stimulate the scalp and improve circulation.
Vitamins A, B5, D, and special conditioners also help prevent split ends. This conditioner is an excellent deep-conditioning treatment for dry, frizzy, and overprocessed hair. It penetrates the hair to give body, pliability, and a healthy glow.

Thick-N-Slick Conditioning Gel is a naturally fresh alcohol-free conditioning gel with superior moisture and sheen. It has an exceptional blend of 100 percent natural extracts. It activates and holds curls longer. Most important, the Silk-N-Shine is a vitamin-enriched non-aerosol finishing gloss that contains no alcohol, water, oil or grease, and enriches the appearance of braids and weaves. This conditioning and moisturizing sheen silkens the hair. It is designed to seal in moisture when used in conjunction with Barry Fletcher Maintenance Products. The results will be astounding. To avoid excess dryness and breakage, remove braids and/or weaves after six to eight weeks.

COLORING

Permanent color is designed to lift the hair's natural pigmentation. This can be stressful on the hair and tends to have a drying effect which leads to breakage. It is important for your stylist to differentiate between types of coloring treatments that best suit your hair texture, semi-permanent or permanent. Alternatives to permanent and semi-permanent color treatments are conditioning colors and rinses. After applying color, use The Moisturizing Shampoo and Revitalizing Conditioner, which leaves the

hair silky clean while nourishing it with protein and pure biological moisturizing extracts.

RELAXERS:
Have you tried the Moisture Therapy conditioning relaxer system?

Finally! An organically inspired alternative prescription of pharmaceutical grade nutrients designed to fortify the natural immunity of your hair and scalp. There have been many associations made between relaxers and dry hair. Surprisingly, however, relaxers can actually be moisture allies depending on the types of relaxer and its application. Glycolic acid works in conjunction with shea butter to protect and hydrate, giving the hair a silky coating. Beware of ingredients such as calcium hydroxide, potassium, lithium, and quinidine sulfide, which are often found in no-lye relaxers.

These ingredients have a tendency to permanently strip the hair of its protective coating of natural oils, also, leaving the hair dry, grainy, and robbed of its moisture rendering it too thirsty to survive. Additional blow-drying and hot curling after a relaxer application poses a triple threat against moisture balance.

NATURAL HAIR

Natural hairstyles have become increasingly popular, and are good alternatives for sisters trying to nurse their hair back to health. A sure sign that natural hair is suitable for you is if subtle signals of hair problems are becoming obvious: accelerated shedding, (which can be remedied with the Mean Protein Reconstructor Conditioner) excessive dryness, and the inability to hold curls. Natural hair would automatically give a stronger texture, but it can be difficult to penetrate. Sisters may still experience shedding if the hair is not kept at its

natural moisture balance. It is important to remember not to use too many drying products on braids, plaits, dreads, or twist. Therefore, the hair still needs to be treated with Liquid Moisture, Moisturizing Shampoo, and Glow-N-Grow. Liquid Moisture is an excellent emollient because its small molecules make it easier to penetrate the hair while in braids, plaits, or dreads.

Most importantly, never wear the hair too tight. If the style is uncomfortable, then it is too tight. Barry Fletcher Products are designed to work on natural hair as well as chemically treated hair.

B NATURAL

An internal remedy to troubled hair and scalp, the B Natural Hair Vitamin is an alternative formula designed to promote healthy hair growth. This vitamin is designed to increase the energy level at the root of the hair, which provides growth. The ingredients in the vitamins are: (1) B6, B5, and B3, which promote health and growth; (2) B12 increases the energy at the root; (3) Vitamin C improves circulation; (4) Vitamin E improves oxygen; (5) Zinc fights bacteria; (6) Iron maintains strength, and (7) Folic Acid helps prevent hair loss. This vitamin is the ultimate in hair restoration.

ROOT THERAPY

Root Therapy is a leave-in conditioner that allows you to feel the power of healthy hair at the root. Feel the tingle as root therapy stimulates the scalp, draws nutrients to the roots, and energizes hair growth. A blend of natural botanical ingredients are easily applied through a squeeze-drop application. Massaging the product into the scalp twice a day increases micro-circulation while enhancing thickness and hair growth.

The Moisture Therapy Hair Care System was designed to strengthen the hair. Barry Fletcher Products are the leading humectant and vitamin fortified products of the new millennium. The moisture-maintenance products have excellent penetrating capabilities, which are essential for maintaining healthy hair. The styling products provide phenomenal results without compromising the overall health of the hair. The products used for braided and weaved styles promote growth while working against dryness and breakage. The products used with coloring treatments nourish the hair with proteins and pure biological moisturizing extracts. The Moisture Therapy Relaxing System consists of key ingredients that work to strengthen the natural immunity of the hair. The B Natural vitamin is the ultimate remedy for troubled hair. Furthermore, natural hair is strengthened by Barry Fletcher Products. This line of products is a must-have for all sisters.

Unless you live in an environment where it is very humid, chances are your hair could use a boost of moisture and oxygen. Since most of us don't have access to an oxygen tank and live in an area where there's relative humidity, you should consider getting moisture for your hair from your hair care products.

When choosing moisture-maintenance products, the key ingredients to look for is humectant. Humectant is designed to help hair absorb moisture. Some humectants are: oil and water, glycerin, propylene glycol, shea butter, gelatin, and sorbitan. Other key ingredients incorporated into moisturizing products are proteins and emollients such as vitamins A, D, and E. The best thing by far would be natural humectants in a jar. So if you see hair in your comb, it's time to get Barry Fletcher Products on the phone, 1-800-Fletch4. Or the Internet: www.BarryFletcher.com.

Moisture Therapy

Hair Diseases and Scalp Disorders

Cylburne Soden, M.D., P.A.
Dermatologist, Silver Spring, MD - Laurel, MD

Hair damage, loss or baldness can be physical or chemical in nature. Scalp infections, systemic disease and hereditary factors can also play a role here

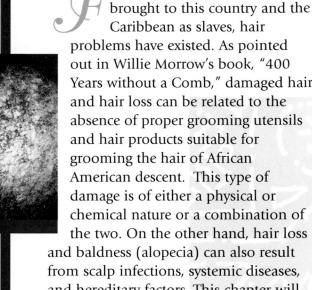

From the time that Africans were brought to this country and the Caribbean as slaves, hair problems have existed. As pointed out in Willie Morrow's book, "400 Years without a Comb," damaged hair and hair loss can be related to the absence of proper grooming utensils and hair products suitable for grooming the hair of African American descent. This type of damage is of either a physical or chemical nature or a combination of the two. On the other hand, hair loss and baldness (alopecia) can also result from scalp infections, systemic diseases, and hereditary factors. This chapter will focus on some of the most frequently treated diseases of the scalp and hair, as seen in a general dermatology practice, which can cause damaged hair and complete hair loss.

Among people of African descent, starting with childhood, some common types of hair problems are tinea capitis (ringworm), Seborrheic dermatitis, acne keloidalis nuchae, androgenic-induced alopecia, Alopecia Areata, Traction Alopecia, and chemically damaged hair. There are other medical causes of hair loss seen less frequently, such as systemic lupus erythematosis, discoid lupus, lichen planus, sarcodosis, and syphilis.

Tinea capitis is an infection involving the scalp and hair. Black children from infancy to the time of puberty are most affected, but adults particularly the black female can be affected. **(a)** Itching of the scalp is usually the first sign. On the scalp, redness, crust, scales, and sometimes black dots will appear in a circular configuration. Thus the term ringworm is used. **(b)** The black dots represent broken off stubs of hair at the scalp level.

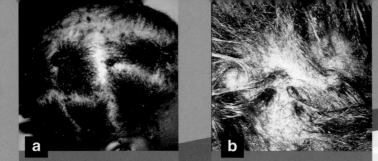

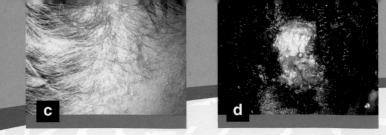

The most common seborrheic dermatitis is another scalp problem that is commonly seen in people of African descent. **(c)** It involves yellow colored flakes and scales adhering to the scalp or flakes lying on the hair. Other areas of the body, such as behind the ears, center of the chest, under the arms, the navel, and pubic areas can also be affected. Associated with this rash is an organism called Pityrosporum Ovale. There are some oils and pomades that can make Seborrheic dermatitis more severe. The use of antidandruff shampoos such as T-Gel, Selsun Blue and Nizoral shampoos can be used to control the problem. These products may make the hair feel brittle and stiff. A softening conditioner should be used after shampooing with these products. In severe cases, a physician should be consulted and antifungal medications such as Sporonox can be taken orally for treatment. Seborrheic dermatitis is a chronic condition and will require continuous care.

Acne Keloidalis Nuchae **(d)** is a disease seen primarily in men of African descent and sometimes in women. It affects the nape of the neck mainly but can extend into the crown of the scalp. Hard small bumps and some hair loss or complete baldness at the nape of the neck characterizes the disease. This condition can spread into the occipital region of the scalp as a folliculitis (inflammation of hair follicles). Irritation from a tight fitting collar, getting the hair cut close with a razor, or close-cutting clippers can make existing lesions worse. Treatment includes the avoidance of close haircuts at the nape of the neck. A scissor cut is preferable. The use of topical steroids, antibiotics, and systemic steroids are the treatments that are most commonly used. Occasionally, surgery or laser therapy is required. Recently the laser has been used to remove completely or reduce the numbers of hairs in the involved areas. This inflammatory disease can sometimes be chronic and should be treated by a dermatologist.

Hair Diseases and Scalp Disorders

Traction Alopecia **(e)** is hair loss resulting from the hair being pulled out. This is a physical means of causing damage to hair and alopecia. The hair either breaks off or is pulled out from the root. Sponge hair rollers, tight braiding, or gluing artificial hair into weak hair, or the process of cornrowing can cause Traction Alopecia. A good rule of thumb in braiding or cornrowing a person's hair is "If it hurts, it's too tight! Take it out!" Traction Alopecia usually occurs at the sides and frontal areas of the scalp. The process of pulling the hair can result in permanent hair loss. To regrow hair, Rogaine, Propecia, topical steroids, or steroid injections are the only products that have been proven safe to stimulate hair growth. A trial of Rogaine can be tried in women and men. A new oral medication called Propecia along with Rogaine can be tried in men. These medications should be used for at least six months to stimulate hair growth.

I have seen at least one skin rash on the shoulders that appear to have been caused by the dye used in artificial hair. The patient had been wearing hair extensions that rested on the shoulders for over15 years. The rash is blackish blue in color and the skin feels hard and wavy. A skin biopsy of the area was positive for dye, which had seeped into the skin. The patient's history was negative for any other chemicals or products, which could have caused this problem.

Male and female **(f)** pattern baldness also affects people of African descent. This is a dominantly inherited condition with uneven penetration among family members. The presence of the hormone dihydrotestosterone is thought to be the major cause of hormonally induced baldness, whether it is male or female pattern baldness. In making the diagnosis of this type of hair loss, as in others, the history is most important. The presence of baldness in other family members on both sides of the family is extremely significant. Male pattern baldness can occur as early as puberty. The crown of the scalp is usually involved first followed by the forehead. The hair in the temporal areas is loss with a letter V shaped indentation occurring. With females, hormonal type of hair loss usually occurs later, most commonly in the 60's or 70's but the pattern of hair loss is similar. In both men and women there is hair thinning and shedding with the hair becoming like that seen in babies (vellus hairs) and then disappearing.

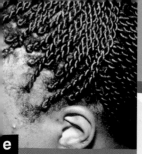

There are two products on the market that have been proven scientifically to stop hair loss and make hair grow. These two products are Rogaine (minoxidil) and Propecia (finasteride). The Rogaine is across the counter being sold at two percent strength and five percent strength. This hair product is thought to work by prolonging the growth phase of hair, the anagen phase. It is applied topically to the scalp twice a day. At this time, only the two percent strength is recommended for the treatment of females. The medication Propecia is the most recent medication for hair growth to hit the market. It is indicated for male pattern baldness but should not be used in females that might become pregnant. It can cause the male fetus to have feminization of the genitalia.

Alpopecia Areata **(g)** is a type of hair loss that involves patches, generalized areas of hair, loss or thinning. It can occur at any age in both males and females. The anagen hairs fall out. The etiology of this disease is not well understood but it is thought to be what is called an autoimmune disease. In some individuals with Alopecia Areata there is an association with such diseases as thyroid disease and vitiligo. Stress is often said to be a factor but has not been proven. **(h)** In most individuals there is no associated disease and the cause is unknown. Most of the time the hair grows back after a few weeks; however, in some it may never return. When the hair returns, it may first be blond or white in color. The treatment of this disease mainly consists of the use of Rogaine and steroids that are administered both topically, orally, and by injection. For this disease, the help of the dermatologist should be sought.

The last hair problem that I frequently see and probably represents the most common hair problem among African American women is chemically damaged hair. The patient usually presents with itching of the scalp, brittle, friable hair, and thinned hair in the temporal and crowned areas. This problem has been recognized since the early sixties when the use of hair relaxers became popular.

With the use of the straightening comb, the hair is heated. A condition called bubble hair may result. This is the formation of air spaces in the hair that's exposed to heat. The hair will break quite easily at these air spaces but does not usually result in baldness. The skin and hair may be burned with the hot comb but brittle, easily broken hairs present over the entire scalp resulting in short and long strains of hair are not usually seen.

Patients presenting with the above description of hair damage almost always have had a common history. There is a history of the use of chemical relaxers and straighteners every 6 weeks for several years. The chemical perm and relaxers have replaced the straightening comb almost completely. With this change in hair grooming techniques among women of African descent, hair breakage, brittleness, and finally baldness are seen by the dermatologist. In the dermatology literature, a disease called the Follicular Degeneration Syndrome (FDS) has been described. Recently, the name was changed to Central Centrifugal Scarring Alopecia (CCSA). With this condition, the most common history is that every four to six weeks for over a 15 or 20 year period, the patient has received a hair perm. Some patients also have used dyes and rinses in combination with chemical relaxers. The patient will often complain of itchy scalp in the crown area, the hair being kinky in the nape of the neck, and thinned at the temples. The disease can represent a spectrum of severity from simple hair breakage to almost complete baldness. Most patients presenting to me with this problem are in their late 30's to early 60's, but I have also seen teen-age patients that show brittle, easily broken hair and an itchy scalp. The severity of this condition is really dependent on how long and how frequently a patient has been getting chemical relaxers. As discussed earlier, scalp fungal infections can also produce brittle and broken hairs. In the patients evaluated for FDS/CCSA, the scalp hairs are tested for fungus and a scalp biopsy is performed to rule out other diseases that might mimic this syndrome. As indicated earlier, there is a positive history for the use of hair perms and relaxers generally at frequent intervals and over a period of several years.

To support the above observations, the history of 17 patients who presented in my office with the symptoms of dry, brittle, breaking hair with alopecia were evaluated for the presence of this condition. All of these patients received a scalp biopsy in the area most affected with itching and damaged hair. The pathology report was either consistent with the diagnosis of Central Centrifugal Scarring Alopecia (CCSA), folliculitis with scarring alopecia or folliculitis of the scalp with non-scarring alopecia. The patients ranged in age from 24 to 56 years with the average age being 38. The length of time for using chemical relaxers or thioglycolates ranged from 10 to 26 years. The average length of use was 19 years. The thiogycolate or "no lye" perm was the most frequently used chemical relaxers. The frequency of application ranged from four to six weeks to six months with the average treatment occurring around six to eight weeks. All patients presented with itching scalps mostly in the occipital area. Conditioning of the hair after chemical relaxation ranged from five minutes at the sink to 20 minutes under a hair dryer. Grooming of the hair on a daily basis appeared to be consistent with all patients using hot blow dryers or curlers. Some patients wrapped their hair at night. With most patients, a licensed beautician had maintained their hair care. By the time patients presented to my office for professional help, many of them were using artificial hair weaves or a wig. At the initial visit the patients complained of itchiness of the scalp usually in the crown accompanied by some tingling. Hair breakage and alopecia were present in all patients usually involving the crown, nape and temporal areas. One patient had desiminated alopecia from the crown of the scalp to the nape of the neck. The texture of the hair ranged from being simply brittle, to breaking off, and coming out by the root. The areas that were most severely involved were the crown and sides of the scalp (parietal-temporal areas). These symptoms are consistent with the description of this condition in the dermatology literature. Women in their 20's and older will show brittle, broken off pieces of hair over the scalp with the hair in the nape of the neck being very short and kinky. The hair is longer on top and is short or absent on the sides of the scalp. Chemical processing may not equally affect all scalp hairs; some hairs are not brittle and do not break as easily as the damaged hairs. Women in their 40's to 60's will often show balding in the crown of the scalp and the parietal-temporal areas. On the histologic level, the inner root sheath of the hair has been identified as the main site of damage. This explains the breakage or no hair growth. In the book entitled, Disorder of Hair Growth, by Dr. Elise A. Olsen, hydroxide relaxers and thioglycolates are identified as causing hair breakage in the nape of the neck and back of the scalp. It should be emphasized that before this disease can be diagnosed, other common diseases such as Female Pattern Baldness have to be ruled out as well as other scalp diseases that can mimic chemically damaged hair. The treatment of this scalp problem requires educating the patient on the potential damage that chemical relaxers, dyes, and rinses can do to the hair.

Patients diagnosed with this condition should not use lye or "no lye" perms (avoid the use of strong chemicals). The current medical treatment for this condition is not satisfactory. It usually consists of treating the scalp and hair with steroids to reduce the inflammation. Rogaine is used to stimulate growth. But what can be done to groom the hair so that it is acceptable and attractive to men and women? We don't want to go back to using the straightening comb.

For the thousands of women that already have the Central Centrifugal Scarring Alopecia as a result of strong chemicals, they must be educated as to what products are not good for their hair. Unfortunately, in an effort to have straight hair, the African American female has had little choice but to use products that can potentially cause great scalp and hair damage. Research specifically for the development of hair care products for the African American, particularly the female is seriously needed to prevent and treat this hair disease that has reached epidemic proportions.

Hair Diseases and Scalp Disorders

Color Me Bad

By Barry L. Fletcher

Learn How

to Pick Your Shade

When you walk into a drugstore determined to color your own hair, nine times out of 10, if your hair is brown and you want lighter hair, you choose blonde. And usually your hair turns an undefinable, unattractive orange. Or you try a home highlight kit and your hair comes out looking and feeling like straw. So you spend the next few months explaining to everyone how you really like the color, even though it was a mistake — and then you wait for it to grow out.

Hair color is marketed to women in dozens of tantalizing commercials. "You too can have a new hair color that leaves your hair in better condition after the color than before." That holds true only if your hair is in good condition from the start. Beware! White women see these commercials and, by a large percentage, still opt to get hair-coloring services professionally done. Black women, being independent and sometimes financially disadvantaged, take on the brave job of doing it themselves. Who do you think comes out with the best results? No matter the race, independence or financial position, the person who has the color professionally done undoubtedly will have the best results. Professional conditioning treatments, proper color selection, application and other trade secrets contribute to our success in coloring.

It is no easy task to color hair at home, and most professional colorists advise against it. Hair-coloring is the knowledge, skill and art of changing the natural pigment of hair to an artificial color. We recommend that you leave the coloring job to a professional hairstylist. But there will always be those who want to color their hair themselves.

Knowledge of specific hair color categories and some simple procedures may increase the success of those "dare to do it at home hair colorists." The following information can also prepare you for a consultation with a professional color specialist:

- Do have adequate lighting.

- Do ask around for an experienced hair color specialist or stylist.

- Do have a consultation with the colorist before a salon colors your hair.

- Do read carefully and follow "specifically" the manufacturer's instructions if you color your own hair; a patch test and strand test should be included.

- Do consider lifestyle when changing your hair color (are you a swimmer, do you sweat heavily, do you take medication, these conditions affect hair color processing and accelerate fading of color).

- When selecting a new hair color, if you are conservative, stay within a few shades of your eyebrow color, darker or lighter.

If you are bold, the "color of the sky" is the limit. "Only my hairdresser knows for sure." That was the answer in the 50's, 60's and even the 70's, when someone asked, "Do you color your hair?" That is, if they asked at all.

Why the big secret over a little gray? Well, sometimes it was a little gray hair and sometimes it was a lot. Back then everyone guarded beauty secrets. Concealing the gray was one way of concealing age. A good hairdresser helped achieve that look with ease. Having their hair color treated regularly gave clients a beauty edge. They stayed close to their natural color except for the wealthy and the daring.

Some went extremely light with their color, too light in some cases. The stigma of "The Unnatural Blonde" still holds true. There are those sharply critical if the contrast of skin color

and hair color is too dramatic; they even believe it somehow represents bad morals. If you think that way it's time to change your mind. Blonde is among the wide variety of today's hair colors.

In the 90's, we used hair color in an open arena. Much of the hush-hush hair color days are a thing of the past. Hair color is now a HOT new topic everywhere, from the runways of Paris and New York to the neighborhood salon. It's not just for covering gray anymore; color can add body to limp hair, boost your fashion image and change your whole personality. Color adds flavor, spice, drama, warmth and individuality. Lighter hair colors and highlights illuminate the hair and add a bright glow to the face. Adding darker hair colors dramatically frame the face and yield stunning images of classic beauty. Red hair color always gets attention. Deep black can be alluring.

Fantasy colors such as lime, pink, purple, royal blue, candy apple red and others are fun and popular; they are usually temporary, but can be made permanent with the help of a little lightener. Today, the hairstylist has endless potential to break barriers with his clients and color.

Deciding to use a permanent color means making a commitment. That's if you want your color to continue to look its best. Color retouches are best every four to six weeks. The idea behind the "color game" is to pretend that your new color is the color you were born with, right? That's why hair color must look consistent and blend with your complexion. (Unless, of course, you're going for the "I'm out there" look). Proper selection and application of color are key to hair color success.

Color Me Bad

"Do-it-yourself colorists" may face some of the following challenges:

- "What color should I choose?

- "How do I know when it's the right time to color my hair and when it's not?"

- "What's the difference in color categories: temporary, semi-permanent, permanent, highlighting and double processes?

- "How do I apply the color correctly?"

- "Why won't my hair color turn out the same as my friend's?"

- "Does hair color cause cancer?

To answer these questions, you must understand the chemistry of hair, the science of its composition, structure and properties of substances. Melanin, texture, density and porosity are all factors in reaching that ultimate goal of great hair color. The following definitions may help your understanding:

Melanin is produced at the core of the hair follicle and gives hair its natural color. There are different types and concentrations of melanin that cause the depth and tone of hair color. Depth is the lightness or darkness of the color.

Tone describes the warmth or coolness of a color. Warm colors have a color base of yellow, orange and red, which creates your blondes and redheads; cool colors have a base of green, blue and violet, creating ash blonde, ash browns, and black hair texture refers to the thickness of the individual hair strand.

Density is the amount of hair you have on your head per square inch, thin, thick or medium.

Porosity is the hair's ability to absorb liquids.

Your hair is either straight, wavy, curly or excessively curly, or it's fine, medium or coarse in textures. When coloring your own hair, you want to consider texture, density and length. These components help determine the amount of color to use and processing time. Checking hair's porosity can also help determine how long the coloring process will take. To determine porosity, observe how your hair absorbs water. Damaged hair will have the highest amount of porosity — it will absorb water and color rapidly. Hair ends may also be more porous than the root because of exposure to the sun and excessive heat from blow-drying and curling irons. Pay close attention to your color processing time to avoid leaving color on the ends too long. Intense reconditioning treatments must precede coloring damaged hair. While preparing to select and apply hair color, remember these two important steps:

1. Always do a preliminary patch or allergy test with the product to assure there is no allergic reaction. This is done by cleaning an area behind the ear, preparing a small amount of the formula you plan to use and applying it to the designated area. Leave it on the skin for 24 hours. If there is no reaction, you can proceed with the color service. If you notice swelling, a rash or other severe irritations, remove the product and do not use it.

2. Always do a strand test, which allows you to preview the color and help determine accurate processing time. Mix a small amount of the formula you plan to use and apply it to a full strand of your hair. Time it as required by instructions. Check the hair by misting the strand with water and wiping off color. Dry hair with a towel to see if desired color is reached. Hair processes faster at the root because of body heat, so remember when strand-testing oxidative or permanent colors, apply the color about one inch from the scalp for about 25 minutes, then 10 minutes for the roots and ends together. For non-oxidative color or deposit-only color, apply color to the entire strand, from roots to ends. Write down processing times and color results. Unsuccessful strand test results may require a consultation or corrective treatment from a salon professional.

A good idea is to stay within a few shades of your natural hair color. First determine your natural hair color. (In the salon we use color charts and hair color swatches to ensure the correct analysis of your natural color and the color you are trying to achieve). Then determine if you would like a darker tone, near the same tone or a lighter one.

Use this basic skin tone and eye-color guide to help select a new color:

- Check your skin's undertone by looking at your throat area. Blue-pink undertones would put you in the cool-toned category; undertones of yellow or golden would put you in the warm-toned category. Neutral skin undertones are described as ivory, beige or brown. The neutral complexions can look good in either warm or cool colors.

- Check your eyes for hints of color. Lighter eyes would signal a need for lighter concentration of color. Medium eyes require a stronger intensity of color. And darker eyes call for a deeper choice. If you have green, blue or brown eyes with red, orange, yellow or gold flecks, you have warm eye color. Green, blue and brown eyes with black, gray, green or violet flecks are cool eye colors.

Light brown, ash blonde, vibrant red, medium red-brown, salt and pepper, or black are the best coloring choices for the cool-toned client. Light blonde, golden blonde, auburn, chestnut brown and dark brown are flattering to a person with warm undertones. Just remember: hair that has a lot of red and golden highlights is warm-toned and hair that has a lot of ash (the absence of red tones) highlights is cool-toned. You can try on a red-toned wig or a brown-toned wig; one will look better on than the other will. Make sure the style is flattering so it does not distract from your color selection.

On the other hand, individual style can play a large part in your hair color choice. If you want, you can break all the above rules and wear whatever color creates self-expression and makes you feel good. If you still can't decide let a professional stylist help.

Hair color comes in two categories: non-oxidative and oxidative. The non-oxidative categories are temporary and semi-permanent; they do not lighten hair, they only add new color and blend gray. The non-oxidative temporary color washes out from shampoo to shampoo, and non-oxidative semi-permanent colors last six to eight shampoos.

The oxidative categories are semi-permanent and permanent. Semi-permanent hair colors, commonly referred to as "deposit only" colors, are oxidative hair colors without ammonia. They are designed to last a lot longer than color rinses. Because "deposit only" oxidative colors are mixed with peroxide, their effect imparts a deeper amount of color.

The "no lift," "deposit only" permanent colors gradually fade after a long time, from 12 to 24 shampoos, according to tonal value of hair. A low volume of peroxide (10 volume) is used with "deposit only" colors, custom formulas, and can be created with deposit only colors by adding a higher volume of peroxide (20 volume). The color becomes deeper and more permanent).

Oxidation is a process in which oxygen is combined with dyes. The dye molecules attach to one another, increase in size and get lodged into the innermost layer of the hair where they can't get out, thus creating the new color.

Permanent hair colors are mixed with peroxide to create a chemical change that is "permanent" in character of the hair. These colors last until they are kut away. They are mixed with peroxide and contain ammonia. When ammonia is included in the color, it decolorizes (lightens) the hair, thus allowing the new color to "take over." Hydrogen peroxide is the agent, which causes the oxidation process.

And for highlighting and double processing (a two-step lightening and toning process), hair is decolorized in order for the new lighter color to show. New growth on highlighted hair will appear at the root in a month or less. Highlighting usually consists of small bits of lighter color created to give the hair a "higher" or "lighter" look. Double processing is easily described by saying "Marilyn Monroe." The color she wore, which was extremely light, was designed

Color Me Bad

by removing all of the pigments in the hair, or decolorizing it, and adding soft pastel colors to tone the hair to a complementary shade.

TEMPORARY HAIR COLOR (NON-OXIDATIVE COLOR)

Temporary hair color, also called rinses, coat the outside strand of the hair, are used to blend gray between regular hair color services, deepen faded hair, brighten lighter hair colors and enhance gray. They do it without damage to the hair. They also contain certified colors approved by the Food and Drug Administration for use in foods, drugs and cosmetics.

It is a great introduction to semi-permanent or permanent color. The colors are not mixed with peroxide and do not cover gray completely, nor do they contain ammonia. A lot of people may be more apt to try this hair color category because it's temporary. You may be familiar with the blue rinse or shampoos, which are a popular choice for neutralizing yellow tone in gray hair; the rinse also brightens the gray hair color. Choosing a rinse a bit darker than your natural hair will blend gray. The downside of rinses is that they run when wet — if you are caught in the rain, sweat heavily or let it get wet in the shower.

There are a large variety of temporary colors. You can select from color mousses, color shampoos, color sprays, gels, creams, crayons, mascara and powders. Temporary colors come in an array of shades: blacks, reds, gold, blonde and funky greens.

Applying them is simple: Always start with a patch test and strand test. Shampoo and condition the hair, then smooth the rinse on the hair in its original form. Note: Temporary rinses come in the form of a shampoo, not to be confused with the permanent hair color shampoos. Read manufacturer's labels carefully; they will tell you how long you can expect the hair color to last.

SEMI-PERMANENT HAIR COLOR (NON-OXIDATIVE COLOR)

Semi-permanent hair color contains no peroxide and you do not mix peroxide with it. It is less damaging than permanent colors and can only deposit or add color to hair. This hair color category will not help the clients looking to lighten their hair. But for those wanting an attractive, warm and friendly glow, this color category might be the answer. It comes in a variety of beautiful colors. from the lightest blonde, sunny auburn to a golden brown.

Semi-permanent hair color is a welcome visitor to relaxed hair. Its no-peroxide properties encourage healthy hair, with or without other chemical services. "Semi-permanent color" and shiny, transparent color work well when used on the same day as other chemical services. The main ingredient is a safe certified stain, much like the food coloring in Kool-Aid.

This hair color type covers gray and enhances natural or pre-lightened hair. Some gray hair is resistant to color and needs peroxide to help the color penetrate the hair shaft. But most minimal amounts of gray hair (less than 35 percent) can be covered with a semi-permanent hair color. Salons use specific color lines designed for gray coverage, so no one knows you are graying. Men like to use these formulas for their gray coverage also. Not to be confused with the lines of color used for gray enhancement. For example, a client with gorgeous "salt and pepper hair" would use the gray enhancers to brighten gray hair and help white hair remain white and free from yellowing stains. Some yellow stains cannot come out because they have been burned or scorched by excessive heat of some sort—curling iron, pressing comb, blow-dryer, etc.

Great for enhancing black hair color, deepening brown, brightening red auburn and adding more gold, yellow or tan to blondes, semi-permanant hair color is a good introduction to color for an apprehensive client. Semi-permanent hair color in any shade works as a nice introduction to color for these reasons:

- It rinses out in six to eight shampoos.

- It's easy to apply

- Your natural hair color returns without damage.

- You can experiment with different shades before deciding your permanent color choice.

Be careful and avoid metallic dyes present in some "gradual

color" products designed to cover gray. Some products contain metallic salts. When it contacts air it decomposes and forms finely divided metallic lead. Most professional hair colors used in salons are nonmetallic. When you try to color over metallic dye with color containing hydrogen peroxide, heat is produced and scalp bums could occur. There are products designed to remove such metals. They are called hair-color removers. They do a great job and can help restore porosity, which improves the success of your color service. Consult with your hair colorist for the proper procedure.

HENNA VEGETABLE TINT (NON-OXIDATIVE)

Derived from a plant grown in Asia and North Africa, this tint penetrates and stains the cortex with its natural plant extracts. Applied with heat, these self-penetrating colors create beautiful shades that resemble nature. Henna comes in brown, gold, red and neutral; henna can also be used as a conditioner. It coats the hair with conditioning properties and once was very popular. What we've learned about Henna over the years is that it prohibits the use of relaxers and other chemicals because it builds up on the hair follicles. Considered permanent, Henna does fade eventually. Semi-permanent colors, or the new transparent colors like Jazzing (r), have replaced Henna in popularity. But Henna remains a good choice for natural hairstyles.

TRANSPARENT HAIR COLOR
(GLAZING AND JAZZ1NG (R)) (NON-OXIDATIVE)

Glazing or Jazzing(r) have become quite popular. It is a shiny, transparent, conditioning hair color that comes in a variety of colors to enhance natural and pre-lightened hair. Glazing and jazzing are applied by using a two-step process, lightening the hair with a small volume of peroxide and an extremely gentle lightener, then applying the color. The processing time is from 5 to 30 minutes, with or without a dryer, depending on the degree and depth of permanency desired. The results are a beautifully colored and conditioned head of hair. Some popular colors are burgundy, wine, grape, black, indigo, cherry, fuchsia, plum, chocolate, cognac, red and gold.

This sheer hair color group falls in the permanent category when placed under the dryer for 30 minutes. Conditioners are contained in the color, which is sealed in with the heat. It can be put on the hair for as little as five minutes with noticeable results. The vibrant certified stains in the color tend to linger. If you want the colors to appear more vibrant, reapply every two to three months.

There is a downside to this color, however. While wearing a style that requires curl activators or moisturizers for daily maintenance, the color will run on clothes and pillowcases when it is wet.

These ultra sheer and beautiful hair colors are great as long as you dry the hair immediately after washing, and I mean immediately. These new transparent colors are my best bet in the color group. With just a small amount of pre-lightening and a low volume of peroxide, glazing, with all its conditioning properties, is a good way to color. Glazing and jazzing can also be used as a semi-permanent hair color by eliminating the pre-lightening step. This product works best as a semi-permanent hair color on lighter hair colors and porous hair.

SEMI-PERMANENT
(OXIDATIVE WITHOUT AMMONIA)

This hair color category does not lighten the hair either. Used mainly to cover gray and add an intense amount of color, semi-permanent hair color uses the least amount of peroxide, 10 volume. A trade secret used in the back rooms of beauty salons, this color category is pushed aside by its permanent hair color counterpart. The reason is the permanent hair color doesn't fade as quickly, and if you need to use peroxide in a hair color you may as well make it count. Twenty-volume peroxide in permanent hair color allows hair to receive more color and to last longer. Semi-permanent colors are great for men to use to blend gray gradually.

Application of this hair color type is simple. Just mix semi-permanent color with the desired level of peroxide and apply to the entire head, using a simple four-section parting of the hair. Start the coloring procedure at the most resistant area of

Color Me Bad

the head, which is usually the front for gray, and continue until all the hair is covered.

PERMANENT HAIR COLOR (OXIDATIVE WITH AMMONIA)

Permanent hair color lightens and deposits color in one single process. That makes it the most popular hair color. It covers gray completely and changes the structure and color of the hair permanently. A beautiful new color can be created. The new color is fixed permanently in place until it grows out or you kut the permanent color out of your hair.

The damaging effects.

Permanent color contains ammonia. Ammonia, when mixed with peroxide, activates the color. There are different volumes of hydrogen peroxides, also called developers, for different lightening effects. The higher the volume of peroxide, the more it lightens and damages the hair. The lower the volume of peroxide, the more color deposits and less damage occurs. Ten volume is used for a mild lift of color and more deposit; 20-volume for general color 1ift: 30-volume for lots of lift and 40-volume gives the most lift or lightening power.

Because of the oxidation process, permanent hair color must be applied about one-half-inch away from the scalp so the body heat does not make the color work too fast on the root area. Even coverage is achieved when the color is applied on the middle or shaft of the hair first, then the roots of the hair near the scalp, and lastly to the ends of the hair, where hair is the most porous.

DOUBLE PROCESS COLORING AND HIGHLIGHTING

Double processing is a two-step process of removing color from the hair and replacing it with light pastel shades. In double processing, one step removes nearly all of the natural pigments from the hair. This step is called decolorization,

and the second process, called toning, adds the soft, light color desired. Highlighting refers to small sections of the hair lightened to create contrast with other parts of the hair. We highlight hair by using peroxides of various volumes coupled with powder lighteners (also called bleach) as a catalyst to speed up decolorization. The color is being removed at a very rapid and damaging rate. Lots of times short hair looks well with highlights because you can keep

Effects of overprocessing.

kutting off all of the overprocessed hair. Highlights are best suited for natural textures with no added chemical treatments. With proper conditioning, virgin hair is highlighted with great success. Highlights can also be done using blonde and other permanent colors. But when we traditionally speak of highlighting hair, we use the powder lightener and peroxide method. The application method of highlighting can be hair painting, using a brush as if you're painting streaks into your hair;, the cap method, using a plastic cap with holes in it to pull the small pieces of hair through for lightening; or the foil method. Foil is used to separate the selected strands from the strands not going to be highlighted.

Professional stylists achieve high success with highlighting techniques in salons because of the broad assortment of toners available to them. A toner is a semi-permanent color designed to subdue the brassy tones or equalize color tone after highlighting. They come in a large variety of pale, delicate shades, which "tone" pre-lightened hair. Store-bought highlighting kits are sold with toners, but the assortment is slim. And for most consumers, the toner shade selection may be difficult to determine. Salons are supplied with the proper colors and toners needed to create highlights of greater enhancement to most skin tones.

A professional colorist can introduce you to techniques of coloring hair that will change your look, and have others' heads turning. There are color combinations that your stylist may suggest to you like using one-, two- or even three-dimensional colors to give you an alluring look. Bold highlights just around the face make an outstanding statement. Chunks of color throughout the hair are becoming popular, and having small portions of lighter hair throughout is common. Blonde and gold are among client favorites. These highlights bring light to the face and brighten up hairstyles.

There are many layers of color in dark hair and each layer must be lightened until the blonde or gold color is reached. Remember that a toner should always be used after pre-lightening to soften the look. Let your stylist try some blonde or gold tones in your hair at least once in your life.

Let's face it, that ski instructor made skiing look easy the first time, too – until you tried it. Do yourself a favor. Don't try to highlight your own hair. Put yourself in the hands of a professional colorist or stylist.

The results of permanent hair color and highlights remain until new hair grows in. Color retouches should be applied at four to six week intervals at the roots. There is a definite line dividing the previously colored hair and the new growth. That line is called the line of demarcation. So when you see "de" mark, color your roots.

The combinations of these chemicals used for coloring and highlighting are abrasive when used with other chemical services, such as relaxers and curly perms. Great caution should be taken to assure the least amount of breakage and shedding during these procedures.

Here are some things to remember while wearing hi-lift, highlighted or double-processed hair:

- Wait at least two weeks between permanent hair color applications and other chemical services.

- Avoid using relaxers with highlighted hair.

- Use a low volume of peroxide to adequately perform color services.

- When retouching permanent color, use permanent color on new growth and semi-permanent color to "perk up" previously colored hair on ends.

- Use vitamin-enriched, deep-penetrating protein treatments regularly.

- When selecting other chemical treatments to be used on color-treated hair, always use appropriate formula relaxers.

- Try setting, sculpting and wrapping styles to combat dryness and retain moisture.

- Use a conditioning styling lotion while blow-drying to protect hair from excessive dryness and add moisture.

- Always use professional salon-sold products on colored-treated hair; grocery store brands tend to be abrasive and damaging and can cause premature fading.

- Have your hair kut before coloring, especially when highlighting. This simple procedure helps prevent that choppy, zebra look. Use a razor kut to improve blending of highlighted hair. Once the hair is kut, the right hair color design can accent that kut.

Another good reason to kut the hair before coloring is not to waste color on hair that will end up lying on the floor.

With all the new advanced technology and knowledge available to stylists, and a little research on your part, you can find a great colorist who will satisfy your needs.

WHY WON'T MY COLOR COME OUT LIKE MY GIRLFRIEND'S?

Everyone has underlying pigment in the hair, which is a great factor in determining the hair color results. Most likely, your color did not start out as the same color as your girlfriend's; also, did you check what volume of peroxide she used? What color line? And just how long did she leave the product on her hair? Most importantly, you shouldn't want to look

Color Me Bad

exactly like your girlfriend anyway. What happened to individuality?

DOES HAIR COLOR CAUSE CANCER?

The answer is no. The Medical Sciences Bulletin reported in 1994 that with 573,369 women tested, "no evidence of positive association between use of permanent hair dye and all hematopoietic cancers for a specific type (Hodgkin's lymphoma non-Hodgkin's lymphoma, multiple myeloma, chronic lymphocytic leukemia and other leukemias)." The report was published in the Journal of the National Cancer Institute. The Harvard researchers went on to say that age at the time of first use, how long you used the products, how often and how long you have been coloring had "no material associations" to blood and lymph system cancer risk.

Everyone has underlying pigment in the hair, which is a great factor in determining the hair color results.

23 The Power and Politics of Black Hair

By Barbara Coles, lawyer, Bowie, MD

In the Name of Beauty and Acceptance.

As we enter into a new millennium, hair and the politics of hair still hold amazing power over African Americans. Whether we want to admit it or not, our opinion of our hair is inextricably molded by the opinions that others have about our hair and what we see in the mirror—or what we think we see. It's just that simple. But unfortunately the painful experiences that have come as a result of hair have made it anything but simple. It's because of this pain that in the year 2000 there is still an ongoing debate about the uses of the other "n" word, yes, "nappy," and the description "good hair." Can I get a witness?

Ask any sister what she thinks about the use of these words to describe textures of hair and stand back. Most will tell you it makes their blood boil! And, it's not about being politically correct. It's about reliving some pain. It's about being on the receiving end of a tasteless joke—a last ditch put-down ranking a close second behind something that begins with "your mama so—" or a pronouncement that you must think you're cute." All based on hair texture.

No matter what "good hair" means in terms of texture, it clearly connotes that anything that doesn't meet the general definition of "good hair" must, therefore, be …"bad hair." No wonder the description makes a woman's blood boil. Who on earth wants to claim the title of "bad" anything? Has anyone ever been proud of something that's associated with or regarded as "bad"? Think about it. Bad usually means more than simply not being good. It usually means not being "as good" as or not being "good enough." Inferior. Can you blame anyone for having negative feelings regarding the whole "good hair" drama?

What about the use of the other "n" word? A recent controversy concerning a white teacher's use of the children's book "Nappy Hair" raised an uproar in New York and reopened the debate. Never mind that the book was used to raise self-esteem or that it tells the story of an African American girl's journey to finally accepting the uniqueness of her hair. Never mind that the majority of the protesters weren't familiar with the story or that a sister wrote it. The title was enough. Clearly, the perception of hair at the close of the 1990's was still the subject of ongoing debate in our community. Whether we want to admit it or not, that makes hair pretty powerful.

In her book chronicling the history of hair among African Americans, Noliwe Rooks explains that denigration of blacks based on the texture of their hair was one of the ways that Caucasians used to make them feel inferior. Although whites started this more than 300 years ago, it is still prevalent today. In fact, African Americans are chiefly responsible for its continuation. Ever heard a Caucasian utter the word, "nappy" to describe hair? I haven't, but I can't count the number of African Americans who continue to use it as a derogatory term in these politically correct 1990's. Talk about self-infliction of pain.

We all know that television is a powerful medium and that our opinions of ourselves stem, in large part, from what we see in that small box. But some of us still don't recognize that our self-value and our opinions of ourselves have been shaped long before television was even invented. In the 1900's, advertisements touted the use of "Curl-I-Curl: A cure for Curls by convincing women that nothing detracts so much from your appearance as "short, matted, unattractive curly hair." (Kansas City Star, Feb. 11, 1997). From 1910 to the 1920's, some of the advertisements actually used bible verses to shame women into maintaining straight hairstyles. After all, I Corinthians 11:15 states that, "If a woman have long hair, it is a glory to her." Peace of mind via chemical straighteners was promised to women in the 1930s and 40s. For example, women were encouraged to chemically straighten their hair if they wanted "beauty, comfort, and lasting peace of mind." Who wouldn't want to be attractive? To glorify God? To have peace? While each marketing strategy used a different angle to lure African American women into buying products, they all had the same message: Women, you've got to change your hair! As a result of this message being passed down from generation to generation, both consciously and inadvertently, sisters have been trying to get rid of one of the things that makes us unique: our hair.

Advertisements like these have been successful because they have made women want what they don't generally have: naturally straight hair. This is a common marketing strategy, and it's not limited to African Americans. Look at the countless advertisements geared toward products that chemically curl "bone straight" Caucasian hair. And look at the cornrowed variations of Bo Derek vacationing on a Caribbean Island. So, does that mean that sisters are spending a fortune to look more Caucasian and Caucasians similarly are spending a fortune to look more African? Or does it simply mean that the billion-dollar industry will do whatever is necessary to continue generating billions by making us think we need to change in order to improve. Go figure!

Every woman has a horror story about changing her hair in order to fit in or in order to look a certain way that she believes is better. Initiation into that "I'll do anything to look better" club usually began at an early age with mothers using the kitchen for double duty, beautification and supplication. We all remember the straightening comb days or, for the Generation Xers, the first time we were given a kiddy perm. Take your pick, either experience probably resulted in burns!

> *Sisters have been trying to get rid of one of the things that makes us unique: our hair.*

And that's not all. As we matured, we wanted more "mature" looks or, at the very least, what we thought were more flattering looks. All in the name of beauty, with a price. Hair coloring gone wrong. Sores from misapplication of relaxers. And the more recent phenomena of "it's mine if I paid for it" has caused a few problems, too. All in the name of beauty. Sisters have bought unnaturally straight synthetic or human hair to compensate for their lack of hair. And then there are the platinum blondes. These include the African American Marilyn Monroe wannabes capitalizing on European traits. All because we want change. In the name of beauty. In the name of acceptance. This fact is just as prevalent on the streets of any metropolitan area as it is on the runways of the most prestigious designer fashion shows.

However, some of the newcomers in the modeling industry are naturally coifed and quite beautiful nevertheless. For example, African model Alek Wek has tightly cropped hair and ebony skin. Clearly, she has a different look than Tyra Banks, Naomi Campbell or Veronica Webb. Unfortunately her different look has not been accepted by, of all people, African Americans. Instead of welcoming and embracing her natural look, some have complained that she's a demeaning stereotype. All because she has a wide nose, full lips, natural hair and dark skin. Shame on her for looking too black! That's a sad commentary, especially in the dawn of this new millennium. Someone's going to have to explain that one to me because I simply can't comprehend why so much negativity has been thrust upon this young lady. Is this criticism unfairly steered toward her because some people think she's too black? As if there is such a thing. Or is it because she hasn't tried hard enough to look more European? Answers to both questions clearly demonstrate that self-hatred is still prevalent in the African American community, especially when it comes to questions about beauty.

While media campaigns on televisions and runway models all have an influence on African American women, there may be an even more powerful force in their lives as it relates to hair: black men! Although black men aren't monolithic and their tastes vary, there is a common belief among black women that black men actually prefer long hair. Some do, and some, acting like they've turned their backs on tradition, are apologetic about this preference. One brother said that he's sorry, but he's always liked shoulder-length hair and he couldn't understand why women with long hair wear their hair in upsweeps. To him, that makes them lose their appeal because their hair looks shorter in that style. After some "tongue acrobatics" and jumping all around the subject, one brother explained that his preference for long hair goes all the way back to his Pentecostal upbringing. He said that women in his church were encouraged to stay away from scissors. One brother even went so far as to say that he questions a woman's sexuality based on her choice of hairstyle. Despite the sheer numbers of heterosexual sisters wearing short hairstyles, he said that he immediately questions whether a woman with a very short texturized style or fade is heterosexual. When a close relative opted for a very short style, he asked her, "So, you're a dyke now?" Not all brothers share his sentiment. In fact, a small minority of

the men who were polled for this article readily admitted that they believe that bald women are very sexy, as long as these sisters have style. Style was a common trait that all the brothers said was important to them. As a result, the majority of brothers responded that they have no preference at all—as long as a sister carries herself in a stylish manner. To them, hair is not a primary concern because a sister who has it "going on" will undoubtedly wear her hair in a manner that is flattering. To these brothers, the complete package matters.

Some brothers actually prefer women with natural 'dos—locks and twists. Still others say that all they want from a woman is healthy, clean hair—even if it doesn't belong to the head to which it is attached! After all, one brother compared a weave to seamless panties: If the rest of the world doesn't know, who cares? Almost all men agree that if worn stylishly and in a way that flatters a sister's features, hair can be very sexy. And, almost all brothers shared the complaint that sisters allow their hair to dictate their life too much. According to these brothers, a sister sleeping with her head hanging off the bed out of fear that she's going to ruin her 'do is a major turnoff. Speaking of turnoffs, one brother aptly said that some sisters act like getting their hair wet is like catching a venereal disease. Now, that just ain't sexy!

Who would have ever thought that certain concepts of hair are traced to religious beliefs? Or that the Bible contains verses about hair and how a woman should treat her hair? In religious circles, hair is viewed in many ways. Some see it as a powerful. Remember Samson's strength? Others view it as a crowning glory. In the New Testament, the apostle Paul stated in I Corinthians 11:15 that if a woman has long hair, it is her glory and that it is a disgrace to have her hair shaved. Paul further explained that a woman's taking off of her head covering and publicly exposing her hair was indicative of loose morals. Because of the belief that hair is sexy and, thus, should be covered, some Christian, Muslim and Jewish women are required to keep their hair covered while in public. Some men cover their hair as well. For example, Sikhs wear turbans to contain their hair because the men never kut their hair. Similarly, Rastafarians don't believe in kutting their hair.

These religious principles have been used successfully to establish that certain people should be allowed to wear their hair in ways that may deviate from workplace norms and employer-instituted requirements. However, cases that have not been based on religious freedom have been harder to win. For example, some women have filed lawsuits claiming that they have suffered racial discrimination because they wore braids. Most of these women have been employed in the service industry. In 1981, an American Airlines operations agent sued the airline in federal court after she was told to remove her braids or to wear a wig to cover them during working hours. The agent lost her suit based on the judge's conclusion that braiding was not the product of natural growth and, thus, was a characteristic that could be easily changed. In other words, she would have had a case if she had an Angela Davis Afro because hair naturally grows into an Afro (for some of us). Some companies like Avis Car rental even had written policies forbidding employees from wearing braids. When two employees filed a lawsuit in 1988, Avis immediately reversed its policy. These employees argued that the ban targeted blacks because braids are worn primarily by blacks, often as an affirmation of African heritage. Finally, an employee of the Crystal City Hyatt in Arlington, VA, was fired in the late 1980's because she refused to change her "extreme" braided hairstyle, even though hotel management allowed an Asian employee to have hip-length hair after deeming this style as "cultural". Excuse me, aren't braids "cultural"? In a settlement, the hotel reversed its policy on braids. According to the Equal Employment Opportunity Commission (EEOC), it has no way to determine how many lawsuits are filed each year as a result of no-braid policies. However, the EEOC has indicated that the percentage of cases alleging discrimination based on cultural and religious differences are on the rise.

Interestingly, some schools have banned braided hairstyles. When a third-grader wore braids to school in 1996, she was told not to return to school unless she changed her hairstyle. Denying that the youngster had been discriminated against, officials at the Grace Christian School said that braids, dye, dreadlocks, gaudy hair ornaments or shaved-in designs are distracting to students. Braids, in particular, were found to clash with the "spiritual and educational mission" of the

school. This conclusion was based in part on I Timothy 2:9 which contains the following statement made by the apostle Paul: "I also want women to dress modestly, with decency and propriety, not with braided hair or gold or pearls." It should be noted that the school didn't completely adhere to Paul's proclamation. In this regard, the school readily admitted that it did not object to students wearing "regular" braids or "traditional" braids. If you missed something in the translation, join the club. According to the school official, "traditional" braids are single or double braids. Clearly, this official hasn't been schooled on the fact that black women have worn braids since ancient times. So much for our tradition. Obviously, it's not relevant in some circles. Or maybe, it's not "regular" enough.

It's amazing. Even though Carol Mosely Braun was able to wear braids and represent her constituents in the hallowed halls of the U.S. Senate, she wouldn't have been allowed to work in the service industry with the same style. Nor could she send her child to some schools. That's very sad commentary. Or maybe we're giving too much credit to her constituents for their "supposed" acceptance of her style. After all, she is a former senator of Illinois, and she didn't wear braids when she first sought office.

The emergence of natural 'dos has resurrected the old questions of the 1960's: Who's really black? And are there hairstyles that aren't black enough? You know, the old "to relax or not to relax" drama. The whole debate about whether a sister should relax, lock, twist or braid her hair really misses the point that sisters have a choice! Thus, they have every right to wear their hair any way they want—as long as they treat it with care and realize that their beauty is not measured by the texture or length of their hair.

Sisters should realize that having a choice is powerful in itself. No longer do we have to be burdened with the old pain and degradation associated with terms like the other "n" word and "good hair" and the length of one's hair. Those old burdens should be left in the past. In this new millennium, we should rein in the power by accepting our hair and its limitations and by celebrating the choices we have and our differences. After all, they're what make us unique. Can I get a witness?

What is Trichology?

By Dr. Tariq Madyun, International Institute of Trichology, Madison, AL

Beauticians

Behind

the Times

As the general public becomes more aware of the correlation between hair and body diseases, the sophisticated hair care professional will find it important to go the extra mile to keep clients informed of the latest developments in hair and scalp care.

Today, at the start of a new millennium, the U.S. population has 78 million baby boomers, one-third of its population, with approximately 1,000 joining this group daily. This cluster is placing more on cosmetologists, yet cosmeticians are pressured to answer questions outside their field of expertise. For years the solution has been to see a dermatologist. However, there is overwhelming evidence that many challenges facing the consumer often have little, and in some cases, nothing at all to do with dermatology. Frustrated with possibilities, where does one turn for remedies?

There is a finely tuned organization of hair and scalp care professionals willing to give new direction to our industry. The vision of a new direction for the hair and scalp industry has been forming in recesses of the minds of these professionals for some time now. The emphasis has been placed on higher standards. In her book "Could This Be Your Hair Loss Problem? Diabetes and Low Blood Sugar," Dr. Sandra Gilman-Baldie points out the correlation between these two maladies and hair loss. She happens to be a member of this elite group. This group is redefining the industry and the roles we play. Schools, manufacturers, educators, students and patrons all have to be educated on the industry's new direction.

One such change is the personal responsibility in the health and maintenance of our hair and scalp. No longer can we look at hairstyles to determine the ability of hair care professionals. The reality is that the average beautician is not equipped to maintain healthy hair. The advice of many industry experts is that if hair care professionals are not continuously educating themselves, or offering better service at a reasonable cost, you may want to look elsewhere. A national standard for this industry is being mapped for the year 2000 or shortly thereafter. This will be spiraled by the higher education being obtained by many of the industry's constituency.

HOW HAIR GROWS

To fully understand hair loss, let's examine how hair grows. All the hair you will ever have in your lifetime you will have at birth. The hair that you have at birth is called the lanugo hair. This hair has a tendency to be replaced by vellus hair shortly after birth. This is the very fine hair you may notice on a woman's face, neck and abdomen. The vellus hair that is found on the head, arms, legs and auxiliary areas of the infant are replaced with terminal hair. Terminal hair is the hair in which we most often experience, hair loss. Fortunately, hair loss does not occur all at once. There are three stages for hair growth: Anagen, defined as the growth stage; Catagen, defined as the transition stage of the hair; the final resting stage being the Telogen stage defined as the stage in which hair growth stops before shedding begins. The amount of hair going through the cycle is represented in percentages: Anagen 85 percent, Catagen 1 percent, and Telogen 14 percent.

HAIR LOSS

Hair loss is a normal occurrence, although the amount of normal hair loss has increased over the last 10 years. It is now considered normal to shed 80 to 100 strands of hair a day, an increase of about 20. This indicates some change in the body's metabolism. The decline in proper nutrition has also given way to poor overall health worldwide. Malnutrition leads to loss of hair integrity and eventually hair loss will result. Hair loss is normal but excessive hair loss is not. The hair is like a barometer for the body. When hair sheds it is an indicator that something is internally out of balance. At this point, it is time to seek specialized assistance from a certified trichologist or dermatologist.

WHAT IS TRICHOLOGY?

Trichology, the scientific study of hair and scalp disorders, is a unique area of study. Though it is not very widely known, it is by no means a new science. It is an area of study that began in London, England, in 1902.

The definition of Trichology is well in keeping with the science of Trichology. Trichology is taken from the Greek word "Tricho," meaning "hair." It is the branch of medicine that has to do with hair, its anatomy, growth and diseases. It involves indepth study of chemistry, physics, biology, anatomy and physiology. As such, trichology is a paramedical field, as trichologists must work closely with medical and other practitioners (i.e. nutritionists and cosmetologists).

TRICHOLOGY GROWING

Trichologists are on the rise in the United States, Canada and the Caribbean. This will be beneficial for the hair and scalp industry. These individuals continue to produce high standards of work. One challenge being faced is sick hair and scalp. The industry has to take a closer look and address these problems. The answer to healthy hair and scalp is not styling, but correct treatment.

THE HISTORY OF HAIR CARE

In the 1920's, hair strengtheners (hair relaxers) were introduced into the market. At that time, only men wore them. Much of this processing was performed in barbershops and salons, others were done in the homes, some by unlicensed practitioners and others just experimented. This practice continued until the 1940's, when this product was introduced to women of African descent. When it was first introduced it created havoc. Severe scalp burns and extreme amounts of hair loss occurred resulting primarily from the chemical strength or overprocessing. Manufacturers had to pull many of the products off the shelves and start over. They studied this challenge, added conditioners to the hair straighteners and renamed the product relaxers. The main conditioner that was added to relaxers was petrolatum (Vaseline petroleum jelly). After the first trouble, women were reluctant to try this product again. This time the average person did not have to go to the beauty shop weekly. The process slowly began to pick up some momentum until, in time, it became acceptable to try this chemical process again.

By the 1950's, cosmetologists were becoming more comfortable and more skilled in using this chemical process (chemical reformation). At that time, the hair was not sectioned and only the new growth was processed. Rather, the chemical was just applied to the head, combed through and

What is Trichology?

shampooed out with a regular alkaline shampoo, rinsed, set on rollers and placed under the dryer for an hour-and-a-half. In spite of the crude methods, gradually, the hair and scalp healed and women of color still had long, beautiful and luxurious hair. This took place in the 50's and into the 60's. Then the "Revolution' came and many abandoned the straightening combs and the chemicals and became black and proud. The hair was worn naturally in the 60's at great cost to the salons.

During the 60's, another technique for hairstyling was quietly being introduced. It was the blow-dry-and-curl. All of these represent relevant parts of the hair revolution. As the 60's began to fade along with the afro, the 70's began to blossom. Things were rapidly changing for women of color. Business opportunities were opening up at an unprecedented rate. Appearance took on a new meaning. Mothers were now entering the workforce at an astonishing rate. So back to the salon they went, as if a new revolution was unfolding. Women began to demand faster service to keep up with this rapid pace. As the demand became greater, stylists had to find techniques to meet the chemical need of their clientele. The blow-dry-and-curl techniques were adapted by hairdressers to meet increasing demands.

It was during the 70's that one man, Mr. Jerri Redding, who had dedicated his life to educating cosmetologists, noticed the trend and made this profound statement, "In 20 years there will be more baldheaded women than men." Mr. Redding was accurate, for 20 years later here we are with at least as many baldheaded women as there are men. Mr. Redding, like many of us today, probably realized the devastating effect of the misused chemicals on our hair and scalp.

Chemicals are not the only challenges that we have that are here to stay. There are more than 70 challenges alone that contribute to hair loss as well as to scaly or itchy disorders. Dr. Joseph Mostly, a world-known trichologist, once said to me in a meeting, "One of the biggest challenges we face in this industry is misdiagnosis." It is obvious that if we do not know how to diagnose correctly, we cannot treat effectively.

Chemical application of products should not be taken lightly, and by no means should this be done at home. For professional cosmetologists who have 1,000 to 1,700 hours of practicing, it still takes effort to apply chemicals correctly. The long-term effect is not worth the short-term results.

MORE THAN 50 REASONS FOR HAIR LOSS

The No. 1 cause of hair loss is androgenetic, or male and female pattern baldness, and there are overwhelming numbers of products on the market for thinning hair. Most of the products are for genetic thinning. However, many people are suffering from other problems, so it would be wise to first identify the type of hair loss being experienced.

Male pattern baldness is known as a dominant disorder, which means that the gene is passed from the mother or father. The location for this malady is very distinct. It is in the frontal area, often referred to as a receding hairline or a thin or bald area in the crown. There is also the well-known horseshoe shape.

Siblings and parents may have full heads of hair while one offspring may experience thinning. Another very important factor is the male sex hormone, testosterone. Testosterone is converted to a more potent hormone known as dihydrotestosterone (DHT) that has been linked to male pattern baldness.

Since the time of Hippocrates, we have known that boys that were castrated never lost their hair. Men, after being castrated, regained their hair. Many of the so-called miracle drugs are aimed at the conversion of DHT to testosterone. Normally, we refer to the gene as the potential and the trait as the manifestation. So, once again, the person inherits the gene, giving the predisposition for the trait. When the right amount of male hormone is in combination, the trait appears. So this helps to explain why one can inherit the gene and still not manifest the trait. Those suffering from hair loss or thinning should consult a trichologist or medical doctor as soon as possible.

Below is a list of some causes for hair loss. It gives a more comprehensive view of the wide range of challenges that hair care professionals have to face. Contrary to popular belief, all hair loss problems are not only caused by stress and heredity:

1. Hypoglycemia
2. Iron Deficiency Anemia
3. Improper use of relaxers
4. Medications
5. Birth control pills
6. AIDS
7. Postpartum
8. Trauma (blow to the head)
9. Trichotillomania
10. Auto immune disorders
11. High fever (in excess of 103°)
12. Freezing (below 0° for extended periods of time)
13. Dental infections
14. Hyperthyroidism
15. Hypothyroidism
16. Death of loved one
17. Too many aspirins
18. Excess vitamin A
19. Braiding too tightly
20. Bonding
21. Scratching
22. Too many nuts
23. Pesticides
24. Mercury poisoning
25. Lupus
26. Syphilis
27. Tumors
28. Chemotherapy
29. Crash diets
30. Fungal infections
31. X-rays
32. Traction
33. Bacteria
34. Folliculitis
35. Pituitary
36. Rollers
37. Herbicides
38. Deficiency of Essential Fatty Acids (EFA's)
39. Menopause
40. Steroids
41. Teasing or backcombing
42. Infected tonsils
43. Massage
44. Hot comb
45. Drugs
46. Operations
47. Calcium deficiency
48. Hypoparathyroidism
49. Adrenal imbalances
50. Marijuana
51. Ovaries
52. Zinc deficiency
53. Magnesium deficiency
54. Chromium deficiency
55. Copper deficiency
56. Protein deficiency
57. Sun
58. Stress
59. Arsenic
60. Insecticides
61. Aluminum
62. Thelium
63. Boric Acid
64. Chloroprene
65. Hepatitis
66. Cirrhosis
67. Kidney failure
68. Copper deficiency anemia
69. Pernicious anemia
70. Anorexia nervosa
71. Bulimia
72. Excessive vitamin D
73. Birth Control inserts

What is Trichology?

Maladies of the hair and scalp are on the increase, so there is ever-growing need for people who are trained in this field. In order to be a trichologist, one must undertake 650 hours of theoretical training and 100 hours of practical training, which must be preceded by a minimum of five years of experience in the hair and scalp industry. Knowledge must be gained in the areas of the causes, symptoms, diagnosis and prognosis of specific hair and scalp disorders. Trichologists treat such conditions as dandruff, psoriasis, Seborrhea dermatitis, dry, oily or itchy scalp, hair loss, hair breakage and thinning. Additionally, it is important that trichologists be able to recognize certain systemic conditions that need to be treated by other medical practitioners such as endocrinologists, dermatologists, neurologists or medical doctors, to name a few, and direct the patient accordingly. One such example is the condition known as Discoid Lupus Erythematosus, which along with other signs involves the destruction of hair follicles. A trichologist is trained to recognize the signs of the illness and many others.

Quite often a person may go to the doctor for a medical checkup, yet the hair and scalp are never included in the examination. If this were done, a number of medical conditions that initially elude doctors could be treated earlier. The hair and scalp are just as important an area of the human body as all the others. Hair, as a tissue of excretion, is a perfect gauge for physical conditions and acts as a barometer for the body systems.

There are specialists available for every area of the human body,such as the neurologist, who deals with the brain and central nervous system, to the podiatrist, who deals with the problems associated with the foot. Trichologists specialize in conditions of the hair and scalp and often sees the first signals of imbalance in both adults and children. So trichology, though seemingly obscure to some at present, is a very necessary profession that has its place in medical treatment.

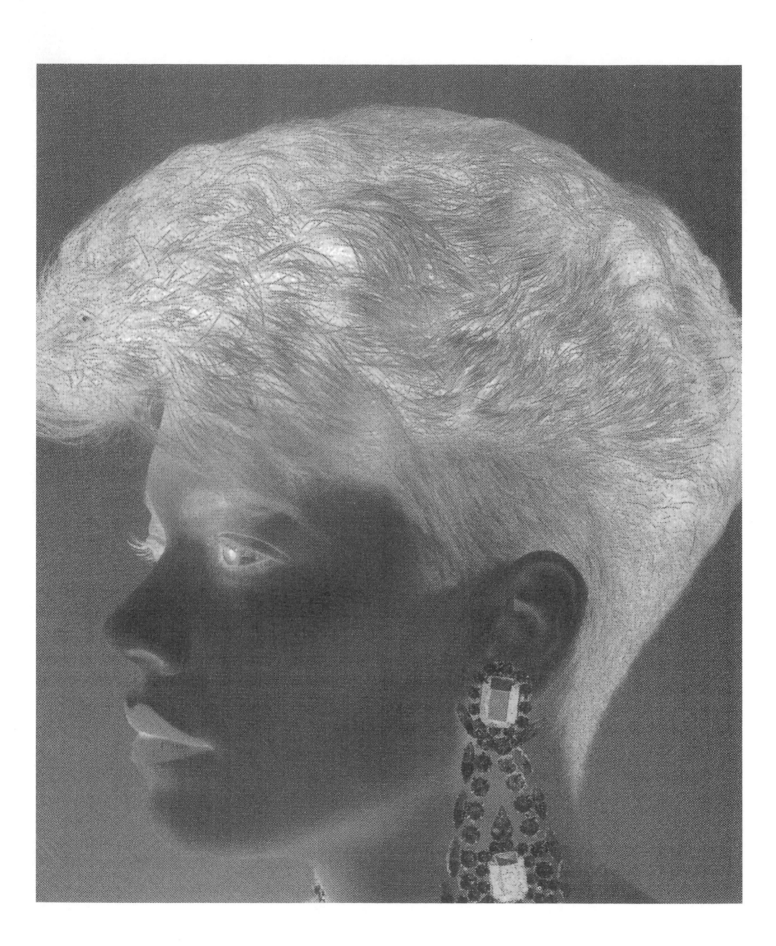

25 Cancer

By D. Smith, M.B.S., M.D., Washington, DC

A cancer diagnosis is a powerful stimulus against procrastinating on warm, kindly and beautiful things. It is a reminder that much of the material things aren't that urgent after all. It is a reminder to take time to watch the sunset with someone you love.

These are the thoughts of a woman who has cancer, who needed to share her feelings with someone who would care and understand. This is written for those affected by cancer. Maybe it's you, someone in your family, or a close friend.

Those dealing with cancer, as someone once said, often feel that "we share a common bond that only victims of cancer know, the feelings of anguish and the loneliness no one else can share."

No two people who have cancer are alike. The same goes for relatives or friends of those battling the disease. But they all face intense fears, anxieties and frustrations that seem new to many of us. Yet, so many others have taken the journey before us. We travel a road paved with great emotion, hope and despair, courage and fear, humor and anger. Perhaps sharing the experiences of those who have walked before us will help us find our own ways of coping.

These days, cancer does not automatically mean death. Today, nearly two million Americans diagnosed with cancer are alive and considered cured, meaning that five years or more after their diagnosis and treatment, there is no evidence of the disease. For them, cancer has become a chronic condition somewhat like hypertension, diabetes or a heart condition. As with other chronic conditions, periodic checkups will be a part of their lifelong routine. Undeniably, they will be more anxious about minor signs of illness or discomfort. Unlike others with chronic disease, they most likely will not need lifelong medications or special diets as a daily reminder that they are ill. Many patients will live for years, grow old and die much as they had expected to do before their diagnosis.

And yet, it is hard not to think about death when diagnosed with cancer. But people should remember the following: 1. A diagnosis is not a death sentence; 2. For some forms of the disease, nine out of 10 people diagnosed can be considered cured; and 3. There are so many sunrises and sunsets left to enjoy. One must always concentrate on living.

Each of us develops over the years an image about our body. We may not be completely satisfied with that image, but usually we are comfortable with it when we are with someone we love. Disfigurement, hair loss, nausea, radiation burns — even fatigue — can destroy your good feelings about your physical appeal.

Chemotherapy plays a big role in our physical disabilities. The drugs often are called "anticancer" drugs. Normal cells grow and die in a controlled way. Cancer occurs when cells become abnormal and keep dividing and forming more cells without control or order. Anticancer drugs stop cancer cells from growing or multiplying.

Surgery and radiation are other forms of treatment often used to fight cancer. Other drugs may be used, too. These may include drugs that can block the effect of hormones. Doctors also may use biological therapy to boost the body's natural defenses against cancer. Depending on the type of cancer and its stage of development, chime can be used:

- To cure cancer.

- To keep the cancer from spreading.

- To slow the cancer's growth.

- To kill cancer cells that have spread to other parts of the body.

- To relieve symptoms that may be caused by the cancer.

Treatment often involves a combination of methods, chemo is used along with surgery and/or radiation therapy. When it is used for this purpose, it is called adjuvant therapy.

How often and how long you get chemo depends on the type of cancer you have, the goals of the treatment, the drugs used and how your body responds. You may get chemo every day, every week or every month.

Because cancer cells grow and divide rapidly, anticancer drugs are made to kill fast-growing cells. But certain normal, healthy cells also multiply quickly, and chemotherapy can effect these cells, too. When it does, side effects may result.

The fast-growing, normal cells that are most likely to be affected are blood cells forming in the bone marrow and cells in the digestive tract, reproductive system and hair follicles. Anticancer drugs also can damage cells of the heart, kidney, bladder, lungs and nervous system.

The most common side effects of chemotherapy include nausea and vomiting, hair loss and fatigue. Other common side effects include an increased chance of bleeding, getting an infection or developing anemia. These side effects result from changes in blood cells during chemotherapy. Most normal cells recover quickly after chemotherapy, so most side effects gradually disappear and the healthy cells have a chance to grow normally. The time it takes to get over some side effects and regain energy varies from person to person. How soon you will feel better depends on many factors, including your overall health and the kinds of drugs you have been taking. While many side effects go away fairly rapidly, some take months or years to disappear. But sometimes the side effects last a lifetime, as when chemotherapy causes permanent damage to the heart, lungs, kidneys or reproductive organs. And certain types of chemotherapy occasionally may cause delayed effects, such as a second cancer, which can show up years later.

It is important to remember that many people do not have long-term problems from chemotherapy. It also is reassuring to know that doctors are making great progress in preventing some of chemotherapy's more serious side effects. For instance, they are using many new drugs and techniques that increase chemotherapy's powerful effects on cancer cells while decreasing its harmful effects on the body's healthy cells. The side effects of chemotherapy can be unpleasant, but they must be measured against the treatment's ability to destroy cancer.

Nausea and vomiting almost always can be controlled or at least lessened. If you experience this side effect, your doctor can choose from a range of drugs known as antiemetics, which help curb nausea and vomiting. Different drugs work for different people, and it may be necessary to use more than one drug to get relief.

Cancer

Hair loss (alopecia) is a common side effect of chemotherapy, but it doesn't always happen. Your doctor can tell you whether hair loss is likely to occur with the drugs you are taking. When hair loss does occur, the hair may become thinner or may fall out entirely. The hair usually grows back after the treatments are over. Some people even start to get their hair back while they are still having treatments. In some cases, hair grows back in a different color or texture.

Hair loss can occur all over the body. To care for your scalp and hair during chemotherapy, use mild shampoos, soft brushes and low heat when drying your hair. Also, don't use brush rollers to set your hair, don't dye it or get a permanent. Have your hair kut short. Short styles will make your hair look thicker and fuller. It also will make any hair loss easier to manage. Use a sunscreen, sunblock hat or scarf to protect your scalp from the sun if you lose a lot of hair from your head. Some people who lose all or most of their hair choose to wear turbans, scarves, caps, wigs or hairpieces. Others leave their head uncovered. Still, others switch back and forth, depending on whether they are in public or at home with friends and family members. There are no "right" or "wrong" choices; do whatever feels comfortable for you.

Here are some tips to use if you choose to cover your hair: Get your wig or hairpiece before you lose a lot of hair. That way, you can match your natural color and current hairstyle if you wish. You may be able to buy a wig or hairpiece at a specialty shop just for cancer patients. Losing hair from your head, face or body can be hard to accept. It's common and perfectly all right to feel angry or depressed about this loss. For some patients, loss of hair from the head can be decreased or prevented by scalp hypothermia (chilling) before and during treatment sessions. This technique has been helpful for patients taking certain drugs, but it is not recommended for all patients. Your doctor can tell you about scalp hypothermia and whether it would be right for you. Remember that your hair will grow back when your chemotherapy is over. In fact, it may begin to return during treatment. Some people will find that their new hair is slightly different in color or texture.

No extensive studies have been done to determine whether certain genetic cancers have the same effect on family members. For instance, out of four generations of one family that received chemotherapy, the side effects were similar. All suffered from nausea and fatigue, but none experienced hair loss. More research needs to be done to determine if genetics play an important role in hair loss.

Cancer is not something anyone forgets. Anxieties remain as active treatment ceases and the waiting stage begins. A cold or a cramp may cause panic. As six-month annual checkups approach, you swing between hope and anxiety. No one expects you to forget that you have had cancer or that it might recur. People must seek their own ways of coping with the insecurity of not knowing the true state of his or her health. The best prescription seems to lie in taking on challenging responsibilities and activities that seek to fill the needs of others, and a generous dash of frivolity and laughter.

You still might have moments when you feel as if you live perched on the edge of a cliff. They will sneak up on you from time to time. But there will be fewer of those moments if you fill your mind with other thoughts rather than focusing on the cancer.

Cancer might rob you of that blissful ignorance that made you believe tomorrow stretched to forever. But in exchange you learn to see each day as precious, as a gift to be used wisely and richly. So take time to watch the sunset. No one can take that away.

See each day as precious, as a gift to be used wisely and richly.

Common Hair/Scalp Disorders in Black Women

By Valerie D. Callender, M.D., P.C., Dermatologist, Mitchellville, MD, and Washington, DC

Hair Stylists

Have a Role

to Play

INTRODUCTION

I write this chapter on scalp and hair disorders with tremendous passion and concern as a medical doctor and as a black woman who also values her hair and expects a healthy scalp. The passion stems from the deep concern I have for the number of women who suffer physically and emotionally with hair and scalp problems. As they struggle to deal with these problems, emotions build up inside that result in crying episodes — at home in seclusion and in my office examination room. This physician/patient encounter usually leaves both of us filled with emotion and sometimes despair. A bond between us exists from thence on and lasts for many office visits to come.

As a dermatologist, I see patients with problems affecting the skin, hair and nails. Hair and scalp disorders represent approximately 20 to 25 percent of all patient visits. Since I treat mainly African American women, the most common complaints that present to my office are dandruff or dry scalp, itchy scalp and hair loss (alopecia). These conditions are frequently ignored by the patient for many months and sometimes years. Over-the-counter products are used to alleviate these complaints and various medicated shampoos and sulfur-containing preparations are bought but seldom help. Stress is believed to be the cause, so medical intervention is delayed. Beauticians or hairstylists who see these women must also recognize the signs of scalp disease and refer them to a dermatologist immediately.

DRY SCALP

Dandruff or dry scalp is a common concern for many women. It is a chronic condition that is likely to recur throughout life. Dandruff produces flakes of skin throughout the scalp and maybe associated with itching. This can be of cosmetic concern because these flakes can also appear on ones clothing. Wearing dark-colored shirts, dresses or suits can cause these flakes to be more noticeable and become a problem. Over-the-counter dandruff shampoos containing tar derivatives, selenium sulfide, zinc pyrithrine and salicylic acid are helpful but can overly dry the hair and cause hair damage. These shampoos should not be used daily as recommended on the label, but weekly or every two weeks. Nizoral A-D shampoo is a new over-the-counter dandruff shampoo that was originally available in a higher strength by prescription only. The active ingredient is one percent Ketoconazole, an anti-fungal agent that is effective in treating the cause and symptoms of dandruff. This shampoo is easier on the hair but also should be used less frequently than what is on the label and followed by a deep-moisturizing conditioner.

Seborrheic dermatitis is an exaggerated form of dandruff. Inflammation or irritation of the scalp is present and symptoms include itching, burning and sometimes soreness. Large flakes appear throughout the scalp and can extend to the forehead, eyebrows, around the nose, inside and behind the ears. In black skin, Seborrheic dermatitis can cause dark or light patches of flaky skin on the face and commonly along the frontal hairline and forehead. This is important to note because hair chemicals applied to the scalp will cause further irritation in those areas and worsen this condition. Over-the-counter products seldom help in alleviating the symptoms and medical treatment becomes necessary. There is no way to prevent or cure Seborrheic dermatitis. However, it can be effectively treated with prescription strength Nizoral shampoo used weekly and topical hydro-cortisone applied to the scalp daily. The scalp will then take several months to heal even after the itching resolves.

ITCHY SCALP

There are many causes for an itchy scalp. Usually the cause is visually apparent to the trained eye and thus the treatment can be determined easily. An itchy scalp can occur from various hair and scalp diseases such as dandruff, Seborrheic dermatitis, eczema, psoriasis and contact dermatitis. All can cause the hair to shed but the latter condition also can be a cause of permanent hair loss.

Dandruff and Seborrheic dermatitis have been previously mentioned. Eczema or atopic dermatitis is a common skin disease that occurs in families. It is associated with allergies, hay fever and asthma. Eczema can occur at any age but is most common in infants and young adults. Common locations include the skin on the face, inside of the arms and behind the knees. The skin rash is very itchy and appears dry. When this condition occurs on the scalp, chronic scratching

can result in open sores, scabs and hair breakage in the affected areas. The treatment consists of mild shampoos, over-the-counter hydrocortisone and, in some cases, prescription-strength hydrocortisone. Oral antihistamines such as Benadryl are used to control the itching.

Psoriasis is a chronic skin disease that commonly affects the scalp, elbows, lower back and knees. The cause is unknown. However, recent research studies have discovered an abnormality in the functioning of key white cells in the bloodstream that trigger inflammation in the skin. This causes the skin to shed itself too rapidly producing large thick scales on the body. Psoriasis of the scalp presents similar to Seborrheic dermatitis but is usually more severe. The thick scales are more compact and usually do not respond to over-the-counter products. Treatment consists of medicated shampoos containing tar derivatives or salicylic acid, prescription-strength hydrocortisone and topical synthetic vitamin D.

Contact Dermatitis

Contact dermatitis of the scalp can be divided into two types, an allergic type and an irritant type. An allergic contact dermatitis occurs in people who are genetically predisposed. It can be caused by an allergy to hair dyes (para-phenylene diamine) or to bonding glue (latex). When these two substances come in contact with the skin, itching occurs within 12 to 48 hours after exposure. If not treated, this allergic reaction can worsen and cause intense itching, skin redness, oozing and eye swelling. This reaction is considered

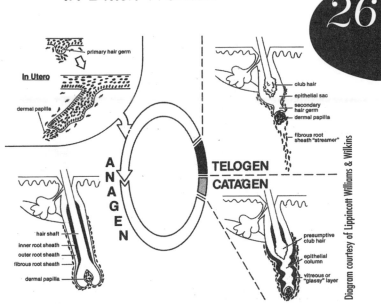

Diagram courtesy of Lippincott Williams & Wilkins

Fig. 1. The life cycle of a hair. The fetal primary hair germ develops into the first anagen hair while still *in utero*. This hair then proceeds to cycle from anagen through catagen into telogen. The secondary hair germ at the base of the telogen hair develops into a new anagen hair.

life-threatening and some patients are admitted to the hospital. Treatment consists of removing the bonding glue or thoroughly rinsing the hair dye with mild shampoo. A combination cortisone/antibiotic ointment is applied daily. Benadryl is taken as needed for itching. Prednisone therapy for a one- to two-week course is sometimes necessary in severe cases. Avoidance of the offending agent (hair dye or bonding glue) is important.

An irritant contact dermatitis of the scalp is usually a gradual process and is caused by hair relaxers (lye and no-lye based) and curly permanent (thioglycolic acid). These hair products can cause inflammation of the scalp and itching. The symptoms occur after each relaxer or permanent and then eventually resolve with no treatment. After many months, and frequently many years, this process continues until thinning of the hair is noticed at the vertex of the scalp. Thus, early treatment can prevent this hair loss. Recognizing the problem and adjusting the hair care practices is the most effective treatment. Choosing a milder relaxer may help along with correct application by an experienced hair stylist. Also, topical cortisone ointments applied to the scalp daily and then as-needed are helpful.

ALOPECIA

Hair plays an important role in one's appearance and self-image. Society has placed a great deal of emphasis on how one looks. Hair and hair styles have social and cultural significance. Our "crowning glory" if lost can be devastating, especially in women. Any sudden or gradual loss can be psychologically painful and may result in depression. Attempts to cover the bald spots by weaves, wigs or hats are done in order to avoid being stared at or ridiculed. So therefore, the medical community should not take hair loss lightly. It should be addressed and aggressively treated like any other type of illness or disease. Hair loss or alopecia is treatable if early medical intervention occurs.

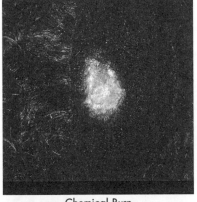

Chemical Burn

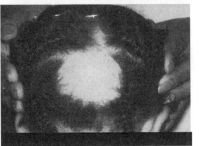

Alopecia Areata vs.
Tinea Capitis-Ring worm

To understand hair loss, one must understand the growth cycle of hair. The average scalp has more than 100,000 hairs. The growth cycle of a single hair ranges from two to six years. Shorter growth phases occur in other areas such as eyebrows and eyelashes, which range from one to six months. Scalp hair grows one-half inch per month or six inches per year, on the average. This varies based on hereditary factors. There are three stages in the hair growth cycle: catagen (transition) phase, telogen (resting) phase and anagen (growing or active) phase. On the scalp, 85 to 90 percent of all hairs are in the active phase and 10 to 15 percent are in the resting phase. The resting phase usually lasts two to three months and at the end of this stage the hair is shed. The loss of 50 to 100 hairs/daily is considered normal. It is important to remember this because any hair loss above this is considered to be alopecia. After the hair is shed, a new hair will then grow within that follicle to replace it.

There are many causes of hair loss (see table 1). In order to correctly determine the cause in each person a systematic approach is essential. There are pertinent questions that must be asked in each individual case (see table 2).

Examination of the skin on the scalp is done in order to determine if there is a skin or scalp condition that initiated the hair loss. We have previously discussed some scalp problems such as Seborrheic dermatitis, eczema, psoriasis and contact dermatitis due to hair chemicals. Another condition, which has been described in the dermatology literature, is the Follicular degeneration of the scalp syndrome or Central Centrifugal Alopecia. The cause of this entity appears to be unknown but a long history of hair chemicals along with a hereditary predisposition to hair follicle damage may probably play a role. An examination of the hair under a microscope is done to check for any signs of hair damage or breakage. A culture is taken of the hair if a fungal infection is suspected. A scalp biopsy is very important and sometimes a necessary diagnostic tool that allows the dermatologist to have the hair follicles under the skin examined. This in-office procedure is done under local anesthesia and takes only ten minutes to perform. The sample is taken from the bald area of the scalp and sent to the laboratory for testing. The results usually take a week. This provides in essence a picture of what the scalp and hair follicles look like to the physician. The biopsy will show if there is infection or inflammation in the skin as well as whether the follicles are damaged. This is important information in determining whether the hair loss is temporary or permanent. If scar tissue in the skin is present, it usually means that the hair follicles have been replaced and ther is permanent hair loss.

Hair loss in women can be caused by hereditary factors. This type of hair loss is called Androgenetic Alopecia or simply "female pattern baldness." It is estimated that over more than million women in the United States can be affected. It's seen more commonly in men. Androgenetic Alopecia begins with a gradual thinning of hair on the top of the scalp. With time, the scalp becomes more visible. There is no itching, scaling, burning or redness of the scalp, in fact, the skin appears perfectly normal. The cause of this condition is a hereditary shrinking or miniaturization of certain hair follicles on the scalp which is predetermined. The active growth phase of the hair shortens and the resting growth phase becomes longer. Eventually this hair thinning can involve the entire top of the scalp.

Currently the only medical treatment for female pattern baldness is Rogaine or Minoxidil topical solution. Once by prescription only, this product is now available over the counter. It comes in two strengths, two percent and five

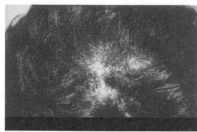
Central Centrifugal Alopecia

percent Minoxidil. The five percent strength is used mainly in men. The side effects of Rogaine include scalp irritation and facial hair growth. So therefore, the use of Rogaine should be used only for female pattern baldness and not for any other type of hair loss, particularly hair loss caused by the use of hair chemicals. Using a product that has the potential of irritating the scalp along with an already irritated scalp may cause further damage and more hair loss. The correct cause of the hair loss must be determined in order to prescribe the appropriate treatment.

Table 1.   CAUSES OF HAIR LOSS

1. Hair/Scalp Disorders

    a. allergic dermatitis
    b. irritant dermatitis
    c. seborrheic dermatitis
    d. eczema
    e. psoriasis

2. Traction Alopecia

3. Alopecia Areata

4. Hereditary (androgenetic) Alopecia

5. Medical Illnesses

    a. thyroid disease
    b. anemia
    c. high fever
    d. lupus
    e. syphilis

6. Surgery

7. Medications

    a. birth control pills
    b. cancer fighting drugs
    c. vitamins
    d. prednisone

8. Radiation treatment

9. Child birth

10. Crash diets

11. Stress

Common Hair/Scalp Disorders in Black Women

In conclusion, ther are many diseases that affect the hair and scalp. I discussed the common ones seen in my practice and their treatments. however, other conditions have been mentioned and discussed in other areas of this book. There are several points that must be emphasized and serve aas take home messages sfter reading this chapter. They include the following:

1. Don't wait to seek help Early medical intervention can prevent end stage scalp disease and permanent scarring.

2. Demand a healthy scalp. Take care of your hair follicles by good hair care practices along with a healthy diet and lifestyle.

3.Work with your hairstylist and dermatologist to accomplish your goal. together as a team we can do it.

Table 2.   IMPORTANT QUESTIONS IN EVALUATING HAIR LOSS.

1. Was the hair loss sudden or gradual?

2. Is the hair loss localized to one area or diffused throughout the scalp?

3. Does the scalp itch or burn?

4. Is it painful or tender to touch?

5. Are there any new medications or medical illnesses?

6. Did the hair loss occur after a pregnancy or surgery?

7. Did any stressful event occur prior the the hair loss, i.e death of a loved one, loss of a job or divorce?

8. Is there a family history of hair loss?

9. Did it occur after a chemical treatment of the hair - i.e. relaxer, hair coloring, hot comb?

10. How long have you been having your hair relaxed, permed or colored?

11. What daily hair care products are you using?

12. Did your stylist perform the chemical treatment or did you do it yourself?

27
Hairy Choices

By Barry L. Fletcher

Weaves,

Braids,

Wigs,

Locks,

Twists

and Turns

Versatility is the spice of life. There's no wonder that weaves have had such longevity among African American women. If you're interested in getting a weave but are apprehensive about it, be aware that while some weaving techniques are more permanent, others are temporary and relatively safe and easy to use.

There are basically five weaving techniques: fusion, stitching, integrating, bonding and clamping. Fusion is the most permanent, and involves mending the hair using a hot glue gun. First, the glue is squeezed onto the root area of the weaved hair (should be weft-less), which is then placed onto the root area of the natural hair. Once in place, the hair is rolled into a cast-like structure using the balls of the thumb and index fingers. When completed, the hair is left to harden into a fixated position.

✎ FUSION

Profusion and French fusion are the two types of glue used in the fusion method. Profusion glue is a surgical liquid adhesive mixed with wax. To remove this glue from the hair, a non-acetone lotion is applied to the glue. The glue is then melted down with heat from a curling iron or pressing comb. French fusion glue is made of Polyurethane, which causes it to harden into a crystal-like substance. In order to remove this glue from the hair, an acetone-based lotion is applied to the glue. The glue is then cracked off using a sturdy set of pliers. If your hair is suffering from excessive dryness and chemical abuse, I suggest you opt for a less permanent weaving method.

✎ STITCHING

The stitching method is less permanent and involves braiding cornrows into the hair, then stitching the weaved hair to each row (or track). To ensure longevity and added security, reinforce the cornrowed sections with a stitch before applying the weft.

✎ INTEGRATION

For those suffering from severe alopecia, in which hair is completely gone from the crown area of the head, there are various methods in which weaved netted fabrics are used. The net is first measured to fit the thinning or balding area. The hair surrounding this area is then braided in a circular formation and used as a base to anchor the netted fabric. The weaved hair is stitched to the net, which then becomes a filler for the bald area.

∽ BONDING

Hair bonding is a more temporary method of weaving and is designed to last at least a few weeks. Like the fusion method, bonding uses glue to secure the weaved hair. The glue is squeezed onto the weft of the weave, as well as the root area of your hair. The two are then bonded together. Glue should be applied an eighth-of-an-inch from the scalp. When wearing a bonded weave, avoid using oily products such as oil-based shampoos and conditioners. These oil-based products will lubricate the hair and scalp and may cause tracks to loosen prematurely.

To remove a bonded weave, apply bonding removal lotion or any hair or body oil to each track. Place a plastic cap on the head, sit under the dryer for approximately 15 to 20 minutes, or leave the plastic cap on overnight. To ensure easy removal, check hair the following morning, make sure it is thoroughly loosened and then remove. You may want to give yourself a hot oil treatment to ensure that the scalp and hair are lubricated and that the glue is completely dislodged.

∽ CLAMPING

Hair clamping is the most temporary of the five hair-weaving methods and has the least damaging effect on the hair. This weaving technique may last for one day, and often is used in fashion shows, photo shoots and special events. Hair clamping involves inserting the clamp into parted sections of the hair and snapping it into a secured position. To remove the clamp, push it down, snap it open and slide out of the hair (see a weave specialist for more details).

∽ IMPORTING AND EXPORTING

In 1997 alone, approximately $60 million worth of human hair was imported into the United States. Hair is imported from countries in Asia and Europe, where it often is purchased from poor people or taken from animals such as the yak.

I use hair mannequins when I teach. These mannequins are also imported from countries in Asia and Europe and, in many instances, have traces of lice infestation in the hair. The hair on these mannequins and the hair bought for weaving come from the same source. It is important to exercise strict hygienic precaution when buying human hair.

When the hair arrives in the United States, it undergoes extensive chemical processing to meet commercial standards. This process involves stripping the cuticle layer, color-treating the hair and converting it into various textures. Sulfuric acid is the main ingredient used in this process and it also kills any traces of bacteria on the hair. And there may be instances when the acid residue is not thoroughly rinsed from the hair. Any contact with this acid could promote scalp irritation and cause damage to our natural hair texture. Therefore, I suggest that after buying human or animal hair you soak it in hot water mixed with neutralizing shampoo for about eight hours, then blow-dry the hair straight or allow it to air dry.

∽ HOW TO CHOOSE SYNTHETIC AND HUMAN HAIR

Hair weaving is a personalized service and should be well-planned from inception to completion. There are numerous hair-types, colors, lengths and textures available to ensure that your finished look meets your expectations. It is best to personally purchase the hair of your choice from your braiding and weaving specialist.

Synthetic and human are the two basic hair-types used for braiding and weaving. Synthetic hair is the more popular of the two because it is man-made, which makes it more affordable. In addition, its soft texture makes it easy to manipulate and mold. In some ways, the ability of synthetic hair to cling to natural hair is an advantage, in other ways it can be a disadvantage. Synthetic fiber has a sponge-like quality, which sucks up the natural oils and moisture from the hair. Therefore, if you choose to use synthetic hair, I recommend you minimize the amount of time it is left in the hair, and do not exceed a four-to-six week period.

For a more natural appearance with your weaves and additions, you may want to use human hair. Be aware, however, that human hair is costly, not as sanitary as synthetic hair and in some instances may cause allergic reactions. You may consider using yak hair instead. Although it is animal hair, the texture is almost identical to human hair, so it offers the appearance of human-like hair without the high costs. The disadvantage is that it tends to tangle and matte easily.

PSYCHOLOGICAL APPEAL

When weaves were first introduced, they were used as fashion accessories predominately by entertainers and high-profile fashion figures who wanted image versatility. Along with the growing popularity of cable television and music videos over the past decade, the visibility of these high-profile images has significantly increased and, as a result, helped reshape our fashion and beauty values.

Hair-weaving, which at one time was considered taboo, has become a socially acceptable fashion statement and a prime attraction to teen divas seeking to emulate their celebrity icons. Of course achieving high-glamour diva status is not the motivation for everyone who opts for a weave. There are far more practical forces at hand, such as: losing your hair at the hands of an untrained cosmetologist; adding hair to give your naturally thin hair a healthier, fuller appearance; trying a weave for a special occasion or perhaps just trying something new. Whatever the reason, if a person feels more comfortable with hair additions, I support them. We all deserve to look our best. But when you allow your hair-weave to become a necessity as opposed to an accessory, it is time for a change.

SHE'S GOTTA HAVE IT

Weaves should be fun. When you start taking them too seriously it's time to stop. There are exceptions, such as when one has a serious hair deformity and is forced to use hair-weaving. In these instances, one should be under a medical doctor's supervision.

There are other instances, however, where women use their hair-weaves as a fashion crutch and in the process allow themselves to become enslaved by their weave. Just like some women will not leave their homes without a full face of make-up, likewise there are some women who will not leave their homes without their weave. This growing obsession develops when women begin to place too much value on their beauty accessories and diminish the value of their natural beauty. In these instances, you may want to stop and question how much credit you are giving your hair-weave for contributing to your beauty and overall image. The chances are, you may be giving it far more credit than it actually deserves.

HAIR BONDAGE

Just like any other living organism, hair conforms to its environment, and if we put hair in bondage for extended periods of time via weaving and braiding, when it is released it will no longer have the same configuration. The same holds true with an individual. For example, if you incarcerate a brother for 10 years, the same brother you kissed when he went in is not going to be the same brother you kiss when he comes out.

Hair needs freedom. When it is strapped down for extended periods of time via braiding or weaving, the hair's natural oils cannot travel from the root area to the ends of the hair, and they eventually suffer from strangulation, suffocation and eventually malnutrition.

Your hair will give you signs that it does not want to be in bondage anymore. When you remove your braids or weave and your hair looks springy and mushy, more than likely it is suffering from redox damage. Redox damage is when the hair follicles shrink because of insufficient moisture and nutrient content. At this point, you will have to kut a good portion of the hair off to get to its strongest portion. The next time you remove your weave, take a good look at your hair and be honest with yourself about its condition. Then decide, is it safe to put my hair back in bondage, or do I need to set it free?

SAVING THE LIFE OF YOUR HAIR

Letting go of your weave to save your hair can be a delicate process and may require you to psychologically prepare for a new, more natural you. For some, the switch may be instantaneous, for others, however, it may be a gradual process, which requires removing one track at a time. In either instance, communicating with your stylist will be the key in accurately assessing the best way for you to make your transition. Length, texture, thickness and the overall health of the hair will be the key determining factors; and the process demands a stylist who is not only sensitive to your personal preferences, but also can be truthful about the condition of your hair.

When considering your styling options, contemplate the long-term effect it will have on the health of your hair. Remember, trends come and go, but your hair will be with you for the rest of your life. If you still have doubts about making your transition, seek an opinion from someone who loves and cares about you. Weigh your options and make an intelligent choice.

TIPS ON HOW TO GROW HAIR WITH THE WEAVE

When utilized properly, hair-weaving can be an asset and could contribute to the growing and maintaining of healthier hair. The beauty of wearing a hair weave is that it allows you to protect your hair while enjoying the benefits of high-maintenance styling, hot curling, blow-drying, etc. This is especially beneficial in professions such as modeling or entertainment, where the hair is subjected to high-pressure maintenance, excessive heat and constant manipulation.

If you are wearing a weave as a fashion accessory, limit its usage to a six-to-eight-week period. Never exceed three months. After you remove the weave, give your natural hair a break for at least a few months. If you opt to relax your hair after removing the weave, then leave the weave off until the relaxer completely grows out, which would be approximately six to eight weeks. After a two-month period, if you decide to put the weave back in the hair, keep its length to a minimum. This will provide a natural appeal and will allow you to fluctuate freely between your weave and your natural style.

BRAIDING

Braiding is a technique that dates back to our ancestry and has been used for centuries to heal and strengthen our hair. Braids are still being used to enhance our image while promoting hair growth. The introduction of synthetic and human hair additions to the braiding process, however, has posed new challenges that need examining when addressing the health of our hair.

Braids can work to your benefit and braiding can be a beneficial styling method if you familiarize yourself with your hair texture and what it is able to sustain, then honor those parameters. For example, if your hair texture is thin, fine or weak, adding too much weight and length to the hair places an enormous amount of pressure on its root, and may lead to permanent damage and hair loss.

Hairy Choices

◉◈ LENGTH AND SIZE

The beauty of braiding is that it allows you to work with a carefree style without the hassle of curling irons, combing or excessive tension on the hair. Instead you are simply placing the hair and moving it around. Braids also offer versatility; they can be glamorous with the free-flowing styles or kut to precise measures. They also can be formal or frolic.

Unfortunately, there is no one fixed formula to recommend when it comes to choosing the size or length of your braid additions. Again, it is a personal preference and is largely determined by your individual hair texture. You may need to try different sizes and monitor the condition of your hair. I suggest that you begin with larger braids and then move to smaller, thinner ones. The first time you apply the braids, leave them in for a maximum of six to eight weeks. Take out the braids and examine your natural hair to see if it is in satisfactory condition. Allow your natural hair adequate time away from the braids and refrain from reapplying the braids and additions for about two weeks or longer.

Under no circumstances should braids be tight. Again, excessive pulling on the roots of the hair may cause damage and retard hair growth. In addition, no hairstyle is worth throbbing headaches and sleepless nights. Part of the appeal of a hairstyle is that it is not only flattering but also comfortable.

Schedule a consultation with a professional braid and weave specialist and communicate clearly your expectations and styling preferences. Experiment with different hair colors and textures before having your hair braided. Remember that your roots will be exposed in a short period of time, therefore, you may want to consider this when opting for colors lighter than your natural hair. When determining the size and thickness of your braids, keep in mind that larger-sized braids are less time consuming and less costly. Micro braids are very striking, but they are time-consuming, costly, and harder to maintain. Most braiders charge by the hour. Keep this in mind when choosing intricate styles that you only plan to wear for a short time.

◉◈ MAINTAINING YOUR BRAIDS

Hair is healthiest and maintains its proper moisture balance when it is clean. For this reason braids and braid extensions should be removed, shampooed and deep conditioned every four to six weeks. Refrain from wearing braided styles such as the Goddess Braids, which are difficult to shampoo. Use lightweight shampoos and conditioners to avoid residue and buildup. To dry the hair, secure braids using a sheer scarf and sit under a hooded dryer for at least 30 minutes. I recommend using a dryer to avoid the risk of mildew, which sometimes occurs when drying the hair naturally.

If you would like to freshen up your braids in between shampoos, apply a small amount of light gel to the braids and then gently smooth using a damp baby brush. Tie the braids flat with a cotton scarf for a few minutes to set. Remove your scarf and spray the hair with a light, oil sheen. To prevent scalp dryness, itching and bacteria formation, spray the hair and scalp with oil sheen or spray antiseptic. You may also saturate a cotton ball or sponge with antiseptic and dab it throughout the scalp.

◉◈ WIGS

Wigs can be an excellent styling choice when searching for a new, exciting yet temporary look. Even with the growing popularity of hair weaves, wigs have maintained a position in the market because

they offer versatility without the minor inconvenience that sometimes accompany hair-weaving and additions. Wigs today can range from inexpensive, generic pieces sold through retail catalogs, to expensive custom-made creations. The selection is vast and includes numerous hair colors, types, styles and textures.

◉ HUMAN HAIR

Human hair wigs are normally fashioned, using the finest human hair textures available, such as Asian, Indonesian and European hair. These textures are less bulky, more manipulative and tend to provide a natural appearance. Virgin European human hair is the best hair texture available for wigs because it has not been processed and has, therefore, retained its strength and natural appearance. On the downside, like natural hair, it will tangle and requires high maintenance. Asian human hair is very coarse and straight; because of this, it is often damaged in the process of making it conducive to our hair texture. However, it remains the most popular because it is least expensive. Indonesian hair has a finer texture and does not require much processing.

The major advantage that human hair wigs offer is styling flexibility. These wigs, just like your natural hair, can be cut, permed, colored and styled. In the same vein, however, just like your natural hair, human wigs are not maintenance-free. All human hair wigs require some styling after they are shampooed. You can blow dry, hot roller set, hot curl, or even wet set and place it under the hair dryer. When properly maintained, human hair wigs will last three to four years. If you wish to avoid high maintenance, consider wigs with a human, synthetic blend.

◉ HUMAN SYNTHETIC BLENDS

Human-synthetic blend hair wigs offer the best of both worlds. They provide the natural look and longevity of human hair, along with its ability to hold its shape after shampooing, unlike human hair, which tends to shrink or draw-up after it is shampooed. Like human hair, these blends can be permed for extra body wave or curled. Human-synthetic blends can last two to three years with proper maintenance and care. Wig and weave specialists can also integrate your natural hair into a wig or wigglet to fill in weak areas, reinforce thinning hair, and provide a lighter, natural appearance.

◉ WIG SIZE

When choosing the wig for you, consider your overall image. If you are petite, do not overwhelm yourself with too much fullness. If you are tall or full-figured, opt for longer or fuller looks to balance your overall figure. Keep in mind that wigs should be used as a fashion accessory, not a crutch.

When fitting yourself for your wig, wear a wig cap to provide a smooth base for the wig, while protecting your natural hair. Place the wig over the cap and be careful not to pull it beyond your natural hairline. Adjust it so that it feels secure without feeling tight or constricting. Your wig should not feel like a hat. It should be comfortable and light. If it feels too heavy or does not cover the hair completely, you have perhaps made the wrong choice.

◉ MAINTENANCE

Environmental factors such as air quality and humidity will determine how frequent you should shampoo your wig. Generally speaking, however, wigs should be shampooed after 12 to 15 wears. Before shampooing, brush straight styles gently and completely using a wire brush. If the style is curly, loosen tangles lightly using a vent brush or pick. Be sure to keep the curls in tact. Avoid using standard hairbrushes; they can create excessive tension and stretching and may damage the hair. When brushing your wig, start at the ends of the hair and then work your way gradually toward the root of the hair piece.

When shampooing your wig, you should include:

- Prepare a basin of cool water (never hot), with a capful of wig shampoo, fully immerse the wig and allow it to soak for two minutes.

- Rinse (the wig) completely in clean, cool water, gently squeeze to remove the excess water and apply hair conditioner for softness and added luster.

- Leave the conditioner on the hair for five minutes, then rinse again in cool water, gently squeeze to remove excess water.

Hairy Choices

- For curly styles, lightly squeeze the curls while the wig is still wet, then gently towel blot the wig to remove excess water, and place a clean dry towel on the hair and allow it to air dry.

Do not comb or brush a wet wig unless you are completely restyling it. After the wig is dry, shake it out and style. Always store your wig on a wig stand. To completely restyle your wig, take it to a professional hairstylist.

When selected and cared for properly, wigs can be a great alternative to experiment with new styles without altering your natural hair. Some hair types can be quite fragile and are often mistreated. For example, some women wear wigs without preparing or protecting their natural hair. In these instances the hairline, front and back, recedes; the hair becomes thinner and in some cases will break. In order to ensure that the fabric inside of the wig does not further damage any fine or already fragile hair, your natural hair should be moistened with light oil and braided loosely and covered with a wig cap before applying your wig.

LOCKS

Considered by some to be the "final frontier" in natural hairstyling, "dreadlocks" or locks are increasingly becoming the styling choice of those seeking "carefree" hair options. These thick, natural coils are becoming what the Afro was in the 1960's and, for many, are a symbol of black consciousness and liberation.

There are several conflicting theories regarding dreadlocks and their origin. Some historians say that the origin is rooted in slavery and that locks grew on the heads of slaves during the Middle Passage as a result

of their inability to comb and groom their hair. Many of the colonists were repulsed by the locks and referred to them as "dreadful." These slaves were then forced to kut their hair and were forbidden to let the locks grow back.

Jamaican descendants of slaves, also referred to as Maroons, are followers of the Ethiopian King Haile Selassie I. Haile Selassie's birth name was RAS Tafari Makonnen, and his followers are often referred to as Rastafarians. Rastafarians are known for their long, untamed, elaborate locks, which they wear in part as an expression of their faith and adherence to biblical scripture, which states never to comb or kut the hair. Rastarfarians were shunned and feared by many because of their unorthodox lifestyles and the intimidating appearance of their long locked hair. Many people dreaded the Rastafarians; it is believed that this is what gave birth to the terminology dreadlocks.

Many of the negative perceptions/misconceptions regarding Rastarfarians are still ingrained in West Indian society; even casual lock wearers are sometimes regarded with mistrust and contempt. The history regarding the origin of the term "dreadlocks" remains controversial and for the most part has negative connotations. For the purpose of this chapter, therefore, we will refer to this hairstyle as "locks."

Today, locks are worn for many reasons that go beyond religion and slavery. Natural hair care salons are popping up all over the country and natural hair care is becoming one of the fastest-growing markets in the black hair industry. As a result, both current and potential lockwearers are seeking information on how to start nurturing their hair. First, keep in mind that it takes time, patience and commitment to develop locks. Secondly, remember that there is no way to unlock the hair. The only way to remove the locks would be to kut them off, kut the hair down to the roots.

There are as many methods of locking hair as there are wearers of the locks, but let us discuss some of the basic techniques used to start and care for your locks. Most people want to know how long will it take their hair to lock. The length of time required depends on the hair texture, wave pattern and locking method used. If the hair has a tight curl pattern, it will take two to four months to lock. If the hair is fine it may take six months or longer. The hair should be at least three inches long and chemical free.

PALM ROLLING

There are three commonly known techniques that are used in the hair-locking process. Hair with a medium to tight curl pattern responds best to "palm rolling." Section a piece of the hair, starting with a horizontal part at the base of the neck. Part this section into smaller equal sections and apply a small amount of gel or setting lotion to each section of the hair. Place the hair between your hands and roll between the palms until the hair forms a cylinder, then clip the rolled strand to the scalp. Continue this process until the entire head is completed. Remember to keep the hair moist using water or diluted setting lotion. Cover the hair with a hair net and dry under a warm dryer. Remove the holding clips and spray the hair using a light hair oil. Repeat this procedure every two to three weeks. If the hair texture is straight or very fine, it may be difficult to lock.

TWO-STRAND TWIST

A two-strand-twist is similar to the braiding method and can be used to lock a medium curl to a wavy hair pattern. Again, start with a horizontal part at the base of the neck and part this section into smaller equal sections. Divide each smaller section into two parts, also referred to as strands. Crisscross the two strands beginning at the roots and follow through to the ends. When you have

approximately one-inch remaining, begin securing the twist using a three-strand braid.

Once you style your hair to lock, do not shampoo the hair for at least three weeks. At the end of three weeks, shampoo the hair and gently massage the scalp. Re-twist or roll any loose or frayed locked sections. The goal is to cleanse the hair and scalp without unloosening the braids or twist. An alternative to regular shampooing is to cover the hair with a nylon wave cap or cotton hair net. Rinse the hair with very warm water and then apply a foam hair cleanser. I recommend Black and Sassy Braid Foam. Let the foam set for five minutes to break down any oil and dirt that is on the hair and scalp. Rinse foam out thoroughly using very warm water, and then follow up with a herbal rinse. Sit under a hood dryer until hair is completely dry and then remove net or cap. If the scalp is flaky or itchy, saturate a cotton ball with an antiseptic such as witch hazel or Sea Breeze and dab throughout the scalp. Follow up using a light hair oil sheen or oil spray.

After several months your twists or braids will begin to tighten, mat together and form baby locks. When properly cared for these baby locks will grow into young adult locks and will require less pampering. Continue using the palm-rolling technique after every shampoo. Avoid using softening conditioners after shampooing; they have a tendency to loosen the locks. Matured locks that are at least one year old can be shampooed and conditioned as often as you like,

Hairy Choices

and without the use of a net or wave cap. Mature locks are characterized by their tight, smooth cylindrical rope-like appearance.

Daily grooming using a light moisturizing hairdressing is essential to maintaining healthy, radiant locks. Avoid using heavy wax or petroleum-based hair pomades; they have a tendency to attract dust and make locks appear heavy and dull. Treat your locks to periodic hot oil treatments to combat dryness. Herbal rinses such as sage, rosemary, nettles, and others can be used to invigorate the scalp and keep the hair smelling fresh. Visit your local herb retailer and concoct your own personal lock potion.

Hair locking is a deliberate, reflective process, and as your hair begins to grow, twist, turn and coil, you will begin to touch and feel your hair with a new admiration and awareness. Some equate the growth of locks to a spiritual, inner-growth, rebirth and maturation, a rebirth and maturation of the

inner-self. Many develop a kinship and feel instantly connected with other sisters and brothers with locks.

There is nothing more attractive than a sister or brother who has well-groomed locks; short or long, impeccably styled, wild or rugged, whatever your choice or experience brings, know that the new positive changes in your hair will bring positive changes in your spirit and, subsequently, your life.

COIL AND TWISTS

Coils

When wigs do not work, and you do not want weaves, locks, or braids, twisting or coiling your natural hair may be a sweet alternative.

Coils—the appearance of locks, without the permanency, is achieved by winding the hair around itself. This style can be achieved on hair that is one-half inch to eight inches long. Section off a small portion of the hair and moisten using a setting lotion or gel and a fine-tooth comb. Grasp the sectioned hair, and beginning at its root, twist the hair around the comb until you reach the hair's ends. Sit under a hood dryer or allow hair to air dry, then spray the hair using a light, hair spray or hair oil. To prevent coils from opening and frizzing while sleeping, tie the hair with a stocking cap, scarf or wave cap. The hair should be covered when showering as well. Coils have a tendency to swell when exposed to moisture.

Twists

Twists are a healthy styling alternative because they do not require chemicals. There are a number of ways that the twist techniques can be applied to the hair. One method involves twisting two sections of hair together, then drying and unraveling to achieve a full, funky finish.

Another locking technique that is used is the Senegalese twists. In creating Senegalese twists, two sections of hair are intertwined together, while simultaneously twisting the individual sections in opposite directions. Sound complicated? Like anything else, it requires practice and patience.

Natural hair can also be twisted into Bantu knots, a tribal style resembling small balls of hair arranged symmetrically on the head. Remember how your mom used to twist your hair into balls after shampooing and then combed out each one? Bantu knots are the same; they only create more attitude. There really is no limit to what can be achieved with natural hair.

28 Born Again

Anonymous

Weaves

Tangled Up

My Attitude

About Hair.

As I sit here and try to recall what prompted me to begin wearing weaves nearly a decade ago, I realize that the subject of my hair is more far-reaching than I thought. I have some unpleasant early memories that surely helped shape my perceptions about my hair.

Take summer camp, between the ages 9 to 12, for example. My parents sent me away for an entire month with nothing more than a tube of Vigoral. After mandatory swimming, no braids, no perm and no electricity in our cabins, my hair looked absolutely atrocious every day. I couldn't do anything with my short nappy hair for four weeks. I felt so ugly that I couldn't wait for camp to end every year. I knew the other children and counselors were making fun of my poorly groomed look.

I went to an all-girls Catholic school from age 5 to 18. The largest class size was about 30 students. Often I was the only black student, or one out of two or three girls. Tuition was expensive for our family, but my parents wanted me to have the best education they could find. Most of my classmates came from wealthy homes, including families such as the Kennedys. The student car lot was larger than the faculty's and staff's, and the cars were more expensive — BMWs, various convertibles, Mercedes. And of course, all my high-school classmates looked like Barbie dolls. Too often, my hair looked awful. I was always late for morning classes because my hair took so long to style; and I was painfully self-conscious. After gym class, the girls would share combs and brushes, but it was always clear that we black girls couldn't borrow a comb or brush from our white classmates.

It should be no surprise that by the time weaves became available, my only issue was how to pay for the procedure. Not only would I finally have long, beautiful, well-groomed hair, I heard that weaving would make my own hair grow like a weed and that it would be healthy, thick and damage free. (That was definitely not true.)

I wore a weave for eight years. I've had every method, too: from braiding, to interlock, to individuals, to infusion, to sewing, to the wefts, to a wig cap and even glue. You name it, I tried it –Each time a stylist gave me a list of reasons why their method was healthier and better than the rest. I was getting my hair redone every four to six weeks, paying anywhere from $250 to $1,200. (That was just for putting it in, not for the hair or styling, etc.) I maintained

135

relationships with six to seven top stylists in different states, and rotated frequently depending on my travel schedule.

My boyfriend is a celebrity, so I was obsessed with always looking perfect, given the numerous events, award shows, interviews and public appearances involved in our relationship. I learned where all the celebrities got their hair done. Soon, their stylists were my stylists. It was nothing for me to fly to New York or Los Angeles to see someone, or fly the stylist to me. I would also get dropped in a heartbeat for those "more important" clients.

Between weaves, despite deep conditioners, treatment, etc., I was always disappointed with how my hair looked. My hairline was becoming thinner and thinner, and I was losing plugs of hair from where the end of a weft was sewn. Some methods of weaving looked beautiful on, but when it was time to remove it, it seemed to require a surgeon's skill. And the folks who took them out (usually a stylist's assistant) notoriously kut my hair, despite their claims otherwise.

It took me a while, but over time I had some revelations. First, I noticed that my hair was always trendy. I got the latest celebrity style that fit my face, personality and lifestyle. Often my hair looked "wiggy," for lack of a better word, and I couldn't really tell until I saw a photograph of myself or caught my hair in a certain light. Second, I began really listening to the advice and theories of these hair people and put their words to the test. Was my hair growing significantly? Did the fact that my hair was braided make it healthier? Were the remedies for dandruff, breakage and dryness working? Having been to some of the nation's best salons, I now believe that at least 75 percent of beauticians have no idea what they're talking about. A cosmetology license does not offer nearly enough credentials for someone to counsel me about my hair. The stylists I referred to earlier usually fell into this group. I noticed that when the poorly trained ones did my hair the bottle labels were turned away so I couldn't see them. And staff were often reluctant to tell me. On the other hand, my experiences with trained hair care professionals always begin with the stylist talking to me about the products and their ingredients. What I could not ignore over time was that the beauticians in this category

were all saying the same thing versus the varied "expert opinions" I got elsewhere. All were into "growing hair" and were truly into care and maintenance. These elite few urged me to consider relinquishing my weave so that at age 50, I could have hair left.

My weave became a type of bondage. I was always self-conscious about a track showing or a thread hanging, or how the wind blew. Though I must be honest and admit that I feel more attractive with long hair, I definitely don't miss anything about my weave. I don't miss:

- Spending outrageous amounts of money

- Gray hairs

- Hair shedding

- Spending six to 10 hours in the salon

- Being at the hairdresser until 2 or 3 a.m.

- The look of my hair when it got old

- Flinching every time someone touched my hair

- Trying to tack my loose tracks myself.

- Unskilled assistants kutting my hair as they took out my weaves

- The headaches from having my hair pulled too tight

- The "wiggy" look in photographs.

- Trying to get my hair clean between tracks.

- The tracks that don't lie flat or were laid incorrectly in the first place

- Begging to be squeezed in for an appointment

Now I'm a free woman. I wear short hair. I don't have a good grade of trained hair, so I'm still learning how to style and care for it. I spend less money, despite getting my hair done every four to five days, and I have had to become more disciplined than ever before. I put healthy hair as a top priority, and it's the main criteria when evaluating a stylist. Do they have a track record and demonstrated clientele with

thick, healthy hair? I no longer rely on my hair to make a statement about me when I walk in a room, take a picture or go to an event. I never realized how much I demanded of my hair! I definitely had to become more self-confident and self-loving. The demand now is for inward beauty to do all the talking!

Though my man misses my long hair, we've had many talks about it and he understands and respects what I am trying to do. He is willing to be patient with me, but I've found that I can be just as fierce with short hair when I want to be. I now understand why many women say it takes a more self-confident woman to go short! I just keep my eye on the prize, take my vitamins, follow my heat-free maintenance routine and remain steadfast in growing hair on my own. I have to believe that 10 years from now a lot of these "beautiful" women that we emulate will have no hair and be forced to wear wigs. You'd be surprised at how many celebrities are almost bald! Along with my short hair also came more humility, more spirituality and more focus on me rather than my appearance. I don't hide behind a look anymore. I have found the courage to be myself.

Hair Maintenance

By Barry L. Fletcher

*L*adies, if you want to ensure that you are treated with the utmost respect when visiting a salon, you need to arm yourselves with the proper information about your hair. The same way you arm yourselves with critical information about your physiological profile, i.e., blood pressure, cholesterol level, etc. You need to arm yourselves with critical information regarding the physiological profile of your hair.

Your hair type is just as unique as your fingerprint; no two types are exactly the same. Once you understand your hair's unique physical properties, you can assess its strengths and weaknesses and choose styles that work for your hair, not against it.

How much do you actually know about your hair's profile? Is your hair naturally straight, wavy, curly, or excessively curly? Is it oily, normal, or dry? Porous or non-porous? You may be a little intimidated by these questions and think that only a trained professional cosmetologist can answer them. Following is a unique system especially designed to help you diagnose the physical properties of your hair. Think of this as the first step toward getting to know your hair. Once you have answered these questions, pose these questions to your stylist and compare notes in order to get an accurate assessment of your hair type.

CONDITION	TEXTURE			
	Straight	Wavy	Curly	Excessively Curly
Oily	os	ow	oc	oec
Normal	ns	nw	nc	nec
Dry	ds	dw	dc	dec

❧ PHYSICAL PROPERTIES OF THE HAIR

TEXTURE

There are four types of hair textures: straight, wavy, curly and excessively curly. The condition of these textures range from oily to dry, and is evaluated based on three properties—porosity, elasticity and density.

POROSITY

Porosity is the ability of the hair to readily accept moisture, chemical or any product into the cortex layer of the hair. To determine the porosity of the hair, hold one strand of hair in between two fingers, take one hand and run your fingers up and down on this strand using the cushion of your fingertips.

If the Hair Cuticle Feels:

1. Smooth and flat to the hair shaft, it is non-porous.

2. Moderately open and slightly rigid, it is porous.

3. Rough and rigid, then the hair is overly porous.

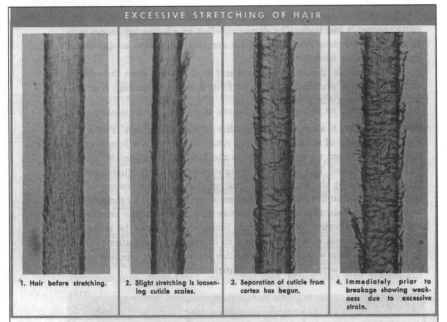

EXCESSIVE STRETCHING OF HAIR

1. Hair before stretching.　　2. Slight stretching is loosening cuticle scales.　　3. Separation of cuticle from cortex has begun.　　4. Immediately prior to breakage showing weakness due to excessive strain.

ELASTIC NATURE OF CORTEX Because of its elastic ability, hair is able to withstand relatively great forces, e.g., normal hair is stronger than copper wire of the same diameter.

In order to give this strength, pliability and elasticity to the hair, the cortex is built like a series of coil springs. These are wound around one another in a complicated fashion, but each is free to move backwards and forwards.

ACTION OF CUTICLE The freedom of movement is one reason for the outstanding properties of hair. These stretching movements are unrestricted by the scales of the cuticle, which can slide in and out, providing a continuous covering for the cortex even while the hair is in the stretched position. This arrangement is of the utmost importance in understanding the wide range of physical properties of hair.

Diagram from Hair Structure and Chemistry Simplified

ELASTICITY

Elasticity is the hair's capacity to stretch. In order to determine the hair's elasticity, we can use the same type of strand test that we used for porosity. The difference is that the hair strand is being stretched in order to measure its elasticity. Take one single hair strand and pull. Apply a moderate amount of tension. You may opt to pull the hair strand out from the root in order to test. Hair containing proper moisture and sebum content should stretch at least a 16th-of-an-inch.

If the hair:

1. Stretches 1/16th of an inch without breaking, the hair has adequate elasticity.

2. Stretches very little before breaking, the hair has little elasticity.

3. Breaks easily, the hair has no elasticity.

DENSITY

Density is defined by the number of hair strands on the scalp per square inch. In many instances people confuse density with the diameter of the hair strand. The average person has 130,0000 strands of hair on their head. People with very dense or thick hair have 150,000 or more strands, and those with thin hair have 100,000 strands or less. Density is then determined or measured by the number of strands per square inch.

It is difficult to determine hair density. In this case you may want to use comparisons. For example, evaluate someone who you think has thin, medium, and thick hair; then use this comparison as a guide to assess your density level. Do not simply rely on your stylist to understand your hair texture, its boundaries and limitations. The above are properties both you and your stylist must evaluate before determining your chemical prescription. Remember two heads are better than one.

Hair Maintenance

It is important to understand the potential hydrogen content (pH) of the products we use on our hair. The pH refers to a product's acidity or alkalinity content. When the hair's sebum mixes with sweat and perspiration, it produces an acid mantle which effects how the hair responds to the product's pH range. For example, individuals that have dry hair and scalp need to use shampoos with a pH range of 4.5 to 5. Normal to dry hair requires shampoos with a pH range of 6.5 to 7.5. For oily hair types shampoos with a pH of 8.0 to 8.5 is sufficient. Shampoos with high pH's can cause discoloration and dryness. PH meters are available for those of you who want to test the pH of your products. This will help you to determine which products are right for your hair. Call your local beauty supply store and find out if they sell pH meters or where they can be purchased in your area.

Remember it is to your benefit to purchase products from companies that essentially know about your hair. Don't get caught up in buying products because they are advertised on TV. Most black manufacturers can't afford to advertise on TV, but the majority of the black manufacturers make products that are specifically designed for our hair type. To determine whether a product is black-owned, look for the "Proud Lady" logo on the back of the product (see product page for product details).

SHAMPOOING

As I travel around the country conducting my classes for professional hairstylists and consumers, I often ask professionals, "what service do you least enjoy rendering in your salon?" The usual response is "shampooing." When I ask my consumers in the hair care seminars what service they like most when visiting a hair salon, they invariably respond, "shampooing." So, what I have discovered is that the service that stylists find least favorable

to them, is the service that consumers enjoy the most, shampooing.

Shampoo is a Hindu word which means "to clean" and this process should never be taken for granted. Most consumers refer to cleaning the hair as washing. We refrain from using this terminology, however, because we do not wish to confuse this process with the way in which we wash our cars, clothes, or our bodies, for that matter. Shampooing the hair cannot be administered any old way. It is a strategic procedure and, if poorly administered, can contribute to dry, dull, rough, tangling, fly-away, static-clinging hair. On the other hand, when properly administered, shampooing and conditioning alone can eliminate the majority of hair and scalp problems and can leave the hair soft, shiny and tangle-free.

PREPARING FOR YOUR SHAMPOO

This segment is designed to help guide you in choosing the right shampoo for your hair texture. Avoid purchasing shampoos that are designed for people with straight and naturally oily hair. Most products that are sold by mainstream manufacturers have a lot of detergent in them.

ACTION OF SHAMPOOS

A WATER / SHAMPOO / OIL AND GREASE

Sticky greasy surface attracts and holds dust and other particles of foreign matter to hair cuticle. Water alone is unable to clean hair because water molecules are unable to pull particles free from cuticle.
Shampoo molecules have a strong attraction for hair, grease and dirt, etc.

B DIRT / OIL AND GREASE

Proper massage during a shampoo insures that shampoo molecules are brought into direct contact with these substances.
Each tail of a molecule is attracted to grease and dirt.
Action of shampoo causes grease and oils to roll up into small globules reducing contact with hair cuticle.
EXCESS shampoo molecules are attracted to imbrications. Alkaline shampoos open imbrications causing tangling and matting during massage movements as fibers rub together.

C WARM WATER RINSE

Currents of warm rinsing water remove dirt and grease because heads of shampoo molecules are attracted to passing water molecules. Tails of shampoo molecules plus attached dirt and foreign matter are bound to heads of shampoo following the rinsing currents of water. Thus foreign matter is removed ONLY during rinsing stages of shampooing.

D CONTINUED RINSING

Excess shampoo molecules are less easily removed from hair shaft. Continued rinsing is essential to cleanse hair of shampoo. Time of rinsing is reduced by restricting amounts of shampoo. Excess swelling of imbrications is prevented by acid, soapless shampoos.

Diagram from Hair Structure and Chemistry Simplified

These detergents have high alkaline content and are designed to strip as much oil off the hair and scalp as possible. We should avoid using these shampoos because normally 80 percent of African-Americans have dry hair. Using shampoos designed for oily hair types will create dry, brittle and overly porous hair.

There are many shampoos available on the market, including conditioning, moisturizing, protein, clarifying, mentholating, dandruff, color treated, soap-less, medicated shampoos and more. Synthetic or soap-less shampoos are either by-products of petroleum or natural fat. The problem with these is that they don't rinse as well. Conditioning shampoos are normally thick, rich, creamy, have built-in conditioners and provide a thick, rich lather. Although lather does not contribute to cleansing the hair, it certainly helps to determine if all the shampoo is completely rinsed out of the hair. Fragrance shampoos leave a lasting scent on the hair and you may want to consider that when choosing your shampoo. I usually suggest oil-based as opposed to alcohol-based fragrance shampoos because alcohol is known to have a drying effect on the hair.

Caution yourself regarding shampoos that make too many claims or gimmick shampoos that say everything you want to hear. For example, I would not expect a shampoo to cleanse my hair properly and then deep condition it all at the same time. It just doesn't happen. Most importantly, whether it is a neutralizing shampoo that's used after a relaxer, a cleansing shampoo used to reduce build-up, or a conditioning shampoo to increase moisture, keep in mind that they should perform those specific functions. Do not expect too much from a shampoo and remember that the most important function is that it cleanses the hair and scalp.

It is always nice to have at least three different types of shampoos to choose from. For example, moisturizing shampoos are designed to coat and protect the hair, protein and clarifying shampoos cleanse build-up from the hair, and mentholated shampoos stimulate blood circulation. You would then fluctuate among the three, depending on the condition of your hair and scalp.

Technique is everything in the shampooing process. At Avant Garde Hair Gallery, we perceive shampooing as the main course among our entrée of services. First, we use a wide-toothed comb or brush to remove all tangles from the hair, starting from the ends of the hair working down toward the scalp area. We then check your scalp for any abrasions, irritations or traces of dandruff. If there is a large amount of dead skin cells on the scalp, we use a fine-tooth comb to lift the dandruff away from the scalp. We then brush the dead skin cells as far away from the scalp as possible to facilitate their removal during the shampoo and rinsing process. The hair is always combed in the direction in which the water is flowing.

In the salon our clients lie back in the shampoo bowl, so that the hair is rinsed while it is away from the face. If you are working from a sink at home, however, you are going to have to rinse from the back of your head, then brush all the hair forward. Next, we select the proper shampoo and we are ready to begin. We guarantee a five-minute free massage, which is part of the shampoo treatment.

SHAMPOOING THE HAIR

When shampooing the hair, use warm water to rinse the hair and scalp thoroughly. Direct the flow of water so that you keep a consistency and eliminate unnecessary tangling. Apply a small amount of shampoo in the front, nape, top and sides of the head. Using the tips of your fingers, begin massaging shampoo into the hair using round, rhythmic and rotating motions. Apply more pressure in the crown and nape area and use relatively moderate pressure on the temple sections and around the hairlines.

After the hair is thoroughly shampooed, rinse with water. Water should flow in the same direction of the hair. Repeat the application for your second shampoo and avoid combing or brushing your hair while it is wet. If you need to manipulate the hair when it is wet, use your fingers. For best results after shampooing, use soft or distilled water. Another excellent idea is to save a container of rain water and use it to rinse your hair when shampooing. A mild conditioning rinse can be used to remove the excessive soap scum trapped

Hair Maintenance

29

THE pH SCALE

COSMETIC SOLUTIONS	REACTION		pH SCALE	EXAMPLES
	A C I D S	STRONG	0	MINERAL ACIDS
			1	
			2	VINEGAR
				BEER
			3	LEMON RINSE
		MILD		COLOR RINSES
			4	NEUTRALIZERS
				HYDROGEN PEROXIDE (Stabilized)
			5	CONDITIONERS
				FILLERS, ACID OR CREAM RINSES
			6	ANTI-DANDRUFF COSMETICS
				SETTING LOTIONS (New Types)
		NEUTRAL	7	SOAPLESS SHAMPOOS
				HAIR CREAMS
	A L K A L I E S		8	SEMI-PERMANENT RINSES
		MILD		SOAP SHAMPOOS
			9	SETTING LOTIONS (Older Type)
				PERMANENT WAVING—STRAIGHTENING
				SOLUTIONS (Alkaline—Thio Type)
				HAIR TINTS
			10	BLEACHES
			11	CHEMICAL HAIR STRAIGHTENER—
			12	(Sodium Hydroxide)
		STRONG	13	AMMONIA
			14	CAUSTIC SODA

(pH 3-9 range marked: SAFE ON HAIR)

Diagram from Hair Structure and Chemistry Simplified

There are five basic types of conditioners, they are: moisturizing, protein, balsam, acid rinse and oil conditioners. Each of them has a distinct purpose. Moisturizing conditioners penetrate into the hair shaft and provide moisture to the hair. Protein conditioners penetrate the shaft and strengthen the hair. It is normally used when the hair is breaking, snapping or is dry and brittle. Protein conditioners should always be followed with a moisturizing conditioner to soften the hair again and eliminate additional breakage. Detangling conditioners are acid-based and allow the hair to transition back to its normal pH, and use a balsam rinse to detangle the hair. Oil-based conditioners are sometimes used for hot oil treatments and actually do not penetrate into the hair shaft. Similar to the acid rinses, it only coats the hair shaft.

in the cuticle. Acid rinse also helps to neutralize the alkaline in the shampoo while shutting down and hardening the cuticle to give the hair more sheen. If your hair is oily, shampoo it every three to four days, normal to dry textures of hair should be shampooed every five to seven days and every 7 to 10 days if the hair is thermally pressed or braided.

When used as a hot oil treatment, it adds moisture, lubrication and sheen to the hair. In cases in which the hair is excessively dry, you will want to use a hot oil treatment. Although the oil will not actually penetrate into the hair shaft, it will provide softness and sheen to the hair.

CONDITIONERS

TYPES OF CONDITIONERS

A conditioner is any substance added to improve the quality of a product. For example, we condition dirt to strengthen and help plants grow. Likewise we use conditioners to moisturize, strengthen and promote the growth of our hair. It is important that we have a clear understanding regarding the capabilities of a conditioner. Many of us expect our conditioners to perform miracles, but a conditioner will, under no circumstance, repair hair that already has been damaged or fractured.

Even if the hair is not suffering from severe breakage, I recommend getting a deep penetrating conditioner at least once a month in order to prevent hair damage. Deep or reconstructive conditioners penetrate the innermost layer of the hair strand and usually require a heat application to ensure maximum penetration. In my salon, we use a steam machine to maximize penetration. If you do not have a steam machine, wrap a hot towel around your head and allow it to set for approximately 15 minutes.

When I was growing up, products designed for black hair were scarce and the ones that were available were often petroleum-based which left a film on the hair, clogged the pores and prevented the hair from receiving its required oxygen. It's quite the contrary today. We have so many products designed for our hair texture that we have to use discretion. Consumers today respond too quickly to marketing buzz words such as sheen, shine, silky, no frizz and extra body, and get lost in the whole natural process of building our hair.

Most products that are used on the hair can carry the claim of being a conditioner to some degree, because technically, a conditioner is defined as any additive, which improves the quality of your hair. For those of you that take care of your hair at home, I would like to introduce you to some natural home-conditioning remedies. You would be surprised at some of the things that you can do to condition your hair without spending a lot of money.

Believe it or not, water is the ultimate conditioning treatment. This is the reason why our grandmothers and great grandmothers used to put out big tubs when it rained and then saved the rain water. They understood the value of water's natural conditioning properties. In some regions, water is extremely hard, which means it contains more chemical preservatives, which tend to dry the hair. Some households accommodate this by using filtration systems to soften the water. When we talk about distilled water, most manufacturers have removed at least 99 percent of the minerals from this water, which makes it less susceptible to bacteria. However, the water is stripped of minerals, which are beneficial to the hair. Rain water, on the other hand, is soft and rich in minerals and serves as a dual purpose; it softens and strengthens the hair.

Water-based conditioners penetrate the hair quicker than any other substance and, when combined with nutrients, minerals, vitamins and proteins, it can be a powerful conditioner. Seaweed, for example, is rich in vitamins, minerals, proteins and iron. Boil seaweed for 10 to 20 minutes in 16 ounces of water or until the water turns to the color of seaweed, then allow it to cool. Once you have completed your shampoo, rinse the hair and massage the seaweed conditioner throughout your hair and scalp. Allow it to stay in for a couple of hours. You may also braid or wrap your hair and allow the conditioner to dry naturally overnight. In the morning, proceed to rinse thoroughly.

There are many products you can use to provide hair with protein, such as egg yolk, mayonnaise, protein oils, wheat and rye. Fruit abstracts are also beneficial to the hair. Basically, what's good for the body is good for the hair. It is just a matter of concocting it in a manner that allows it to penetrate into the hair shaft. Oils work excellent as superior coatings. I have a keen admiration for peppermint oil because it not only coats the hair, but also stimulates the scalp and promotes hair growth. For that reason, in my deep penetrating conditioner, I use peppermint oil along with a host of vitamins that are added to improve the hair's quality, body, pliability and sheen.

Additional ingredients to look for in your shampoos and conditioners are panthenol, lanolin, almond, or sweet almond oil, hydrogenized carotene protein and pine tar which have been used for centuries to help eliminate flaking and itching associated with dandruff. Natural herbal extracts, alpha hydroxy acids, shea butter, salicylic, glycolic acids, cooling metals, calm or mild, help moisten the hair. You should also be certain that all of your products are pH balanced.

You can experiment with some of the previously mentioned formulas, however you should talk to your professional hairstylist about prescribing a natural conditioner that's custom designed for your hair type. For example, if my client's hair needs strengthening, I may prescribe a mud or protein pack. Let's take rye flour, which is rich in proteins, which will nurture the skin, scalp, as well as the hair. This is prepared by using one cup of rye flour mixed with three cups of water, one teaspoonful of yeast and four tablespoonfuls of honey, place this mixture in a clear container for a couple of days to increase its potency. Apply conditioner onto the hair and scalp. Place a plastic cap on the head and allow conditioner to set for approximately one hour or until the rye

Hair Maintenance

flour hardens on the hair. Then remove the cap and rinse the mud pack off the hair.

If your hair is severely damaged and you want a natural tonic to stimulate the scalp and the opening of the folic pores of the hair so that you can condition it, you must have some stimulating agents. So we have to think about the fermentation process when it comes to actually treating our hair, which is a living substance. Fermentation of hair conditioners is no different than fruits for wine and grain for alcohol, or vegetables for juices. We can use our natural proteins such as vegetables, fruits and herbs for the simplest method of fermentation. Create the following mixture by adding a little water, honey and sugar, then mix and stir and let the mixture set for a few days to begin the fermentation process. We recommend no longer than two to three days for the fermentation process. You want to use your products during the beginning stages of the fermentation because after it reaches its height, you will end up with strong bacteria, or an unpleasant odor will develop. Once you ferm your hair conditioner, you should strain and refrigerate it and keep it for a few days.

I am not advocating every old-fashioned remedy. Some of them work, some don't. For example, beer had a reputation at one time for being a food substance that would strip the chemicals from the hair. There is no scientific evidence to date, that supports this finding. Beer is believed to help revert relaxed hair because it is so rich in protein and quickly dissolves into the hair. The only thing that is certain about beer is that the alcohol content opens up the cuticles of the hair strand, which facilitates the hair's ability to accept protein into the hair membrane. While this promotes a stronger hair texture, it also makes the hair feel coarse and dry.

So, with some remedies, you have to use your judgment and weigh the pros and cons. Once you understand your hair's fabric and texture, you will know which ingredients offer you the best benefits in your journey to conditioning your hair. Although I spoke extensively regarding external conditioning, conditioning your hair internally is truly the most effective anecdote to healthy hair, and this is achieved, of course, through a proper diet (see chapter on nutrition and hair).

SETTING LOTION

When shopping for setting or wrap lotions, look for ingredients such as Hydrolyzed carotene, amino acids, jojoba oil, panthenol, glycerin, natural botanical abstract, humectants and vitamins. Avoid setting lotions that contain alcohol because it has a very drying effect on the hair.

Setting lotions with thicker consistencies usually have more built-in conditioners and can be used as moisturizers or activators. They also provide more control and are good for sculpting, wrapping, curling, detangling and conditioning the hair. Setting lotions are available in spray, lotion foam, or liquid form, either regular or concentrated.

Concentrated Setting Lotions

Concentrated setting lotions are excellent for fine, thin, soft hair textures because they provide a firm hold, while making hair appear thicker and fuller. These lotions also provide curl longevity, improved elasticity, and heat protection from thermal styling tools. Keep in mind that you can always dilute your setting lotion to your preferred consistency.

Foam Setting Lotion

Foam setting lotions are very popular today because of their ability to lift and swell the hair while providing pliability and control. The disadvantage of using foam setting lotion is that it dilutes the potency of the lotion and tends to leave a film on the hair.

OILS

Jojoba Oil

Some of the oldest products ever used on the hair and skin have their origin in the oil family, and over the years, have sported a variety of names. Jojoba oil, for instance, is one of the oldest products used by Native Americans and is derived from the seed of the jojoba plant. For centuries the jojoba plant was used to heal kuts, wounds and treat the skin and hair. Today, jojoba oil is still one of the most widely used essential oils in hair and skin-care products.

Petroleum

Petroleum is another very popular oil, and unlike jojoba oil, it is artificially manufactured. Petroleum is available in gel, paste and cream form and its texture varies from light to very heavy. Although petroleum (mineral oil) has no nutritional value, it is popular because it can be used for a variety of purposes and is not costly to produce.

Cod Liver Oil

Cod liver oil is a vegetable oil and is known for its ability to evaporate quickly and penetrate the hair and skin. This oil is easily shampooed from the hair and is recommended to use on babies' hair as well as adults. Cod liver oil is also referred to as fish oil, and is an excellent softening agent for dry hair and scalp. Be mindful that cod liver oil does not offer the same heat protection as the plant oils.

Castor Oil

Castor oil comes from the castor bean and is used as a lubricant in the cosmetic industry. It has a very thick consistency and tends to clog the pores. Although it has an odor in its natural form, there are odorless brands available.

Soy Bean

Soy bean is one of my favorite oils because of its natural conditioning properties. Soy bean has very small molecules, which penetrate easily into the hair strand. It also contains vitamin E, which has great healing properties, and because of its low cholesterol content, soy is often used for cooking. Its ability to withstand heat and protect the hair from blow-drying, pressing and hot curling makes it particularly valuable as a hair maintenance agent. Soy can easily be shampooed from the hair and it also provides luster and sheen to it.

Tallow

Tallow is a waxy substance and is derived primarily from animals like cattle, goats and sheep. Although tallow has a waxy texture, it is not greasy. In fact, it may be one of the first non-greasy products to be used by our great-great-grand parents as a hair emollient, lubricant or lotion. This product is not very popular today, and has been replaced by man-made waxes like petroleum. Do not confuse tallow with pig or hog fat, which was used to make lard or cooking grease.

When shopping for oil-based products, carefully examine its ingredients. I often examine the many different ingredients that are combined into one product. When there are too many different types of oils mixed into one product, I consider that product to be a mutt. I also believe that some manufacturers mislead consumers regarding the ingredients used in their products. Most consumers are not aware that mixing six, seven, and eight different types of oils into one product to achieve their desired results is not always necessary. Once you understand the various properties of waxes, greases, and oils, you can use this information to guide you in protecting and strengthening your hair.

✆OIL BASED CREAM OR POMADE

Light oil-based cream pomades are making their way into the market as a popular styling aid. Pomades are sometimes preferred over liquid oils. This is simply a personal preference. Some people prefer to dip their hand in and feel the texture of the product, as opposed to pouring a portion of it into their palms and massaging it in. However, the creamy texture of the pomade does help to retain moisture longer than the liquid oils and provides a concentrated dosage. Most pomades include mineral oils and petroleum. The better ones will include vitamins A, D and E and Shea butter. Shea butter is an African seed oil that is used in a variety of products today. You may also look for herbal abstracts.

What I like most about light cream-based emollients or pomades is that they work as a buffer to protect the hair from heat applied via blow-drying, pressing and hot curling and produce strong curls without producing a hard, fixed finish. Pomades also repel moisture and humidity and therefore, provide longevity to finished curls or styles.

When choosing pomades, look for one that contains very little wax. Although wax has a lot of positive attributes, such as its ability to repel moisture, while coating and protecting the hair, it is just a concentrated form of petroleum. And, like petroleum, wax produces a build-up on the hair and is very difficult to shampoo out. In order to remove wax build-up, use a clarifying shampoo at least once a month.

SPRAY SHEENS

Sheens or greaseless non-aerosol finishing glosses have become very popular products over the last three or four years. They have their origin in the silicone family and the main ingredient includes cyclomethicone. Silicone is designed to reflect light, seal in moisture and detangle the hair. I suggest using greaseless finishing glosses as a finishing spray only. If used in conjunction with the hot curling iron, it will cause one's hair to smoke. Opt for vitamin-enriched spray sheens.

HOLDING SPRAYS

Although I have cautioned you against using maintenance products, that contain alcohol, holding spray is an exception to this rule. The alcohol content in holding spray is necessary for quick drying results. There have been some holding sprays that have claimed to be alcohol-free. Usually, they are too wet and often cause the hair to revert. Most holding sprays use SD40 alcohol, however they should also contain some type of emollient. There may be oil-based

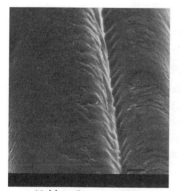 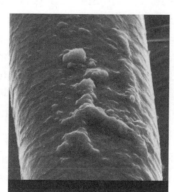

Holding Spray on Hair   Holding Spray over Dandruff

Photos courtesy of the Gillette Co.

fragrances present in your holding spray as well, which may give it a little more shine along with the hold.

When applying a holding or sheen spray, remember to hold the spray at least six to eight inches away from the hair. This technique helps you avoid using a concentrated amount in one given area. Finish off with short quick bursts to help mystify the spray. Only spray (holding spray) when needed and do not get into the habit of using holding spray daily; it should be used to assist curl and style longevity and resist humidity. If you are not wearing much of a style, then obviously you do not need a holding spray. In most cases, you only need a minimal amount anyway.

AEROSOL VERSUS NON-AEROSOL

Aerosol usually comes in a can form and uses a gas compression to release the oil and holding spray. Personally, I have never been a big advocate of aerosol holding or sheen sprays. Its use has really been sensationalized. Some people prefer spraying sheen onto the hair, however the hair will not reap any added benefits from its usage. Non-aerosol holding and oil sheen sprays come in a pump bottle and are safer and just as convenient to use. Aerosol holding spray is designed for a very light hold, not a concentrated hold. In order to receive a light hold using non-aerosol holding spray, just hold the spray bottle further away from the head and spray in quick spurts.

I would never recommend a product that is potentially damaging to your health. So when a client asks whether I recommend aerosol or non-aerosol spray, I refer them to the excessive warnings on the back of the container of aerosol holding and oil sheen sprays. They read as follows: Keep away from flames; do not puncture because the can may explode; do not spray in your eyes; do not inhale spray. (How do you avoid that?) Do not smoke when using; allow the product to dry completely after use; keep out of temperatures above 120 degrees, and keep out of reach of children. Ultimately, misuse of this product could be fatal. Now who would take that kind of chance, using a product? Is it really worth it, when you can obtain the same effect by using a non-aerosol spray?

If you want an even distribution when creating sheen on the hair, I suggest using a cream emollient as opposed to an oil sheen spray. Cream applications allow you to massage the oil into the hair and scalp beginning at the scalp and working through to the ends of the hair. This process allows each hair strand to enjoy the benefits of your emollient. When you spray your oil onto the hair, it does not penetrate into the scalp and, therefore, remains on the surface of the hair. As a result, some areas of the hair are deprived of the oil's nutritional benefits.

MOISTURIZERS AND ACTIVATORS

Non-aerosol conditioning sprays (better known as moisturizers) are excellent to use in conjunction with curl perms, chemical relaxers, or on naturally dry and excessively curly hair. Most conditioners basically contain distilled water, glycerin and a few other ingredients. The fewer ingredients in a product, however, the better. You do not want a product that will make the hair excessively oily.

Activators, which are available in lotion form, have basically the same ingredients as conditioners. The activators contain more ingredients, however, and may include distilled water, glycerin, protein, aloe Vera, panthenol and a variety of oils such as jojoba, lanolin, mineral oil and vitamins A, D and E. This lotion has a variety of purposes and acts as a moisturizer, detangler, conditioner, activator and wave revitalizer. It can be used on body perms, cold waves, texturizers, braided or naturally twisted hair.

GELS

Consumers and stylist alike rely too heavily on gels. They have been overrated, and are often used as a crutch. In high humidity areas where people want to maintain their styles for a certain length of time, consumers feel like they have to resort to gelled-down, frozen fixations when it comes to their hairstyling options.

Gels seem to be one of the most difficult products to perfect in the beauty industry. A lot of them now are claimed to be alcohol-free, however these gels dry, harden and leave a

dreadful flaky film on the hair. There are now gels available in a thin consistency. In my opinion, you can achieve the same result if you use a setting lotion.

There are a multitude of gels that are now available on the market, including sheen, moisturizing, holding, protein and styling gels, and when they are used on the hair excessively, they all leave a flaky finish. Dark-colored gels are more popular because they blend naturally with dark hair textures and the gel is not as visible when it begins to flake. Clear gels are excellent for color-treated and gray hair.

When selecting your gels, check the active ingredients. Whole wheat, protein, aloe vera extract and a variety of other herbal extracts have excellent attributes. Wax and glycerin are also beneficial. When experimenting with gels, purchase a small

Hair Maintenance

four-ounce size first and try a few gels until you find out what works best for your hair. It wouldn't hurt to put a little on your hand first to examine its moisture, consistency and shine. Some gels work better on relaxed versus natural hair.

Place a little oil on your hair before applying gel. Popular styles today, such as the straw sets and twisted styles, require a combination of both. When using gel as your primary styling agent, minimize the longevity of the style. The longer the gel remains on the hair, the more it dries it out.

If you wish to preserve the hair, opt for a setting lotion as opposed to gel, or use gel only as a secondary agent to accompany your setting lotion. If you are wet-styling, sculpturing and molding, mix a little gel with your setting lotion. Setting lotion can achieve the same effect as a gel, but it penetrates the hair with proteins and moisture conditioning treatments and, as a result, is more beneficial to the hair. Gel lays on the surface of the hair and transforms from a shine to a dusty finish. It is best to limit gel to usage around the edges of your hair only.

Sometimes I joke about people who wear brick-hard finger waves and other hard, gelled-down styles. Usually, after four days, the hair and scalp begin to itch. I have seen people use all kinds of apparatus, trying to break through the gel and get to their scalp. Once you break up and disturb the gel pattern, the hair begins to look flaky. After excessive usage, you will experience severe hair breakage and it will look like little packmen were running around on your head and chewing away on your hair. After talking with a dermatologist, I was informed that hard gel styles cause scalp infections. When styles such as these are left in for long periods of time, the space between the hair and scalp becomes a breeding place for yeast and bacteria. This is the reason why a lot of sisters who wear these styles end up with scalp disorders and infections.

If you are going to use gel to mold, finger wave, sculpt or scrunch your hair, rinse the gel thoroughly from the hair and shampoo and condition your hair on a regular basis. Gelled styles should be removed after four days; they should not exceed one week.

ACTIVACTOR GELS

Activator gels are nice if you wish to provide the hair with a more natural look, especially if your hair has a little texture to it. Activator gels can also be used to set the hair. If your hair is very thin in the crown area, activator gel can be used to thicken that area.

In order to achieve more pliability and avoid excessive dryness and flaking, you may want to opt for an alcohol-free concentrated wrap, setting lotion or mousse instead. If you find that these emollients are not providing adequate fullness and control, then add a little gel in the areas where you need them.

PRODUCT AWARENESS

I can remember a time when shampoos, conditioners and a good greasing were the only products that we were really concerned about. Now we have freeze-control and volume-enhancing products; texturizing products, hair thickeners and root boosters. It is amazing! To be brutally honest, however, there are not any new discoveries in hair care products. Manufacturers tend to only find new marketing strategies to promote existing products. For example, if we complain about frizzy hair, manufacturers will create a frizz control product. When consumers want to move away from chemical hair straighteners, manufacturers create temporary straighteners. When we want more volume in the hair, they create volumizing products. In actuality, there are products that many of you have in your bathroom right now that can be used to solve most of your existing hair challenges. For example, a mild chemical relaxer application can be used to reduce frizz (this may require assistance from a professional stylist). If the hair needs volume, use either a gel, a concentrated wrap, or setting lotion in the root area of your hair. This is the same as a root booster. Regarding mousse and straightening balms, a lotion right off your shelf contains many of the same ingredients that can be used to achieve the same results.

In other words, you can avoid spending excess money on a lot of these new products that are on the market by using products you already have. So don't get caught up in the hype. Personally, I am fed up with sisters falling prey to manufacturers and their bogus product claims. I was really insulted by the introduction of the so-called chemical-less hair relaxer because it was marketed under false pretenses. There is no way to permanently straighten hair without the use of some form of chemical. So there is no such thing as a chemical-less relaxer. Consumers are also being misled by these so-called shampoo conditioning colors. Consumers are led to believe that they are shampooing semi-permanent color into their hair when it is actually permanent color.

Black women spend three to five times more on hair and beauty products than the entire U.S. population, and have become prime targets for manufacturers who wish to profit from this market's consumer dollars. It is to your benefit, therefore, to increase your awareness regarding the products that you are purchasing. The average African American woman uses approximately five to six different products on her hair just to achieve a shampoo and style. In most cases, we simply need to give our hair a good cleansing and allow it to rest.

MAINTENANCE PRODUCTS AND TOOLS

The silk wrap scarf is made out of a light material, which allows the scalp to receive its proper oxygen. In most cases, when we use heavy fabrics to tie our hair down, it causes the scalp to perspire and suffocate. When the scalp perspires it causes the hair to flatten and lose its body and fullness.

Silk wrap scarves are used to keep the hair in place while one is sleeping. Its adjustable Velcro allows you to regulate the tension of the scarf and create your comfort level. I recommend using a wrap scarf when wearing straighter styles and short looks that are cropped around the outer perimeter. Wrap scarves can be used on all hair lengths and textures and can also be used to provide more shape to natural hairstyles while reducing frizz.

Silk wrap scarves can also be used to reduce drying time on wet styles or wraps. Most salon stylists use the sanex strip to wrap the hair before sitting their clients under the hair dryer. The fabric that is used for sanex strips are paper and, when wrapped around the head three or four times, impairs the ability for heat to penetrate to the hair. Silk scarf fabrics are not porous, so the heat is able to penetrate through the fabric easily and therefore speeds up the hair-drying process. Most importantly, silk wrap scarves look pretty; they can actually look quite sensual. When preparing for bed, you can even match it up with your sexy lingerie. For the ultimate in sleeping pretty, use the U-Shaped BF Sleep Neat Pillow. This pillow comes with a silky-finish pillow case that will help to maintain the hairstyle while you sleep.

Last but certainly not least is the hair net. This is a netted type fabric with elastic around the edges, and is designed to maintain the curl that is created by the roller set. Hair nets can also be worn at night before going to bed. Gather all the curls toward the crown of the head, then place the hair net on the head to prevent the curl from smashing while you are asleep.

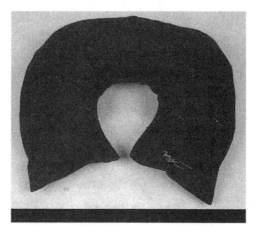

Hair Maintenance

THE HAIR DRYER BONNET

For those of you who do not have a hooded dryer at home, or would like to enjoy the convenience of a travel-friendly hooded dryer, the hair bonnet is an excellent alternative. This convenient portable hood can be attached to the end of your blow-dryer and is easily adaptable to any size nozzle. Most bathrooms that are located in hotels are now equipped with blow dryers which makes the hair bonnet

conductive for traveling. The hair bonnet can be used for setting, conditioning and treating the hair.

DRY SETTING

Dry setting is a method that requires a concentrated wrap or thick setting lotion to reinforce existing curls. To dry set, dampen the hair strand from its root to its end. Part the hair into sections and roll each section according to the direction of the style that you would like to achieve. Set the dryer on low heat, place the bonnet over the head and allow the hair to dry approximately 5 to 15 minutes. Drying time will vary according to the hair length and the amount of setting lotion used. When preparing for bed, wrap the hair and secure it in place using a hair net or a wrap scarf. Keep in mind if you are going to administer a dry set in the morning, your time may be limited. I suggest, therefore, that you first familiarize yourself with a regimen that is designed for dry setting your particular hair texture, then devise a system. Once this is in order, you can dryset your hair at any time.

WET SETTING

I usually suggest wet setting the hair because it seals in the hair moisture, makes it more pliable, and offers curl longevity. The wet set can be sculptured, molded, wrapped

or rolled, depending on the particular kut and style of the hair. The bonnet is extremely beneficial for wet setting because it helps concentrate the heat directly to the hair set. Also, always keep the hair dryer set on a low heat temperature.

HAIR ROLLERS

Mesh rollers have lots of holes in them and are either made of plastic or a wiry-type material with a little cloth covering. To guarantee a smooth, straight set from the root area to the ends of the hair, use a pin to place tension on the roller while bracing it in place. Most consumers have difficulty using the pin method. this is why it's used primarily in the salon.

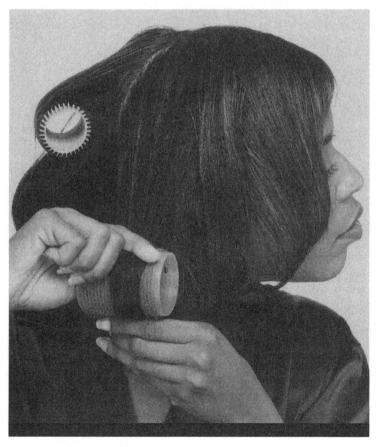

Clip on Rollers

Clip on rollers come in a variety of colors, including pink, black and purple, and are usually found in drug stores. They have a round cylinder-like shape and a case that clamps over the top, which secures the roller onto the hair. The disadvantage of clip on rollers is that they don't provide the hair with a lot of tension, so when the hair dries after it has been shampooed and rolled, it leaves a little wave pattern at the hair's roots, and sometimes an imprint on the hair as well.

Velcro Rollers

Velcro rollers are used when dry setting the hair because they allow the hair to adhere to the roller. Like the clip on rollers, Velcro rollers do not provide a lot of tension at the root area but it is good for reinforcing your curls. I do not suggest that you sleep on Velcro rollers since they have a tendency to stick to the hair.

Sponge Rollers

I am sure most of you are familiar with this type of hair roller; they are one of the most popular do-it-yourself types. The disadvantage of sponge rollers is that they tend to absorb all the natural moisture from your hair. In addition, as they begin to wear, they tend to sink in the middle, producing an overly tightened curl.

Although sponge rollers are comfortable to sleep on, I don't suggest sleeping on this type of roller at all. If, in fact, these are the only rollers that you can endure, then protect the ends first using hair end papers. Place the end paper in a vertical position on the topside of your hair strand, place another on the bottom side of the hair strand then proceed to roll.

Magnetic Rollers

Magnetic rollers are usually plastic and have a shiny, smooth surface with a few random holes. Once the hair is rolled around the magnetic roller, a clip is then used to secure the roller to the base of the hair section. Magnetic rollers do not provide much tension for the hair, and are cumbersome to deal with because of the clip. However, they are superior to most clip-on rollers and leave the hair smooth once the set is dry.

Roller Rods

Roller rods are used primarily for cold waves and curly perms. They come in a variety of sizes and are excellent for dry and wet setting. Roller rods have an elastic band that goes over the top of the hair's section and secures the hair in place. Not only does this provide more tension at the root area, it also gives us the option of allowing the hair to hang. In other words, if you have a longer hairstyle, and just want curls on the ends, you don't have to roll the hair all the way to the scalp. If you want a large bend, use the largest rod that you can find. When rolling the hair, make certain that you wrap the hair around the roller at least one-and-one-half times to secure the curl.

The same way in which consumers take the time to learn how to properly apply their makeup, every African-American consumer should take time out to learn how to roll their hair. It is essential for obtaining and maintaining healthy hair.

HAIR ACCESSORIES

Hair accessories have developed tremendously over the past 15 years. We no longer just rely on a rubber band and a few bobby pins to secure and accessorize our hair. We have escalated to fancy clips, wedgies, head bands, scarves, rain bonnets, scrunchies, jewels, hair pins, multi-sized bobby pins, and we have replaced the rubber band with cloth, elastic pieces. Hair accessories have become key accomplices in helping us make our transition from day to evening and from fun and frolic to formal. Accessories can add glamour to our evening look and festivity to our day. They also have practical purposes, ranging from protecting the hair from the external elements, to securing the hair while exercising.

Hair accessories are a very important part of our maintenance program. We need to understand that even when we are using an accessory, our hair still requires the same loving care. Even if you choose to comb your hair into a ponytail

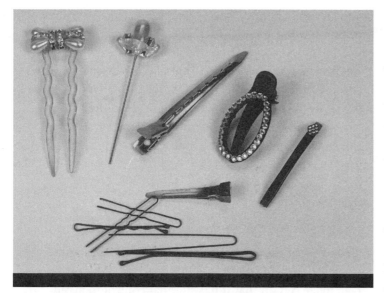

and secure it with a scrunchy or an elastic band, you still need to properly shampoo, condition, and set it, using a moisture-balance setting lotion.

An accessory can be an important styling asset when all else fails or when you are having a bad hair day. You should prepare for those days and have alternative accessorized styles available to maneuver and convert your hair into something fun, useful and expressive.

✐ AFRO COMB

The afrocomb has its origin in Africa and is still a very symbolic part of our heritage that carries with it strong historical values and cultural significance. At one time comb carving was considered an art, which possessed strong spiritual significance. Although the comb was used as a tool to adorn and beautify, its unique design and sculptures were used to symbolize and depict messages surrounding spirituality, fertility, family and love. The comb did not make the journey to America on the slave ships, and was left on the shores of the motherland buried along with its true historical significance.

The commercial version of the comb, also referred to as the afro-pick, made its way into American culture in the 1960's during the civil rights and black awareness era. During this

time, black people used artistic expressions, including hair styles, apparel, poetry and song, to make social, economical and political statements in support of black empowerment. The afro-pick managed to prevail throughout the 1970s and now, 30 years later, you may still find a pick lodged in the back pocket of a brother's baggy jeans or secured in a side pocket of a sister's purse.

Although the comb has lost most of its original significance, it still remains a popular and respected styling tool, and has in its own right, evolved over the past 40 years. Combs are now designed in numerous shapes and sizes and are tailored to accommodate your individual styling needs. Fine combs are used for short Kut hair, detangling combs are used for long hair, and rat-tail combs are used to set and apply chemical relaxers to the hair. Finger and claw combs are used to style, while kutting combs are used to assist in kutting the hair into desired styles. The choices are endless. For more information on the rich heritage of the comb and its origin, read the book entitled, "400 Years Without A Comb, The Untold Story" by Dr. Willie Morrow.

✐ NATURE OF THE COMB

Combing and grooming our hair has very soothing psychological and emotional benefits. It's amazing how one can regain his or her composure by just looking in the mirror and grooming the hair with a few strokes of the comb or brush.

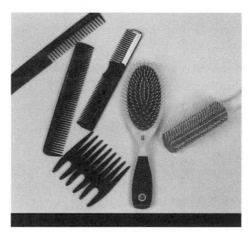

For the most part, everyone needs at least two combs in their possession: One wide-tooth comb to detangle the hair and a multi-purpose comb for styling. Avoid using combs that have little ridges on the teeth of the comb. These combs are primarily used for lifting the hair. Excessively curly hair wraps around the teeth of this comb like tendrils from a climbing plant. When the comb moves through the hair, it should be able to slide through without tugging and pulling. Discard combs that have irregular or broken teeth. Essentially, the teeth of a comb should be smooth, round, and non-abrasive. Avoid sharp edged combs; they can also be damaging to the scalp.

COMBING TECHNIQUES

When combing the hair, a skilled practitioner starts at the ends of the hair and gently works his/ her way toward the scalp. Snarled or matted hair should be handled delicately, and knots must be separated without tugging the hair and scalp. Combing the hair, beginning at the scalp and forcing the comb through to the hair's ends, places stress on the hair and initiates damage and breakage.

USE OF THE COMB

Combs are used to perform a variety of tasks, including parting styling, as well as removing dandruff and debris away from the scalp. Caution ! When it comes to virgin or natural hair, improper combing is the primary cause of damage and breakage. Make certain you choose the proper comb for your hair texture, and do not comb the hair too vigorously or too frequently. Excessive combing places unnecessary strain on the hair, and careless combing promotes split ends. The pressure is at its greatest when combing the ends of the hair and, when approaching the ends, handle with care.

If you have children, when shopping for your combs, ask yourself if it's too dangerous for a child to play with. If it is, chances are it is not safe to use on your hair and scalp either. Don't make the mistake of thinking that just because your

hair is resistant or wiry, coarse, that it's strong. We often overestimate the strength and, as a result, we sometimes torture our hair by using combs and brushes that are not suitable to groom an animal's hair. So use discretion when choosing these simple but valuable tools. When used incorrectly, they can cause serious damage to the hair and scalp. On the other hand, when used correctly, they can contribute greatly to a healthy hair care maintenance regimen.

HOODED DRYER

Hooded drying is the best method to use when drying the hair because it uses indirect heat and seals in moisture from setting lotions and conditions. When choosing your hooded dryer, make certain that it has thermal control to avoid excessive heat exposure to the hair and scalp.

BLOW DRYERS

A power tool used for quick drying and styling of the hair. An efficient blow dryer can range between 1200 to 1600 watts. Blow dryers should be light to medium weight in order to fit comfortably in your hand and provide better control. Make certain that the blow dryer has a protective screen over the fan mechanism, which is located in the back, in order to prevent the hair from being sucked into the dryer. Choose dryers that have long cords for added mobility and adjustable heat setting.

Choose blow dryers that accept adaptable nuzzles and diffusers. There are two types of nuzzles: a comb and a condensing nuzzle. The comb nuzzle is used to add greater tension and heat to the root area of the hair. A condensed nuzzle is designed to direct the flow of air into a concentrated area. Unlike the nuzzle, a diffuser is designed to soften the air flow from the blow dryer and helps soften and retain natural curl pattern. They also aid in removing of roller marks that are caused by wet sets.

Beware of the new model blow dryers, which claim to have automatic censors which will adjust the heat from the blow

Hair Maintenance

dryer to the temperature of your air. I question how this can be achieved when blow dryers, when in use, should be held six inches away from the hair and scalp and should not have direct contact with your hair?

CURLING IRONS

For consumer purposes, use an electric curling iron versus a thermal curling iron. Electronic irons provide better heat control, as well as more even heat distribution. In addition, they are lighter in weight which makes them easier to handle, equipped with a clamp, (which allows you to handle both ends of the barrel), and are more consumer friendly.

You should avoid using curling irons on a daily basis and should not depend on them for your daily style regimen. Over use of the curling irons is the largest contributor to hair thinning and splitting. Curling irons should be limited to using within the first three days after shampooing of the hair and the temperature control should be set to moderate heat.

FLAT IRON

Flat irons are similar to curling irons in that they are used for straightening, waving and krimping the hair. They come in various sizes and can also be used to press the hair. The small flat iron provides greater accessibility to hard-to-reach hair areas on the head. Larger flat irons are used primarily for longer hair. For a slightly smaller flat iron apparatus, refer to a straightening tong.

MINI PRESS STICK

The mini press stick is a small electrical pressing comb, which allows you to press the hair line without applying too much heat to the scalp.

Good for touching up edges prior to a relaxer.

FLATTENING CLIPS

Flattening clips are made by kutting plastic into oval shape pieces and gluing each piece to the inside of a clip. The clips are then used to flatten wraps and straight styles prior to being placed under the hooded dryer to dry your hair. They can also be used as a nighttime regimen. The wedge portion of the clip should be directed away from the crown of the head.

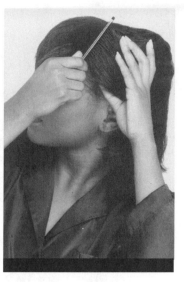

HAIR AND BOBBY PINS

Both hair and bobby pins come in various shapes and sizes. They differ, however, in their usage and application. I suggest using bobby pins with rubber coating on the tips. If

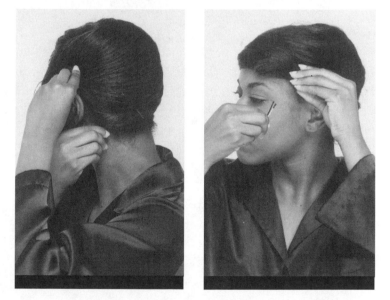

you choose to wear bobby pins, you should not let the pins have direct contact with the scalp. Bobby pins should either be removed before sleeping or positioned in a way that will avoid scalp discomfort. When choosing accessories, including hair and bobby pins, opt for plastic versus metal. Plastic is less harmful to the hair.

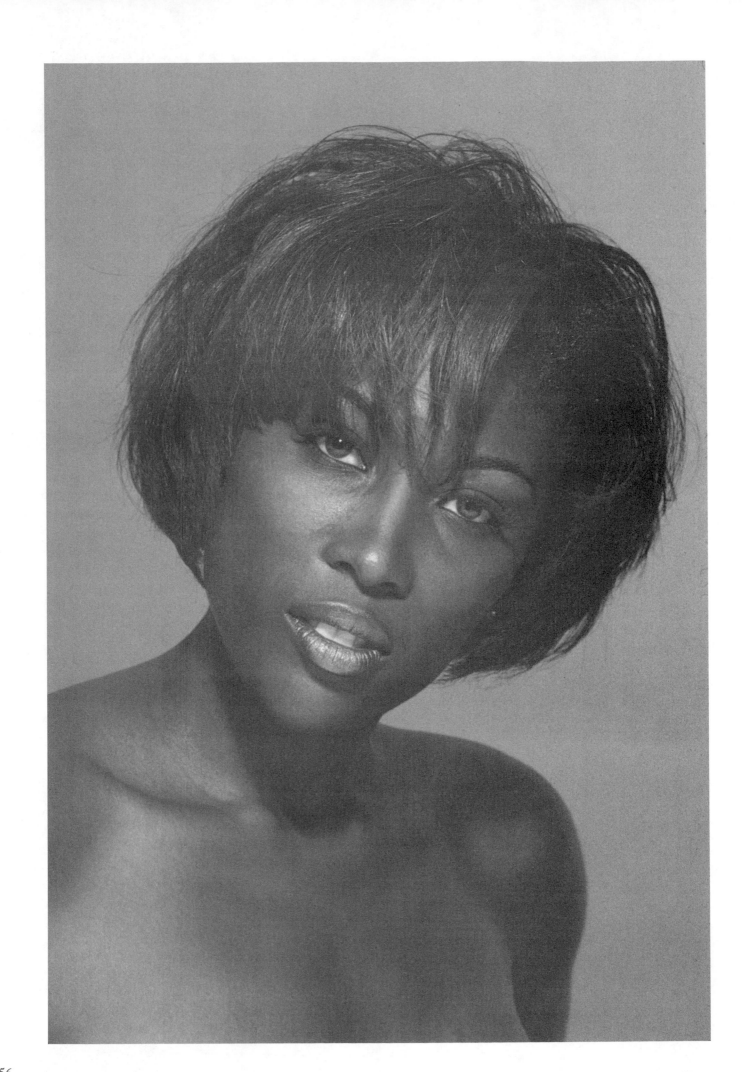

Thermal Relaxing

30

By Barry L. Fletcher

Press-and-Curling at Home; "Is It a Black Thing?"

Press-and-curl is a technique handed down from generation to generation. The pressing comb was introduced by Madame C. J. Walker in the early 1900's when there was a lot of speculation about Walker's hair-straightening system. Some black people accused her of trying to emulate European beauty standards. Walker rejected these allegations and proclaimed that her system was designed to help black people maintain and grow their hair. Walker discovered that when the hair is straight it is easier to comb. This places less stress on the hair, reduces breakage and promotes hair growth. In addition, the straight texture provided black women with more flexibility and styling options. This ability to express themselves and broaden their beauty options, gave black women a new sense of pride, and helped to raise their self-esteem.

Although I consider pressing-and-curling one of the safest methods used to rearrange the physical composition of the hair, it's still risky and requires careful administering. There are techniques involved in pressing that a lot of stylists seem to take for granted. State Board's Examiners around the country are partly to blame because they do not require stylists to have practical training to pass the State Board exam. In most states, practitioners are not required to demonstrate a pressing comb application, which indicates that it must be a "black thing." This is the main reason why black hairstylists need to take press-and-curl more seriously. It is a "black thing," and 80 percent of the people wearing press-and-curls are doing it themselves in their homes. As a result, salons are missing out on a viable part of salon service.

THE PRESSING COMB

The pressing comb is made of metal or brass, and once it's heated, is pulled through the hair to smooth its outer cuticle layer from an open to a closed position. This principle is basically the same as ironing the wrinkles out of a shirt. The same way in which heat from the iron softens the fabric so that the wrinkles give way to the weight or pressure of the iron, the pressing comb softens the hair so that the curl pattern gives way to the weight or pressure of the pressing comb. Most people still refer to this historical styling apparatus as the "pressing comb." If you want to get more technically advanced, you can call it a "thermal texturizing tool."

HEAT CONTROL

The advantage of using the pressing method is that it is fast, safe and chemical-free. The disadvantage is that you can easily scorch the hair if you don't use the proper temperature or heat control. First we need to prepare the iron for proper temperature control; this process is referred to as tempering. Heat your brass pressing comb using a stove designed to heat pressing combs or anything that will heat this brass material, i.e. an electric oven coil, a portable burner plate, or the top of the cooking stove. Allow the comb to exceed normal pressing temperature. Next, immerse the heated comb into pomade, grease or wax and allow it to simmer, then cool. This method seals in and connects the brass molecules. When molecules are not connected, it leaves a rough, uneven surface, which affects the pressing process. For example, if you were to place the iron in a stove or on top of a stove or open flame and only one area of the comb is actually being heated, this is because the molecules are not connected. When connected, the entire iron heats up at the same degree of temperature, so you end up with an even press. The petroleum or emollient is used as a filler connecting and smoothing the molecules on the comb's surface. In addition, it helps to remove the comb's original wax finish or polish which sometimes causes new irons or combs to stick and cling to the hair. Each time you heat the iron, you get a more even temperament.

PROTECTING THE HAIR

So, how do we protect the hair from the heat of the pressing comb? There are four pressing agents commonly used to protect the hair when administering a press-and-curl; they include petroleum, grease, wax and a light liquid oil. These products help lock the cuticles into a flattened position, and provide a smooth protective coating on the hair shaft. Avoid using wax, grease and pomades that are too thick; they have a tendency to remain on top of the hair shaft, weigh the hair down, and take away from its natural body.

There are several methods that are used to monitor heat control when pressing and curling the hair. Some people use a white piece of paper, end wraps, paper towels, or some use toilet tissue. When you apply a pressing comb to any of the above after taking it off of the stove, and it browns very rapidly, you know that the iron is a little too hot to apply to the hair. Keep a damp towel accessible at all times during this process so that you can cool the iron down at will. If you have a problem controlling the heat from the pressing comb, you may want to practice on a mannequin's head as opposed to a human's head to develop your skills. If you don't have access to a mannequin, you can use a human hair wig and press it out.

PREPARING FOR THE PRESS

Those who press their hair regularly, oftentimes experience an oil or grease build-up on the hair. In this case, you will need a good cleansing or clarifying shampoo to remove the build-up before pressing the hair. If you are preparing to have your hair pressed for the first time, you will need to treat the hair, using a good conditioning shampoo and deep penetrating moisturizing conditioner.

Apply heat to the hair immediately following the conditioner application. A heating cap or steam machine can be used to ensure deep penetration. Deep penetration is important in this instance, since the hair will need as much moisture, strength and protection as possible to withstand the excessive heat application from blow drying, pressing and hot curling. If the hair still feels dry after shampooing and conditioning, add a light oil to the hair and massage throughout the hair and scalp. Before blow drying, make certain to apply a protective agent or blow drying lotion. There are many advanced moisturizing, alcohol-free products that are now available for wrapping, setting and sculpturing that can be used as protective drying agents.

BLOW-DRYING TECHNIQUES

In order to move swiftly through the blow-drying process and achieve maximum results, it is always best to adopt a systematic approach. Comb the hair out neatly and section it into four parts using the T-Shaped parting System. Begin by

parting the hair down the center of the head, part across from ear to ear. Concentrate on one section at a time and use hair clips to secure the remaining sections down and away from the section that you are working on. Blow-dry the hair beginning at the roots and work your way toward the ends. Detangle as you blow it dry. If the hair is excessively curly, use a wide-tooth comb along with a wide-tooth nuzzle or comb attachment. When the hair is approximately 75 percent dry, add your hair emollients. I suggest a light hair oil, then completely blow-dry the remainder of the hair in the direction of the style that's desired.

✐◌ PRESSING THE HAIR

Once the hair is completely dry, we are ready to follow up with our pressing technique. Part the hair again into four sections. Concentrate on one section at a time, and use horizontal partings to divide each section into smaller subsections beginning at the nape area. You may elect to use either a brass or electric pressing comb. The pressing comb can be purchased with or without a thermostat.

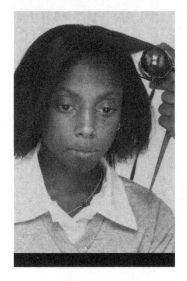

Use the teeth of the comb to stroke through and soften and detangle the hair. Press over the hair a second time using the back of the comb to exert more heat and pressure to the hair while smoothing it straight. As you continue to press each section, keep in mind that you want to press the hair according to your desired style. For example, if your hair is styled straight all over and flat on top, press everything straight down from the head. But if you are going to wear the hair full, then you want to press the hair out to a 90-degree angle away from the head. The hair will follow your lead.

31
Is Your Hair Flaking Out on You?

By Barry L. Fletcher

Dealing

With

Dandruff.

More than 70 percent of the general population suffers from a condition called Pitarias Simplex, better known as dandruff. Those who do not, have concerns about it, or will experience it at some point in their lives.

Don't confuse dandruff with dry scalp. Improper maintenance procedures, such as sitting under the dryer too long, or not thoroughly rinsing shampoo or conditioner from the hair can cause dry flakes on the scalp. These flakes can appear to be dandruff, when in fact they simply may be dry scalp or dried residue from your shampoo or conditioner.

Dandruff, although accepted as a common condition, is classified as a disease and can spread from one person to another. There are two types of dandruff. The most common involves the loss of dry, flat epithelial scales from the scalp. The other type is oily, and its flakes are large with a yellowish appearance.

There is still a degree of doubt surrounding the exact cause of dandruff. Some theories suggest that it derives from worry, strain, stress or excessive cell production in the basal area of the epidermis. There is a row of cells located at the base of the scalp that is constantly reproducing. As new cells form, they push the older cells up toward the scalp's surface. This process takes about 30 days to complete. However, when the growth rate is accelerated, the older cells are pushed upward at a faster than usual pace and begin to accumulate on the surface of the scalp. This cellular accumulation is what we refer to as dandruff.

Several methods have been used to remove these excess scales from the scalp and hair, while destroying the causative microorganisms that accelerate epidermal cell reproduction. Infrared light has been used to help slow down the rapid reproduction of cells. So have medications and shampoos that include coal and pine tar, metallic sulfides, ohexachorophenol flowers and sulfur. Good hygienic practices, such as frequent shampooing and sanitizing your maintenance tools, will help to minimize and control dandruff. Also avoid using other people's combs and brushes.

Seborrhea Dermatitis

There are other scalp disorders, including Dermatitis, Seborrhea Dermatitis and Psoriasis, which all appear to be simple cases of dandruff but actually are more serious and require the attention of a professional dermatologist. Dermatitis occurs when the scalp experiences an allergic reaction to high levels of alkaline found in certain products. This allergic reaction causes the skin and scalp to shed.

Psoriasis is another scalp disorder and can be identified by traces of blood on the scalp or large scaly patches on the scalp, arms or legs. Another symptom of Psoriasis includes the presence of little pinholes in the nails. If any of these symptoms are present, be sure to see a dermatologist. Seborrhea Dermatitis manifests in the form of a scaly ban surrounding the hairline, and should also be treated by a professional dermatologist.

If you don't mind me asking, what kind of flakes are you waking up to?

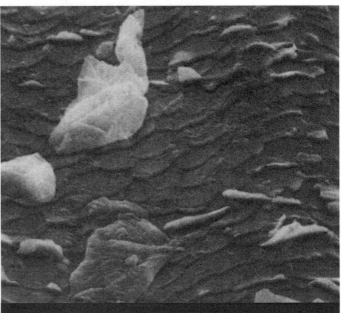

Photos courtesy of The Gillette Co.

Dandruff Magnified

Is Your Hair Flaking Out on You?

Beauty From Within

By Christal M. Jackson, freelance writer, Washington, DC

*I*t was a ritual in my house. Every Saturday evening my mother would shampoo my hair. She would stretch me out across the counter top, and my head and woolly locks would dangle into the kitchen sink. This was the only way she could shampoo my hair without me putting up too much of a fuss. I did not like the soapy water getting in my face. While scrubbing my scalp and caressing my locks she would talk with me about whatever popped in my mind. We both dreaded this process, but it was necessary to get me ready for Sunday morning. I couldn't figure out what all the fuss was about. Why did we have to go through so much fuss for Sunday? I liked my hair just the way it was. Seemingly, God did, too, because I was born with it.

Sunday in the African American community has been one of the most celebrated days in our cultural experience. For those who grew up in the black church, we knew that on Sunday we would put on our very best for church, and part of that included our best hair. When I was to be a dazzling princess, my crown of locks needed to be at their best.

After shampooing and conditioning my hair, there were the taunts from my brothers that the next phase of this journey was going to be painful. They based this on the fact that I shrieked with agony and begged mama to hurry every time. My favorite scream from the kitchen while sitting next to the stove was "You are burning me."

Before pressing it, she would dry my hair and pack it with Royal Crown hair grease. Twenty-some years later I can still smell the stuff and hear my hair frying. In the strangest way I actually looked forward to the finished product. It was sort of a love-hate relationship. I would have beautiful curls and my do would be admired by many on Sunday morning. This early life experience taught me the value placed on hair in the African American community. As I grew older, my mother no longer would fight with me on Saturday nights. I was now a regular at a nearby beauty shop. I loved going to the beauty shop. There were always so many people and not to mention a snack machine. Getting my hair done was a celebrated event. At the shop there were all types of hair; long and short, curly and straight, natural and weave; you name it, the beauty shop could take care of it.

As a result of being raised in the South — Mississippi and Texas — hair was silent status in the black community. People would go through great lengths to make sure their hair was looking right. The

Hair loss, hair breakage, hair thinning, hair deformities and hair health begin with the way in which we view our hair.

irony of looking right has always been looking close to white. Thank God that trend is changing as we develop more appreciation for African beauty.

Like all African American women, I struggled with my self-image. Much of my problems were issues surrounding my hair. I survived seasons when I thought that the longer I wore it (hair) the better it would look. That was not true. Then I went through a season of trying to capture the most stunning style, and I was certain that I would be completely satisfied. That was not true. Before I knew it, I was asking my hairstylist to change the look every other visit. Every now and then she would put up a fight, but for the most part she knew that it

I bequeath to every black woman who reads this, healthy, free and confident hair that spells True Beauty.

came along with the turf. I, like many females, suffered from a bit of hair/image confusion. I thought that my hair was a defining principle of who I was. Wrong!

It's a new day, and my hair is only an accessory. It is not the defining principle of who I am. I now know that my hair mirrors what is going on internally.

During my teenage years when I was able to partner with my mother about decisions concerning my hair, my styles reflected my level of maturity and my own internal struggles with identity. My styles were always based on some picture in a hair book of what I viewed as beautiful only to find that I could never capture the look of the photographed image because it was not me. Now that I have a little life experience under my belt there is a totally different approach that I take to determine what look I want to project.

I remember my first adult hairkut. I was a junior in college and had discovered my beauty. I felt as though my long

locks that I had grown for the past 20 years were hiding my beautiful African features. I was hiding behind my hair. Hesitant but freely I asked my stylist to clip away, and I trusted her decision because I felt a connection with the person that I had trusted with the maintenance of my precious locks. That is important. Never trust your hair to someone you do not feel comfortable with. While my stylist kut my hair, I watched it fall to the ground. And I admit there were moments when I had to remind myself that it was only hair falling.

But I freaked when she handed me a mirror. Everyone complimented my hair, but their words were of no comfort. My emotions swung like a pendulum. After laughing hysterically, my stylist passed me a hand mirror so I could get a better look. Wow, I could see my cheekbones, my eyes, my lips, my nose, my ears, my eyebrows, my forehead and I loved her. It was me. It took some time for me to get used to the new look, but the more comfortable I became with the style the more I loved it. Since that kut, I have not stopped. Later I kut it even shorter.

I no longer have anxiety attacks about my hair. I'm in control of what it looks like; it does not control me. Hair has become a great accessory. I feel just as confident today with a lot less than I did when I suffered from the fallacy that long hair was better. This is by no means an indictment against sisters who choose to wear their hair long, but if it is long because it provides a false sense of security about true beauty then contact your stylist today. Be enlightened and know that what you feel about yourself screams from underneath long hair as well as short. Be free and celebrate your beauty and recognize that your hair is merely a statement of what's going on inside of you. I bequeath to every black woman who reads this, healthy, free and confident hair that spells TRUE BEAUTY.

Sister Hair-Talk

By Kevin Merida, Journalist, Washington, D.C.

33

Sister talk. Sister hair-talk. Words, phrases, imagery: Self-esteem. Assimilation. Pain. Trauma. Horror. Disruption. Conformity. Smooth jazz. Roots. Pride. Beauty. And if you don't see any beauty, you've got to create some beauty. One cornrow at a time.

Sister talk. Sister hair-talk. "So bad, girl, had to wear a wig to work." Oh, no she didn't. "I walked in with my Halle Berry look and homeboy's jaw hit the floor." I hope he picked it up.

Sister talk. Sister hair-talk. You hear it at the grocery store, at the mall, at the job, the health club, the nightclub. You know you hear it at the salon. Hair-talk central. It doesn't matter how black women are wearing their hair. Processed, natural, straightened, curled. They're talking about it.

Believe that. Let's listen in, cyber style.

Denise Hendrickson, a federal government worker, sent this e-mail to her sister, Cheryl, a New York marketing consultant: "I don't think I told you that I took my professionally braided hair out the next day. $100.00 right out the window...but they were just too tight, despite my pleading with the stylist to loosen them. I guess she did loosen them according to her definition of 'loose.' I think they (braiders) are so accustomed to pulling your scalp so tight that it's too difficult for them to do it any other way. I couldn't sleep or move the braids to any other position without pain. I probably would have made the mistake of enduring the pain if I thought I looked 'cute.' I guess I too could have fallen into accepting the very primitive notion that braids are supposed to hurt the first couple of days if, again, I thought I looked cute."

"But I didn't look cute.… So enduring pain was simply not an option. Something told me to turn around and run and not look back when the braider greeted me at the door with her hair line 9 inches beyond her forehead. On the part of her scalp where she apparently was still able to grow hair, it existed in the form of thin and thinning, partially kinky, fully kinky, partially straight, fully straight (overpermed) partially eaten off clusters. She was sporting quite a variety of what appeared to be hair mishaps."

"That's the look that many of the African hair braiders have. I don't know whether the very sad state of her hair was due to just the serious misapplication of perms, years of violent braiding, or both. But it was a very sad sight to be forced to view."

"I went to her because of a strong recommendation from Renee (whose hair probably looks the same under the weave she's been wearing for 20 years). Bless her heart. I probably should not have shared this story with you. I can see you now with a concerned expression on your face. You probably are really concerned now with my therapy needs."

"But on a more positive note: I can see that the siesta lochs that Rita has are going to be absolutely beautiful on her. It is definitely going to work.... Not for everyone, though. But there's something about Rita's look. I don't know whether it's her facial features or manner of dress, but it will look awesome, I believe. But again, it's not for everyone. I don't see it for me. I don't think I see it for you, but then again, I don't know."

"I don't see it for Baja, who says she may do it... (after marrying Herb) because he doesn't like dreads. While she was saying that, an image of him and his 'Jheri curls' flashed in my mind. I said nothing of course."

"Well, I'm done with my novel. As you can see, I was well-rested last night. Talk to you later." That was an actual e-mail. Raw, uncut.

And this is an actual, heartfelt statement from Susan Eldridge about hair and liberation: "What my hair means to me is freedom…Freedom to be me, whether I'm happy to be nappy or relaxed and silky straight. I have choices. If I want to wear braids or twists or locks or a pressed-and-curled 'do,. I can do it because my hair represents versatility. This versatility allows me to wear it short, cropped and natural one day or washed and wrapped the next."

That's freedom.

Shirley A. Harper, of the FBI, reveals a hair problem that has plagued many women. "The majority of my life I have had a problem with thinning and hair loss," she says. "I have very thin hair that does not accept chemicals very well. I started wearing a wig because of chemical damage to my hair."

Then, in the fall of 1998, she started going to Hair Zen Master Barry Fletcher. Avant Garde started treating her hair in a way that was tailored to its texture. Every two weeks, Harper's hair was treated with the Fletcher products Social Security, Glow-N-Grow and Major Moisture.

Voila!

"In the spring of 1999, I was able to remove the wig and get a chemical curl," says Harper. "My self-confidence has greatly improved. My family and friends tell me that I look younger without the wig. Hair plays a great roll in a woman's life, in the way she feels about herself. When a woman's hair is looking good, she feels attractive and gets more respect for her overall appearance. I am 61 years of age and I thank God that my dull hair is now shiny. I can go without wearing a wig. I feel great and never looked better.

Now, it's one thing to talk about the treatment and conditioning of hair. It's a whole different thing to talk about style. Not styling. Just style. Which brings us to the relationship between men and women. Which brings us back to that question: What's hair got to do with it? Which brings us to Rhonda Collins, a Virginia businesswoman.

"I am convinced that long hair is now, and always will be, a Man Magnet!!!" she says. Three exclamation points. So you know she's serious about that. "I've always kept my hair very short because I like the fact that I can wash my hair and head out the door within minutes. But after a while I felt I needed a new look and decided to let my hair grow long. My hair's length is now down below my shoulders and I am amazed at the attention I'm getting from men."

And she means all men.

"The guys on my job, the fellas I grew up with, strangers on the street. Even my 18-year-old brother's friends seem to be flirting a little," says Collins. "When I questioned an old family friend, he confessed that most men find hair that falls in your face and hangs down your back erotic and sexy. It also adds an element of femininity and definitely makes an impression."

Having said that, Collins has mixed feelings about her own analysis. "If women were bent on pleasing men," she says, "we'd wear our hair long and loose, which is their overwhelming

preference. But when it comes to a hairstyle, women follow fashion, not men."

And fashion is often just a geographical/class/state-of-mind prison. "It's amazing how quickly people recognize social class in hair," says Collins. "There's a hairkut that belongs to Wall Street, there's one that belongs to Hollywood and one that belongs to the 'Hood'."

"Hair sends a message," she continues. "It can make a woman feel and look sexy/demure, wild/reserved, innocent/devilish. It can make a woman look cheap, unsophisticated, neglectful or sloppy. Then you address texture, shape and style and all of a sudden you are more polished and credible."

"I have thought at length about the messages that we read into hair. That brought me to the realization that some of us are still 'hairstruck' in the traditional sense. There are still some folk who judge the viability of a potential mate on the merits of their hair. In other words, is the hair a 'good enough grade' to impress others. Don't even laugh. Y'all know it's true. I have chosen to wear my hair close and natural for the last four years and don't ever plan to change my style."

Deep.

Unfortunately, not all stories turn out so well.

"Going natural is not for everyone," says Arnessa Howell, a reporter for the Bureau of National Affairs. "For me, it wasn't about correctness, about getting back to my African roots, as you might have heard some say. It was simply a form of expression. I needed a change. I decided to make that change by doing something different with my hair. Nothing more, nothing less."

And so here's what she did: "During my state of naturalness, I tried about every style option out there to refresh my unchemically treated 'do. After the braids came flat twists, individual twists, cornrows, twist outs, French braids and yes... the curly weave. With the latter style, I was once again influenced by the hair chameleon herself, Miss Janet. On occasion, I even got my hair pressed. But I was dissatisfied with the 'frozen' state the hair would get in whenever it

remained in one position too long. And don't dare let it be a warm day. My hair would frizz out at the first drop of perspiration."

So, what does a woman do when faced with such hair angst?

"I have returned to familiar territory," says Howell. "After plaiting, tucking, coaxing and greasing my virgin hair for six years, I got a relaxer. The date: Sept. 3, 1998."

No regrets?

"By no means do I regret getting a relaxer," Howell adds. "There's just as much versatility in the styles: weave, color, spirals, straight. Still, there are times that I see a woman walking down the street with braids or an Afro puff and I can't help but reminisce about those natural looks of [the] past."

Phyllis Bell, one of Fletcher's clients, has a horrific tale: "One sunny fall day, I decided to shampoo and condition my hair before going outside to wash my car. After shampooing, I reached into my hall closet for my jar of conditioner and, in a moment of inspiration, I thought why not leave the conditioner in my hair to intensify my beauty treatment. After finishing the car, I thought why not take a nap before rinsing the conditioner out. Hours later, I rinsed out the conditioner and looked in the mirror to begin styling my hair. Then, for some reason, I remembered [the] conditioner had a strange odor. Then I remembered my ear was stinging when I laid down for my nap. Then I remembered that I had placed a jar of perm in front of my conditioner."

Oops.

Bell paid for that mistake.

Fortunately, the mistake was not permanent.

"An unusually savvy hairstylist managed to kut off most of my now seaweed-dead, seriously overprocessed hair and create a beautifully short and sassy 'do," says Bell. "Needless to say, I read all labels first these days and leave hair care to the pros."

From the practical to the thought-provoking we now go.

Julie Brown, a magazine sales representative from Kentucky, raises an interesting question: How does the American idea of beauty affect the black woman?

"When I started researching black hair care, I intended to focus solely on presenting hair care techniques designed to help black women who want to grow their hair out. But, while I searched for information on how to grow out healthy black hair, I noticed a recurring negative perception."

There is this thing many black women have about straight hair equating beauty. "Straightening my hair has become as natural as breathing,' says Brown. "But, who said it had to be straight?"

Good question.

The straight hair-is-beauty equation has for years motivated a lot of black women to chemically straighten or press their hair as often as necessary to maintain a texture they believe renders them glamorous.

Pearl Cleage, the poet and essayist, wrote in her 1993 article, "Hairpeace," about how much time she spent worrying about her hair after it was freshly pressed. Cleage describes her hair-pressing experiences as "self-hate horror stories." Too many black women are conditioned to believe that wearing natural hair is unacceptable.

Here's Brown's perspective on that: "It is true that blacks must be able to adapt and assimilate into mainstream America in order to acquire some level of success. But where is the line between assimilation and conformity? What happens to our daughters' psyche when we make them slaves to the pressing combs, smoothing away and slicking back each curl that proudly stands as evidence of our African heritage? And, ultimately, what do our daughters feel when those freshly pressed coils revert to their natural texture? Disappointment. I still feel that same disappointment…even though it's to a lesser degree because I have learned the natural state always returns…every month when I touch roots that seem to impatiently scream, 'We don't want to be straight!'"

In author Gerald Early's 1992 essay, "Black Like…Shirley Temple?" he describes his daughters explaining to him why they wanted chemical relaxers in their hair. Why? Because they were tired of being ridiculed for wearing natural hair and they just wanted to fit in. They just wanted to be like everybody else.

Like Shirley Temple.

Which brings us to the issue of self-image.

Bernardine M. Lacey, a health professor at the University of Michigan, says: "Anyone who has seen Whoopi Goldberg wrap a T-shirt around her head and say, 'Look, I have long hair,' can relate to the part that hair plays in a woman's self-esteem. Since the time of Cleopatra, women have been interested in hair as an adornment. Long hair has always been the envy of women around the world. More important, black women have copied what has been described as 'good hair' by straightening or relaxing their hair to achieve less curl."

The main point, says Lacey, is: "all hair is good hair if kept clean and well-groomed."

And now we conclude with someone who knows something about the trappings of celebrity, what it means to be in the public eye. In her world, looking good is not a luxury. It is an expectation. Annette Allen, wife of pro football running back Terry Allen, doesn't believe she can afford to have an off day in the hair department.

"It is important that my hair look good every day," she says. "Being in the spotlight, I am always concerned about my appearance. I feel the pressure to look good, the public's expectation that someone like me should always be 'put together.'"

"Because of the burden of always looking 'presentable,' I often use my curling irons, and then I risk damaging my hair. I am always in search of a hairstyle I can maintain weekly, one that requires less curling so that my hair remains healthy. When choosing a hairstyle, this is important to consider. "When selecting a stylist, I prefer a man because often men are easier to deal with. Their attitudes don't change with the wind and they give nice kuts. It's important to me to find someone I can be honest with, who won't be offended by my styling requests. I mean, I know what I want. Finding a good stylist is the beginning to healthy hair."

Brothers Testifying 34

By Kevin Merida

Black women are regal.
Cute.
Sassy.

Fly.

Domineering.

Demanding.

Nurturing.

Extraordinary.

Hip-hop.

Hopping mad.

Professionals.

Prima donnas.

But that's okay.

Black women are mothers.

Single mothers.

Sisters.

Grandmothers.

Grandmothers who are mothers again.

Black women are goddesses.

Don't forget that.

Black women catch the early bus, the late bus, go home tired, cook dinner, clean the house, wash the clothes, supervise the homework, and don't get enough credit.

Let's say that.

Black women take care of men.

And men abuse them.

And men take advantage of them.

And there are not enough real men for them.

(I know there are a lot of good brothers out there, doing the right thing, taking care of their business, taking care of their black women. But this is not about us, this is about them.)

So hear me out.

What's this got to do with hair?

Black women like to dress up.

Look pretty.

Get their nails done.

Get their toes done.

Get their hair done.

Get their hair done right.

Get their hair done perfectly.

Locked, braided, trimmed, permed, pampered.

Whatever.

Just do it right.

So they can dance.

And dine.

And be wined.

And feel like queens.

Because bad hair days are out.

Because black women are too special for bad hair days.

That's about it, for me.

The end.

The rest of this chapter is all about other black men commenting on black women's hair, specifically some notable brothers in the hair care business kicking what they think and what they know. Testifying, you might say.

"First of all, I love all types of hair. But let me tell you what I love about black women's hair." That's Roger Gore talking. Roger Gore, CEO of G'Natural Products of

Prince George's County, Md. What does he love about black women's hair? "Everything. I love the different moods it generates from its different textures. I love the different sexuality it generates from its different lengths. I love the romantic side it generates from its different colors.

"Hair trends come and go, but black women's hair is forever. You can unleash their creativity and sensuality when you style and kut black women's hair. I love it! I love it! I love it! Natural, permed, set or curled. I just love it! Black women's hair has a mind of its own. If you treat it right and take good care of it, it will do anything in the world for you. But treat it wrong and, well, you know what will happen. So black women do me one favor: keep it real and never lose your style. I love your hair. I love ya!"

Larry Massenburg, owner of a Richmond salon: "With the growing hair problems of today, I'm still in love with the hair of a black woman. First of all, I love that the hair of a black woman comes in so many different textures. It has made me a student of beauty culture. Therefore, I have to be prepared as a stylist when a black woman sits in my chair. I also think that a black woman's hair is very sexy. What makes it sexy is the right style that matches the personality of the black woman."

"Personally, for black women, sexy hair can be summed up in one word: short. Let's face it, short hair is sexy, sophisticated and easy to take care of. Short kuts are sexy not only for black women but for all women. What makes short kuts so sexy are that they compliment today's bold fashions. And even if they're high-tech, they feel great to the touch."

Floyd Kenyatta, founder of the Black Hair Olympics and global ambassador for Paul Mitchell's product company: "What I love about black women's hair is that the black woman truly represents all women of color. Within the black race you can find all hair types. To cater to the woman of color gives you the ultimate opportunity to specialize in every variety of hair. My greatest fulfillment exists when I'm the master of transformation. It is a pleasure to see the joy in a client's eyes when you transform her hair from kinky to curly, curly to wavy, kinky to straight…and still accent it with color

if she desires. To work this magic and get paid for it? This is what I love about black women's hair."

Rick Stewart, sales manager for Barry Fletcher Products: "Black men no longer want hair they can't touch or feel at any given time. We want to run our fingers through a woman's hair. We want to feel that sensation…like holding a soft body next to us. Nothing hard. We don't want it hard. We want hair that flows and floats, like it's silk on a windy day. Manicured to protect its health and beauty. And we want it sexy, in a style that fits the woman. When I see a black woman's hairstyle, I want it to turn me around, turn me into a commentator, make me tell her she's beautiful."

Tell the truth, Rick.

Black women are lovely.

Gregory Quattlebaum, a sales rep for a P.G. County newspaper, adds the "regular Brother" perspective with a little impromptu poetry: "She was the woman of my dreams; I am her man, it seems. In our love she would scream because I had created some steam and ruined her hairdo, you know what I mean."

More Quattlebaum: "Our black queens and princesses share one thing in common. They are wearing their hair like no other woman can."

Ok, enough glorification. This is the part of the essay — the end of it — in which we must keep it real. This is the part of the essay in which we tell what brothers DON'T like.

"I hate weaves, man," says Darrell Britt-Gibson, all of 15 years old, representing the high-schoolers. "Don't girls know that it looks fake?"

You mean you can tell automatically if a girl has a weave?

"It's like a barnyard, our school. It's like a whole bunch of horses galloping around in our school."

Barnyard? Horses?

"Weaves are made out of horse hair," Darrell explains.

Interesting. We didn't know that.

But why do black girls wear weaves?

"Because black girls love hair."

Why don't they just sport their own natural hair?

"Because they don't have any hair. They're bald."

Ooooh. So, Barry Fletcher's theory is right? Black women are losing their hair?

"Yeah, a lot of black girls are losing their hair…At age 12."

We now close with the thoughts of Wilkins McNair, who runs a Baltimore-based Accounting firm.

What turns you off, Wilk, about black women and their hair?

"What I don't like are those wild colors," he begins. "Like when you see a sister who is blonde and you know damn well she isn't blonde."

And here's another thing: "When you see her today and she has four inches of hair, and the next day she has 12 inches."

Here's something else: "I don't like ornaments and hair stacked like it's a Bart Simpson hairdo."

That's two things, Wilk. But we feel you on the ornaments. Those can be dangerous. "I don't want to get my hand in her hair and get it kut by some kind of tools," Wilk says. "I mean, like what are they doing? Basically, they're trying to do it for attention. And they don't realize they basically look simple."

When Wilk sees women with these outlandish hairstyles, he does an instant evaluation. "I'm wondering: 'Where do you work? Just by your presentation, there are certain jobs I know you don't have.' I already know that."

But he always returns back to love.

"Don't these sisters realize their natural beauty?"

Let's hope more and more of them do as time passes on.

35 Epilogue

*T*his book started with a question and probably will end with more. In my years as a professional, I've accumulated quite a bit of knowledge about maintaining healthy hair. While researching this book over the last three years, I've learned quite a bit more about the growth and loss of hair.

In the course of this research, a nutritionist told me that the mercury a dentist uses for fillings is one of the most toxic substances that we can put in our bodies. It simply poisons the enzyme that forms vitamin B12. This can cause neurological diseases, homocysteine, which damages the lining of arteries, and hair loss, as well as other problems. A medical doctor told me that people carry too much stress atop their head, and because of poor circulation, we must massage our scalps more often. And when I sought answers from dermatologists about black women and hair loss, some hid behind words like "genetics," "hormonal," "diet" and "chemicals." But I believe black women's hair loss is an issue that has not been thoroughly studied, thoroughly challenged. There's a lot more work to be done.

Now more than ever, empirical studies are necessary.

Regardless of gender or ethnicity, the sad reality is that all hair reaches its optimum strength and condition after a person reaches puberty and begins to thin when she hits her 20s. The average person only experiences 15 years of strong, healthy hair. According to the New England Journal of Medicine, "by age 35, almost 40 percent of women demonstrate some sign of hair thinning."

But that doesn't mean anyone should give up on the attainable goal of a lifetime of healthy hair. I hope this book gives new meaning to the ill-conceived concept of "good hair, bad hair." Any hair that grows on your head is good hair. Black women should be happy for what they have naturally: the world's most versatile hair texture.

But just because black women have options, there's no rule that says they have to exercise them all, going from one relaxer to another, color after color, one blow dryer to the next.

Don't get me wrong. I don't buy into the theory that sisters emulate European standards of beauty when they relax their hair. That is nonsense. The fact that sisters weave, lock and braid their hair, relax it and sometimes wear wigs are examples of their receptivity to their hair's versatility. And when all else fails, they can go back to their natural texture. It's like going back home. It's a natural reaction to life.

My approach to cosmetology is simple: learn it all and do it all well, regardless of the nature of the services. But the best cosmetologist still needs his client's help. That's where you sisters come in.

Black women need to take a more hands-on approach in diagnosing the texture and condition of their hair. This new-found knowledge will fortify a woman's ability to understand chemical applications, holistic treatments, natural hair care methods, and hair growth remedies, etc. From this point on, you should create your own beauty coalition, consisting of a medical doctor, a dermatologist, fitness center – including a nutritionist -– and a professional cosmetologist. This combination will ease some of the angst and anguish associated with black women and hair loss.

Hopefully, this book will give you more confidence and a greater sense of empowerment to help you on your journey to a healthy, long-lasting relationship with your hair. This project has been a labor of love for me. I've had two decades of experience in obscuring beauty flaws and maximizing beauty's potential. I have learned that the true integrity of beauty comes from within. Too much emphasis has been placed on its outward reflections. So many times I feel that black women rate themselves less attractive because of a traumatic hair experience or a bad hair day. This could not be further from the truth. Perhaps too many rely too much on their hair for their self-esteem.

So I ask you this question, my sister, What makes you a beautiful black woman?

I wish you Godspeed. Have a safe and successful journey!

Epilogue

Contributors - Credits

Gye-Nyame Na Obeye (Only God Can Do It !). I thank him for blessing me with two wonderful parents, Audrey and Leon Fletcher. Their hard-working spirit, love for family and will to help other people were my inspiration for wanting to contribute to society. I would like to sincerely thank my family, friends and clients for their agape love and support. Special thanks in loving care of Judy E. Dowtin, whose precious memories will be with me always. Thanks, Judy, for "Wigs" and "Locks" contributed to the Hairy Choices Chapter. I would like to thank a dear friend of mine who sat next to me in the sixth grade. Ray Charles Leonard made a believer out of me by going on to become Sugar Ray Leonard, five time World Champion Boxer. Seeing is believing. Thanks Ray. Thank you, Floyd Kenyatta, for taking me under your wings and honing my skills and attitude. I want to thank Thomas Hayden, Ann Bray the late Gary Bray and Olive Benson for helping me win a Rolls Royce in the New York Beauty Classic Competition and win a position on the USA Hair Olympic Team.

I want to thank John Atchison of New York for being a role model and teaching me the importance of a good hair kut. Thank you Charlene Carol of Boston for raising money for me during the Hair Olympic tryout competitions, and thanks to Dr. Willie L. Morrow for his insight and wisdom.

I do in deed want to thank Dr. Wanda Nelson, president of the National Beauty Culturists' League Inc. The oldest association for African American hairstylists, spanning more than 81 years of existence. Thanks Dr. Nelson for presenting me with an Honorary Doctor's Degree. That's right! You can call me Dr. Fletcher now. I want to thank all the members of N.B.C.L. for their support, and I would like to encourage all hair designers to join as members under the "Education First" direction of Dr. Nelson. It is my privilege to thank Susan L. Taylor and Mikki Taylor for seeking my expertise, allowing me to contribute to Essence magazine and share with your readers.

Thank you James Sparlock, Bonnie Krueger and Jocelyn Amador of Sophisticates' Black Hair magazine for allowing me to reach out to their readers. I would like to extend my gratitude to Jamie Foster Brown of Sister 2 Sister magazine, Marcia Caster of Heart and Soul magazine, Lafayette Jones and Monica Daniely of Shades of Beauty magazine, Terri Winston and Quention Curtis of Salon Sense magazine, Eddison Bramble and Danessa Myricks of Hair Web. Com,

Kate Ferguson of Today's Black Woman magazine, Bernard and Sheila Bronner of UpScale magazine, Jocelyn Dingle and Kierna Mayo of Honey magazine, John and Eunice Johnson of Jet and Ebony magazines. Also, thank you to Earl Graves of Black Enterprise magazine.

Please let me take a moment to thank my wonderful staff who are always there for me. Carol Harper, President of Barry Fletcher Enterprises and my right hand. My sister Jean Jackson, Rochelle, Caroline, Patrice, Kirk, Charles, Tina, Leslie, Nakhesha, Brice, Shelly, Malisa, Joe, Kathy, Karen, Pam, Iris, Billy, Alvin A. Bratton, C.P.A. and tax attorney, Darlene Wright Powell, attorney at law, Zeta Griffith, Sabrina Chinn and Tina Templeton.

I want to say thanks to the Hair Gangsters (my style team): Larry Massenburg, Roger Gore, Bruce Johnson, James Mack, Joe Chisley Bruno, Rick Stewart, John McClenney II, Robert Young, Keith Jones, Richard H and Victor Bushrod; just to name a few. My Gansterettes (the female team): Carol Morrow, Rene' Matthews, Lisa Pope, Wendy James, Vanessa Davis and Brenda Arnold.

Special thanks to the late Darrow Bronner, Janet Wallace, Bobby Bennet, Rudy Armstrong, Al Carter, Mike Chaves, Joe Dudley, Sr., Preston Blue Torain, Khayan B. Lewis, Diva-Pennae, Lucia Rodgers, Pneuma Life Publishing President, Derwin B. Stewart and Ken Williams of Action Beauty Supply.

I really appreciate the time and patience of my models, who worked hard for this book. Thank you to my cover model Nina Shay and models Tiki Firdu, Aundrea Posey, Tokunboh (Toks) Shoson, Christle Alexander, Kafi Smiley, LaShonda Buckley, Felicia Smith, Omar Hunter, Judith Pitt, Patrice Bowie, Gina Jordan, Arnesa Howell, Patrica Burroughs, Angela Houston and Angela Mason. I am going to shout out some love to some of my celeb friends: Chaka Kahn, Tina Turner, Dr. Maya Angelou, Julian Bond, Halle Berry, Kathy Hughes, Iman, Les Brown, Chante' Moore, En Vogue, Lisa Fisher, Sam Fine, Johnnie Gill, Reggie Wells, Toni Braxton, Eartha Kitt, Donnie Simpson, and Prince, thank you for all your support and kind words.

I would like to thank Oprah Winfrey, Bob Johnson, Tom Joyner, Tavis Smiley and Queen Latifah for representing.

CREDITS

When great minds come together, powerful information is exchanged. I am very grateful to have such intelligent, talented and sharing individuals contribute a variety of information that works synergistically to answer the question at hand: "Why are black women losing their hair?" I really want to thank you all from the basement of my heart to the balcony of my mind: A'Lelia Bundles, Donna Britt, Kevin Merida, Cylburn E. Soden, M.D., P.A., and Virginia Soden, M.S., R.N., Cylburn E. Soden, Jr., Valerie D. Callender, M.D., P.C., Dr. Tariq Madyun, Dr. Sandra Gilman-Baldie, Cheryl Lynn Hendrickson, Dr. Akmal Talib Muwwakkil, Toya Watts, Bruce Britt, D. Smith, M.B.S., M.D., Robert Erdmann, PhD, C.C.N., Rashida Johnson, Barbara Coles, Christal M. Jackson, Doris Hill and Bruce Wendell Branch. I thank these people for their contributing testimonies: Dr. Wanda Nelson, Susan Eldridge, Rhonda Collins, Arnesa Howell, Phillis Bell, Julie Brown, Shirley Harper, Annette Allen, Dr. Bernadine Lacey, Floyd Kenyatta, Larry Massenburg, Anthony Stewart, Roger Gore, Vanessa Davis, Denise Hendrickson, Gregory Guattlebaum, Doria Jones, Lisa Adora Johnson and Tonya Blount.

Many thanks to my managing editor who worked long hours because she believed in this project. Her judgment was invaluable. Ann Johnson has my deepest gratitude for her acquiescent contributions to this educational guide. I am obliged to you for all of your help. I am forever indebted to my senior editors, Kevin Merida and Cheryl Hendrickson, and my special coordinating editors Sonya Johnson and Cheryl Burgess, M.D.

Thank you to Frantz of Frantz Photography for bringing everything into focus, as well as the other photographers; Keith Cephus (Iman), Mathew Jordan Smith (Halle Berry), Charlie Pizzarello (Chaka Khan) and Dwight Carter (Maya Angelou), Lois Greenfield (Eartha Kitt). Also special thanks to the makeup artists', Kim Lee, Naima Reed and Sheila Bradley Dillard.

Thank you to all my contributors. Without you, this book would not have been possible.

Acknowledgements, Contributors - Credits

Toxic Minerals

(helpful hints)
By Robert Erdmann, PhD, C.C.N., Data Doctors

ALUMINUM

Sources include anti-perspirants, tea, toothpaste, aluminum cookware, dental work, foil, baking powder, anti-acid medications, processed cheese, and herbs.

Combat it with Organic Silicon (Liquid Bio-Sil, better than bamboo extract). Also useful are Magnesium, B6, Penacillamine.

ANTIMONY

Sources: Food, smoking, industry and metallurgy.

Combat it with Glutathione, CoQ10, NADH, B complex, Vitamin C, Whey protein, and MSM.

ARSENIC

Sources: Seafood (oysters, clams, mussels), pesticides, insecticides, drinking water, smog, industrial exposure.

Combat arsenic with Whey protein, zinc, glutathione, selenium, MSM, Vitamin C.

BERYLLIUM

Source of Beryllium is not clear. It may come from smoking.

Combat it with Lithinase, Ca/Mg supplements.

BISMUTH

Sources: Used in anti-acids, cosmetics (lipstick), glass, and ceramics.

Combat it by removing sources and giving Vitamin C, selenium and MSM.

SILVER

Sources include silver activated charcoal filters, seafood, metal and chemical process industries, photographic processes, jewelry making, and coal-fired power plants.

Combat it with selenium, lipoic acid, C.

THALLIUM

Sources: Foods, tobacco, contaminated water, some fertilizers.

Combat it with liquid silicon, potassium, selenium, and MSM.

TIN

Sources: Tin cans, dental fillings, water supply (pipes).

Combat it with zinc and selenium.

URANIUM

Source: Widespread due to nuclear testing but generally considered to come from food grown in areas with high uranium in the ground.

Combat it with Vitamin C and lipoic acid.

ELEMENTS REGARDED AS NUTRIENTS (HELPFUL HINTS)

CALCIUM

Never give calcium without also giving magnesium. Calcium stimulates the sympathetic nervous system.

Blood pressure cuff on calf muscle should reach 220 without cramping.

SULFUR AMINOS

1. L-Methionine
   Lipotropic
   Anti-fatigue
   Anti-hair loss
   Detoxifier

2. L-Cysteine
   Preventing hangovers
   Helps iron absorption promotes healing
   Protects against smoking, stimulates WBC activity
   Heavy metal
   Chelator Anti-aging

3. Taurine
   Lowering cholesterol epileptic seizures
   Heart muscle
   Retina Cerebral Palsy

L-HISTIDINE

1. Stimulates stomach acid

2. Vasodilating CVD

3. Hypotensive CVD

4. Peptic ulcers

5. Anemia

6. Allergies

7. R. A.

8. Removal of heavy metals

9. Red and white blood cells

10. Sexual pleasure

11. Can bring on menses

L-GLUTAMINE
"ESSENTIAL NON-ESSENTIAL"

1. Gastrointestinal mucosa
   gastritis
   "Leaky gut"

2. Any rapidly dividing cells

3. Building muscle

4. Brain fuel
   Glucose alternative

5. Alcoholism

6. Allergies
   Secretory Iga

7. Immune system
   Fuel for macrophages
   Fuel for lymphocytes

Adults may profit from an extra 10 to 12 grams a day.

TAKING FULL SPECTRUM BLENDS OF AMINO ACIDS

Unexplained hair loss

Brittle nails

Skin problems

Anorexia

Stress

Slimming, especially if on low protein

Pre & post operations

Cold intolerance

Dizziness

Digestive problems

Low blood pressure

Body building

Weak immune system

Vegetarian diet

May be cancer

STRESS ACTIONS-REACTIONS
PHYSIOLOGICAL REACTIONS

Protein breakdown

Retention of salt

Mineral withdrawal

Retention of water

Mobilization of fat

Blood Pressure increase

ENTERIC NERVOUS SYSTEM STIMULATED

Capillaries to individual cells restricted

Restriction of nutrient intake

Restriction of waste product excretion

NUTRITIONAL NEEDS SKYROCKET

Pituitary Needs	Adrenal Needs
Protein	Vitamin A
Vitamin E	Vitamin E
Riboflavin (B2)	Riboflavin (B2)
Pantothenic acid (B5	Pantothenic Acid (B5)
Choline	Lenolenic Acid
Vitamin C	Vitamin C

VITAMIN C accelerates the rate of hormone production, delays breakdown of hormones, improves their utilization, detoxifies harmful substances, and helps alleviate Vitamin B5 deficiency.

GOOD TIMES TO DO TESTS
- When the doctor says "it's all in your head."
- When you're suffering but the doctor cannot figure out why.
- If you want to make sure your metabolic pathways are not sluggish or retarded.
- You want an alternative check on your kidney function.
- You want to check on mineral balance.
- You want to check on your susceptibility to disease conditions.
- You have a neurological problem and you want help.
- You want an indirect check on abnormal intestinal flora.
- You want a check on amino acid hormone precursors.
- You want to check on nitrogen balance.
- You want to know about your metabolism for any reason.

CADMIUM

Main source is tobacco.

Combat with zinc, Vitamin C.

LEAD

Sources: Paint in older houses, an artifact of hair darkening agents, lead acetate or dyes, can be in the water supply.

Combat it with Vitamin C, sulfur amino acids, Ca, Mg, zinc and baked beans.

MERCURY

Main source: Amalgam (silver) fillings. Second source is mercury containing fish, there can be other sources.

Combat it with selenium, chlorella, garlic, MSM, cilantro, Vitamin C.

NICKEL

Source: Each cigarette contains between two to six mcg of nickel. Margarine, partially hydrogenated vegetable oils, nickel coins, workers in electronic industry and metal plating.

Combat it with zinc and removing sources.

PLATINUM

Source: Hair treatments, drugs, possibly dental work.

Combat it with Glutathione, MSM, Zinc, C, B3.

MAGNESIUM

Magnesium is an intracellular mineral, and over 99 percent of the population have low intracellular magnesium. Magnesium Taurate seems to be one of the bio available Magnesium.

SODIUM

Low result should be viewed as a screening test with no clinical significance, but it may be a sign of electrolyte mineral imbalance or adrenocortical dysfunction.

Confirming tests can be whole blood sodium, urine sodium, or adrenocortical tests.

If you want to give sodium, use sodium rich foods (celery) or celtic salt.

POTASSIUM

Low potassium may reflect low body stores, but functional adequacy cannot be interpreted. It is highly unlikely that a patient has a true K elevation at a cellular level. Blood K may be elevated but this is usually indicative that cellular K is low. Statistically, most patients tend to be low of cellular potassium.

Confirming tests include: Blood cell K, whole blood K and Na/K ratio, urine K and Na/K ratio. An electrocardiogram may show abnormalities when K is low in serum/plasma or whole blood.

Treat low K with high potassium foods, Jerusalem artichokes, tomatoes, oranges, bananas, etc.

COPPER

Low in copper transport diseases such as Wilson's and Menke's diseases. Otherwise, low copper is usually reflective of tissue levels.

High hair copper is very sensitive to external contamination perms, dyes, and bleaches as well as purification agents in swimming pools and acidified water flowing through copper pipes. If from hair treatment, then Ca, Mg, Na, K, Ni, etc., are also usually affected. High can come from low levels of competing elements such as zinc and molybdenum.

Confirming tests for copper include packed blood cells, 24-hour urine collection with a provocative challenge using d-penicillamine (cuprimine).

ZINC

Most patients especially adult men are low in Zinc. Zinc is needed for the enzyme carbonic anhydrase (controlling the transfer of oxygen and CO_2). Zinc is stored in the prostate gland and hypothalamus (short tern, memory). Probably accounts for the reason women tend to have better memory than men and why men tend to get enlarged prostates as they age.

Confirming tests: Zinc-tally taste test, use either packed blood cell or whole blood zinc, 24 amino acid urine test to assess zinc dependent carnosinase activity.

MANGANESE

Caused by dietary insufficiency, or intestinal malabsorption or excess phosphorus in the diet. Low Manganese is associated with low cholesterol, but giving manganese does not seem to increase cholesterol.

High levels found in ALS patients, and possibly with dopamine and serotonin depletion.

CHROMIUM

Hair is a good indication of tissue levels and is better than plasma/serum or urine tests, and is seldom affected by perms, dyes, and bleaches. Required for normal glucose, cholesterol, and fatty acid metabolism. It potentates insulin function. Low increases atherosclerotic plaque and increases LDL cholesterol, impairs stress response, leads to corneal opacity, impaired glucose tolerance, and increased need of insulin by diabetics. Ingestion of highly processed food, inadequate soil levels, GI dysfunction, aging, and insufficient Vitamin B5 can lead to a deficiency.

COBALT

Hair is not sensitive to external contamination. The dietary content of cobalt is highly variable. Vegetarians are often lower than meat eaters. Hypochlorhydria and pancreatic insufficiency can cause low cobalt readings.

VANADIUM

Can be really high in patients with psychiatric problems.

Combat it with chromium.

MOLYBDENUM

Body stores can be depleted by excess intake and retention of copper. Low dietary levels come from eating highly processed foods.

BORON

May have beneficial functions related to calcium and magnesium, and may be needed for membrane function. In females, low boron correlates with urinary calcium loss and decreased estrogen levels. Somewhat sensitive to external contamination. Soaps and shampoos are common contaminates.

Appendix
Toxic Minerals

IODINE

Essential for the thyroid, but used in other organs as well, ovaries and liver for example. Low levels result in changes in the skin and hair, weight gain, and reduced cellular oxidation. Breast cancer and breast dysphasia have been linked to low iodine. Hair levels vary according to ingestion and clinical conditions—very sensitive to external contamination.

Iodine rich foods include: Most seafoods, cod, oysters, clams, shrimp, lobster, halibut, herring, sunflower seeds, Kelp, and Irish moss.

To combat elevated iodine, increase urinary output, magnesium intake, most B's, especially B12, and, to some extent, sweating.

Low iodine can cause goiters, Hashimotos's disease, Gull's disease, myxedema, and hypothyroidism.

Excess iodine can cause Grave's disease, Thyroiditis, and Hyperthyroidism, and can even cause goiters. Give lots of B 12 with these thyroid problems.

LITHIUM

Needed to stabilize intra-cellular membranes. Lysomes. Lithium is found in low levels in foods and water.

PHOSPHORUS

As with calcium and magnesium, assimilation is regulated by vitamin D. Hair does not correlate with dietary intake, as it may be effected by abnormal calcium, phosphorus, or Vitamin D metabolism and abnormal magnesium levels. It is a major component of bones and teeth, and phosphorylation chemistry is part of carbohydrate, protein, and lipid metabolism.

SELENIUM

Hair levels are very sensitive to external contamination of anti-dandruff shampoos, and elevated levels are almost always, external in origin. Excess selenium interferes with sulfur metabolism of sulfur amino acids, structural changes in hair and nails, garlic breath, metallic taste in the mouth, tooth and skin discoloration.

Excess selenium can cause mottled teeth (as also fluoride), but personally, I like to see levels at least one to two standard deviations higher than average levels.

STRONTIUM

Does not seem to be very significant.

SULFUR

Some hair conditioners, elevated S levels, and hair straighteners reduce S levels. A diet severely lacking in protein would result in a deficiency. It is needed by Phase II detoxification by the liver.

MSM as a sulfur source does not cause any acidity in the body when metabolized. Again, like selenium, levels above average seem healthy.

Are black men really the problem?

Glossary

Absorption – assimilation of one body by another; act of absorbing.

Ace inhibitors – classification of drugs to treat high blood pressure.

Acid – a substance having a sour taste; able by metals to form salts and capable of dissociating in aqueous solution to form hydrogen ions.

Activate – to make active; to start the action of hair coloring products.

Aerosol – colloidal suspension of liquid or solid particles in a gas; aerosol container filled with liquefied gas and dissolved or suspended ingredients which can be dispersed as a spray or aerosol.

Albino – a subject of albinism; a person with very little or no pigment in the skin, hair or iris.

Alkalinity – the quality or state of being alkaline.

Allergy – a disorder due to extreme sensitivity to certain foods or chemicals.

Alopecia – abnormal hair loss, baldness.

Amino-acid – any one of a large group of organic compounds; the end product of protein hydrolysis.

Ammonia – a colorless gas with a pungent odor; very soluble in water.

Ammonium sulphide – a combination of ammonia and sulphur.

Ammonium thioglycodate – a combination of ammonia and thioglycolic acid to form the chemical; reducing agent used primarily in permanent waving and hair-relaxing solutions and creams.

Androgenic – any of the steroid hormones that develop and maintain masculine characteristics.

Aniline – a colorless liquid with a faint characteristic odor, obtained from coal tar and other nitrogenous substances; combined with other substances, it forms the aniline colors or dyes that are derived from coal tar.

Antibiotic – germ killer.

Antihistamine – medicine for allergies.

Antiseptic – a chemical agent that prevents the growth of bacteria.

Antitoxin – a substance in serum which binds and neutralizes toxin (poison).

Atom – the smallest quantity of an element that can exist and still retain the chemical properties of the element.

Autoimmune – related to or caused by autoantibodies.

Bacteria – microbes, or germs.

Barometer – an instrument for measuring atmospheric pressure.

Basal – of, pertaining to, located at, or forming a base.

Beta blocker – a drug that inhibits the absorption of adrenaline by interfering with betareceptor action.

Bleach – a chemical process involving the removal of the natural color pigment or artificial color from the hair.

Bond – 1) the linkage between different atoms or radicals of a chemical compound, usually effected by the transfer of one or more electrons from one atom to another; 2) it can be found represented by a dot or a line between atoms shown in various formulas.

Booster – oxidizer added to hydrogen peroxide to increase its chemical action; such chemicals as ammonium persulfate or percarbonate are used.

Braid – three or more pieces of hair interwoven to create a three dimensional section that extends from the head.

Bristle – the short, stiff hair of a brush; short, stiff hairs of an animal, used in brushes.

Brittle – easily broken or shattered.

Calcium – a brilliant silvery-white metal; enters into the composition of bone.

Capillary – any one of the minute blood vessels that connect the arteries and veins; hair-like.

Carbon dioxide – carbonic acid gas, product of the combustion of carbon with a free supply of air.

Carcinogenic – the ability to cause cancer.

Action – an ion carrying a charge of positive electricity; the element which, during electrolysis of a chemical compound, appears at the negative pole or cathode.

Caustic – an agent that burns and chars tissue.

Cell – a minute mass of protoplasm forming the structural unit of every organized body.

Centrifugal –moving or directed away from the curvature or axis of rotation.

Chlorine – greenish yellow gas, with a disagreeable suffocating odor; used in combined form as a disinfectant and a bleaching agent.

Cholesterol – a waxy alcohol found in animal tissues and their secretions; it is present in lanolin, and used as an emulsifier.

Chronic – of long duration; continuing, constant.

Citric acid – acid found in the lemon, orange, grapefruit; used for making a lemon rinse.

Coiffure – an arrangement or dressing of the hair.

Color filler – a preparation used to recondition lightened, tinted or damaged hair.

Compounds – 1) made of two or more parts or ingredients; 2) in chemistry, a substance which consists of two or more chemical elements in union.

Conditioner – a special chemical agent applied to the hair to help restore its strength and give it body in order to protect it against possible breakage.

Configuration – the arrangement and spacing of the atoms of a molecule.

Cornrow – a braid pattern that lays flat against the scalp in a row.

Cortisone – drug used to relieve arthritis.

Cuticle – the very thin outer layer of the skin or hair.

Cystine – an amino acid component of many proteins, especially keratin; it may be reduced to cysteine.

Cytotoxic drugs – used to treat cancer as a group of chemotherapy treatments.

Dandruff – pityriasis; scurf or scales formed in excess upon the scalp.

Degeneration – the process of degenerating.

Dehydrotestosterone – type of angren male hormone.

Density – the quality or condition of being close, thick, compact or crowded.

Depilatory – a substance, usually a caustic alkali, used to destroy the hair; having the power to remove hair.

Dermatitis – an irritation of the skin; dermatitis resulting either from the primary irritant effect of the substance or more frequently from the sensitization to a substance coming in contact with the skin.

Glossary

Developer – an oxidizing agent such as 20-volume hydrogen peroxide solution; when mixed with an oxidation dye, it supplies the necessary oxygen gas.

Diffuse – scattered; not limited to one spot.

Disease – an abnormal condition, consequence of infection.

Diuretic – tending to increase the discharge of urine.

Dystropic – disorder caused by defective nutrition.

Effluvium – a usually foul smelling outflow or rising vapor.

Elasticity – the property that allows a thing to be stretched and return to its former shape.

Element – a simple substance which cannot be decomposed by chemical means and which is made up of atoms which are alike in their peripheral electronic configurations and in their chemical properties; 2) any one of the 100 ultimate chemical entities of which matter is believed to be composed.

Emulsifier – a substance, as gelatin, gum, etc., for emulsifying a fixed oil.

Enzyme – an organic compound, frequently a protein, capable of accelerating or producing high catalytic action that will promote a chemical change.

Epidermis – the outer epithelial portion of the skin.

Epithelial – membranous tissue, usually in a single layer, composed of cells.

Etiology – the study of causes or origins (the cause of disease or disorder by diagnosis).

Extensions – extra hair attached and used to add length, texture or color to hair.

Feminization – to make or become feminine.

Flat twist – two pieces of hair crisscrossed to create a rope-like pattern that lays flat against the scalp; similar to the cornrow braid.

Follicle – a small secretory cavity or sac; the depression in the skin containing the hair root.

Folliculitis – inflammation of a follicle.

Fungus – a vegetable parasite; a spongy growth of diseased tissue on the body. Ranging in form from a single cell to a body mass of filamentous hyphae that often produce specialized fruiting bodies and including the yeasts, molds, smuts, and mushrooms and ring worms.

Fusion – the act of uniting or cohering.

Gel – comprised of a solid and a liquid which exists as a solid or semi-solid mass.

Genetic – the genesis or origin of something.

Genitalia – the reproductive organs (the external sex organs).

Germicide – any chemical, especially a solution that will destroy germs.

Hair bulb – the lower extremity of the hair.

Hair consultation – to receive advice or be counseled about your hair; how to care for it and be advised about the hair services you may desire.

Handroll – a hand-made curl that is created by winding the hair from the scalp to the ends.

Heredity – the inborn capacity of the organism to develop ancestral characteristics.

Hormone – a chemical substance formed in one organ or part of the body and carried in the blood to another organ or part which it stimulates to functional activity or secretion.

Humictants – have the ability to absorb or hold moisture.

Humidity – moisture; dampness.

Hydrogen – the lightest element; it is an odorless, tasteless, colorless gas found in water and all organic compounds.

Hydrogen bond – (physical bond) that bond formed between two molecules when the electron of a hydrogen atom, originally attached to a fluorine, nitrogen or oxygen atom of a molecule, is attracted to the nucleus of fluorine, nitrogen or oxygen atom of a second molecule of the same or different substance.

Hydrogen peroxide – a powerful oxidizing agent; in liquid form is used as an antiseptic and for the activation of lighteners and hair tints.

Inflammatory – characterized or caused by inflammation.

Imbrications – cells arranged in layers overlapping one another; found in cuticle layer of hair.

Induced – to lead or move by influence or persuasion.

Injection – the act of injecting a fluid that is injected.

Iodine – a non-metallic element used as an antiseptic for kuts, bruises, etc.

Ion – an atom or group of atoms carrying an electric charge.

Keratin – a fiber protein characteristic of horny tissues: hair, nails, feathers, etc; it is insoluble in protein solvents and has a high sulfur content.

Keratinization – the process of being keratinized.

Lacquer – a thick liquid which forms a flossy film on the nail.

Lanolin – purified wool fat.

Laser – any of several devices that convert electromagnetic radiation of mixed frequencies.

Marcel – a series of even waves or tiers put in the hair with the aid of a heated iron.

Medulla – the marrow in the various bone cavities; the pith of the hair.

Melanin – the dark or black pigment in the epidermis and hair, and in the choroid or coat of the eye.

Metabolism – the process of chemical and physical processes involved in the maintenance of life.

Micro-organism – microscopic plant or animal cell; a bacterium.

Moisture – diffuse wetness that can be felt as vapor in the atmosphere or as condensed liquid on the surfaces of objects; dampness.

Molecule – the smallest possible unit of existence of any compound; (consists of two or more atoms chemically combined).

Natural hair – hair that has not been chemically processed in the past two years.

Neutralize – render neutral; counter-balance of action or influence.

Nitrogen – a colorless gaseous element, tasteless and odorless, found in air and living tissue.

Nucleus – the active center of cells.

Occipital – of or pertaining to the occiput or occipital bone.

Ooze – Leak slowly, slime.

Orally – of or pertaining to the mouth.

Organic – relating to an organ; pertaining to substances derived from living organisms.

Oxidation – the act of combining oxygen with another substance.

Oxygen – a gaseous element, essential to animal and plant life.

Paramedical – of or designating the work of paramedics.

Patch test – see predisposition test.

Penetration – act or power of penetrating.

Perm – a chemical process that makes straight hair curly.

Peroxide of hydrogen – a powerful oxidizing agent; in liquid solution is used as an antiseptic; used in tinting and lightening treatments.

pH – symbol used in expressing hydrogen-ion concentration; it signifies the logarithm, on the base of 10, of the reciprocal of the hydrogen-ion concentration.

Pigment – any organic coloring matter of the body.

Pliability – flexibility.

Polypeptide – strings of amino acids joined together by peptide bonds, the prefix "poly" meaning many.

Pore – a small opening of the sweat glands of the skin.

Porosity – ability of the hair to absorb moisture.

Potassium bromate – a metallic element of the alkali group, used in medicines as a sedative.

Prednisone – an analog of cortizone used as an anti-inflammatory agent in the treatment of arthritis.

Processed hair – hair that has been chemically colored straightened, curled or treated with permanently altering cosmetic products.

Protein – one of a group of complex nitrogenous substances of high molecular weight found in various forms in animals and plants; they are characteristics of living matter.

Puberty – the period of life in which the organs of reproduction are developed.

Relaxer – a chemical process that makes curly hair permanently straight.

Resistance – the difficulty of moisture or chemical solutions to penetrate the hair shaft.

Salicylic acid – aspirin.

S-bond – a solid, non-metallic element, usually yellow in color; it is insoluble in water.

Sebaceous glands – oil glands of the skin.

Sebum – the fatty or oily secretions of the sebaceous glands.

Selenium Sulphide – a non-metallic element resembling sulphur in its chemical properties.

Glossary

Shampoo – to subject the scalp and hair to washing and rubbing with some cleansing agent such as soap and water.

Shed hair – dead, detached hair which has been removed from the head.

Sodium – a metallic element of the alkaline group.

Sodium hydroxide – a powerful alkaline product used in some chemical hair relaxers; caustic soda.

Sodium lauryl sulphate – a metallic element of the alkaline group, in white or light yellow crystals; used in detergents.

Sodium perborate – a compound, formed by treating sodium peroxide with boric acid; on dissolving the substance in water peroxide of hydrogen is generated; used as an antiseptic.

Solution – a homogeneous mixture of a solid, liquid or gaseous substance.

Solvent – a liquid which dissolves another substance without any change in chemical composition.

Spironolactone – a steroid used medically as a diuretic.

Stabilizer – a retarding agent or a substance that counter-acts the effect of an accelerator; preserves a chemical equilibrium.

Steamer, facial – an apparatus used in place of hot towels, for steaming the hair, scalp or face.

Stearic acid – a white fatty acid, occurring in solid animal fats and in some of the vegetable fats.

Steroid – organic compound having a 17 carbon atom ring as a gasis and including the sterols and bile acids, many hormones. Certain natural drugs such as digitalis compounds, and the precursors of certain vitamins.

Sulfur, sulphur – a solid, non-metallic element, usually yellow in color; it is insoluble in water.

Sulphur bonds – sulphur cross bonds, in the hair, which hold the chains of amino acids together in order to form a hair strand.

Symptom – a change in the body or its functions which indicates disease.

Syndrome – symptoms occurring together characterizing a disease or condition.

Synthetic – man made – created artificially.

Tar – Thick liquid derived from coal, seaman.

Tension – stress caused by stretching or pulling.

Texture, hair – the general quality as to coarse, medium or fine, and feel of the hair.

Texturing – the process of manually twisting, braiding, rolling or shaping the natural hair to have texture. The texture is not permanent; it will only last like a wet set.

Thioglycolic acid – a colorless liquid or white crystals with a strong unpleasant odor, miscible with water, alcohol or ether; (used in permanent wave solutions, hair relaxers and depilatories).

Tinting – the process of adding artificial color to hair.

Topically – of or pertaining to a particular topic or topics.

Twist – two pieces of hair crisscrossed to create a rope like pattern to the hair.

Virgin hair – normal hair which has had no previous bleaching or dyeing treatments.

Vitiligo – a skin disorder characterized by the occurrence of whitish non-pigmented areas surrounded by hyperpigmented borders.

Weave – the process of intertwining or attaching loose hair extension to the natural hair. A weave can be achieved using several braid methods.

Zinc – metallic element.

Book References

1. All About Hair Care for the Black Woman: Naomi Sims - Double Day and Company – New York, 1982

2. Hair Structure and Chemistry Simplified: A. H. Powitt – Milay Publishing, 1986

3. The Essence Total Maker (body – beauty – spirit) – Crown Publishing, 1999

4. No Lye! The African American Woman's Guide to Natural Hair Care: Tulani Kinard – St. Martin's Griffin – New York, 1997

5. 400 Years Without a Comb (the untold story): Willie L. Morrow – California Curl Publishing – SanDiego, CA, 1990

6. Andre Talks Hair!: Andre Walker – Simon and Schuster, 1997

7. Let's Talk Hair: Pamela Ferrell – Cornrows & Company Publishing, 1996

8. Fine Beauty: Sam Fine – River Head Books – New York, NY, 1998

9. Hair Matters (African Ancestry): Rodcliff-Darden, Bessie M. Darden – Bessie Published 1996

10. NappyHair: Carolivia Herron, Joe Cepeda – Published, 1997

11. Ultra Black Hair Growth II (another 6 inches longer one year from now): Cathy Howse, 1994

12. Plaited Glory: Lonnice Britencem Bonner – Crown Publishing, 1996

13. Where Beauty Touches Me: Pamela Ferrell – Cornrow & Company

14. Black Is My True Love's hair (Rediscovered Fiction by American Women): Elizabeth Madox Roberts – Image Perfect Communication, 1992

15. Hair Raising: Beauty, Culture, and African American Women: Noliwe M. Rooks – Rutger University press, 1996

16. Healthy Hair Care Tips For Today's Black Woman: Cheryl Talley Moss – Talley Publishing, 1999

17. The Black Woman's Guide to Beautiful, Healthier Hair in 6 Weeks!: Carolyn Gray – Life Changing Publishing, 1999

18. Healthy Hair Care Tips For Today's Black Woman: Cheryl Talley Moss – New York University Press, 2000